Discrete Dynamical Systems

Discrete Dynamical Systems

Theory and Applications

JAMES T. SANDEFUR

Georgetown University, Washington DC

CLARENDON PRESS · OXFORD
1990

Oxford University Press, Walton Street, Oxford OX2 6DP
Oxford New York Toronto
Delhi Bombay Calcutta Madras Karachi
Petaling Jaya Singapore Hong Kong Tokyo
Nairobi Dar es Salaam Cape Town
Melbourne Auckland
and associated companies in
Berlin Ibadan

Oxford is a trade mark of Oxford University Press

Published in the United States
by Oxford University Press, New York

British Library Cataloguing in Publication Data
Sandefur, James T.
Discrete dynamical systems : theory and applications.
1. Dynamical systems. Mathematical models
I. Title
003
ISBN 0–19–853384–5
ISBN 0–19–853383–7 (Pbk)

Library of Congress Cataloging in Publication Data
Sandefur, James T.
Discrete dynamical systems : theory and applications / James T. Sandefur.
p. cm.
1. Differentiable dynamical systems. 2. Chaotic behavior in systems. I. Title.
QA614.8.S25   1990   515' .352—dc20   90–7555
ISBN 0–19–853384–5
ISBN 0–19–853383–7 (Pbk)

Text typeset by the author using TEX

Printed in Great Britain by
Courier International Ltd
Tiptree, Essex

To Helen

Preface

The study of dynamics is the study of how things change over time. Discrete dynamics is the study of quantities that change at discrete points in time, such as the size of a population from one year to the next, or the change in the genetic make-up of a population from one generation to the next. In general, we concurrently develop a model of some situation and the mathematical theory necessary to analyze that model. As we develop our mathematical theory, we will be able add more components to our model.

The means for studying change is to find a relationship between what is happening now and what will happen in the 'near' future; that is, cause and effect. By analyzing this relationship, we can often predict what will happen in the distant future. The distant future is sometimes a given point in time, but more often is a limit as time goes to infinity. In doing our analysis, we will be using many algebraic topics such as, factoring, exponentials and logarithms, solving systems of equations, manipulating imaginary numbers, and matrix algebra. We will also use topics from calculus, such as derivatives and graphing techniques. The mathematical theory generally builds on results developed earlier in this text.

After reading this text, you should be able apply discrete dynamics to any field in which things change, which is most fields. The goal, then, is to not only learn mathematics, but to get develop a differently way of thinking about the world.

My own interest in this material is somewhat backwards. Several years ago I became interested in a topic of current mathematical research, chaos. One result of the theory of chaos is that there are certain situations that change over time in an apparently random manner, and no amount of analysis will enable us to make accurate predictions for more than a short period of time. While this topic is extremely complicated, the ideas behind it can be presented without a lot of mathematical background. As I studied these chaotic models, I came to learn more and more about situations in which we **can** make accurate long term predictions. In fact, discrete dynamics has a long and useful history in many fields of study, but has been largely ignored by mathematicians until the recent interest in chaos.

My idea was to write a text that shows the many cases in which mathematics succeeds in its ability to make predictions. By understanding these cases, we will have a greater appreciation of situations in which math sometimes 'fails', that is, chaos. Thus, while chaos is discussed in this text, it is introduced as a later step in the mathematical understanding of the world.

Acknowledgements

As with any multi-year project, there are many people to thank. I would like to thank all my colleagues at Georgetown University and, in particular, Professor Ronald Rosier. It was through a summer program he directed that I got the idea for this text. His continued support and encouragement over the years has been invaluable. I would also like to thank Ms. Anita Dickerson for typing much of this manuscript from nearly illegible notes, and Professor A. Paul Stokes for his help in producing many of the figures in this text. I am grateful to those who read my manuscript and gave me helpful suggestions. These include Professors Ray Bobo, Andrew Vogt, Robert Devaney, and David Hart.

While many students endured my lectures as I developed the ideas in this text, I would particularly like to thank three: Mr. Lawrence Letellier and Mr. Tony Pribadi who gave me the idea on the gambler's ruin, and Ms. Pamela McGuire who gave me some ideas in genetics.

Finally, I would like to thank my wife, Helen Moriarty, without whose support this project would never have been finished.

Notes to the teacher

While it is not necessary to have a calculator or computer to understand this material, it would be helpful. With the aid of a calculator or computer, students can study many complex and interesting applications right from the start. Once a simple mathematical relationship is found, students can easily run their own math experiments and make their own hypotheses about what will happen. The verification of these hypotheses will have to wait until the appropriate theoretical model is developed.

Some of the earlier material in the book can be carried out using a computer spreadsheet. Experiments can be run on spreadsheets, such as guessing a monthly payment on a loan that over a given period of time makes the end amount owed equal to zero. Spreadsheets can also be used to make graphs similar to some graphs in this text.

Chapters 1 and 2 are essential for the rest of the text (excluding Section 1.6). Chapters 3, 5, and 6 could be studied in any order, but Chapter 4 depends on Chapter 3. Chapter 7 depends on Chapters 3, 4, and 6.

Applications are for the most part independent of one another. Thus, particular applications can be omitted.

The easiest method for compiling tests is to pick what you want as an answer, then work backwards to get a question with that answer. I must admit that it is difficult to develop good modeling questions.

Contents

Introduction to dynamical systems

1

1.1 Introduction to discrete dynamical modeling

Dynamical modeling is the art of modeling phenomena that change over time. The normal procedure we use for creating a model is as follows: first we identify a real world situation that we wish to study and make assumptions about this situation. Second, we translate our assumptions into a mathematical relationship. Third, we use our knowledge of mathematics to analyze or 'solve' this relationship. Fourth, we translate our solution back into the real world situation to learn more about our original model.

There are two warnings. First, the mathematical relationship is not the solution. For example, suppose we wish to model a square that has an area of 4 square meters. One mathematical translation is $x^2 = 4$, where x is the length of one side. Notice that this is not a solution. Analysis gives the possible solutions, $x = 2$ and $x = -2$. The second warning is to make sure that the solution makes sense in the situation being considered. In the example of our square, $x = -2$ does not make sense. Translating the solution $x = 2$ back to the real world, we learn something about our square, that is, its sides are of length 2 meters.

Often, none of the mathematical solutions makes sense, so the original assumptions must be reconsidered (or the mathematical calculations need to be rechecked).

In this text, we will consider situations in which the state of the system at one point in time depends on the state of the system at previous points in time.

Example 1.1

Suppose we start a savings account of 1000 dollars on January 1, 1983, and that the bank pays 10 per cent interest on its accounts, compounded annually. Then on January 1, 1984, we will have 1100 dollars in our account (our original 1000 dollars plus 10 per cent of our 1000 dollars as interest). Now the 'interesting' thing about this model is that on January 1, 1985, we do not have 1200 dollars, but to our satisfaction we have 1210 dollars in our account. This is the 1100 dollars we already have plus $(0.10)(1100)$ – our 10 per cent interest rate times our balance. Note that (a) knowing what is true today (we have 1000 dollars in the bank) and (b) having knowledge about the world that relates today to some day in the future (1 year from today we will have 10 per cent more money), we can predict how much money we will have at any time in the future (barring some unknown factor such as taxes, changes in interest rates or a bank failure).

Let's now translate this situation into the language of mathematics. This is not difficult as long as you remember the definitions and you always write in complete sentences. We will let January 1, 1983, be time 0; January 1, 1984, will be time 1; January 1, 1985, will be time 2; etc.

So January 1, 2001, will be time $2001 - 1983 = 18$. All other days are irrelevant, since the money in our account stays fixed until January 1 of the next year. We now let $A(0)$ be the amount (in dollars) that we have in our account at time 0, that is, $A(0) = 1000$. Likewise $A(1) = 1100$ and $A(2) = 1210$. Our goal will be to **predict** how much we will have in our account at time n where n is some future year. For example, if $n = 18$ (year 2001), what is $A(18)$?

We are now able to write our savings account problem as

$$A(1) = A(0) + (0.1)A(0)$$

which is read as: the amount at time 1 is (or equals) the amount at time 0 plus interest on the amount at time 0 (10 per cent of $A(0)$). This can be simplified to $A(1) = (1.1)A(0)$. Likewise

$$A(2) = (1.1)A(1), \quad A(3) = (1.1)A(2), \quad \ldots, \quad A(18) = (1.1)A(17),$$

and so forth.

We need a shorthand expression for the above equations. Verbally, the equations say that **the amount in our account next year is the amount in our account this year plus interest on the amount this year.** Let this year be year n. Then next year is year $n + 1$. The amount in the bank each of these years is denoted $A(n)$ and $A(n + 1)$, respectively. Thus the statement above is read mathematically as

$$A(n + 1) = A(n) + (0.1)A(n), \quad \text{for } n = 0, 1, 2, 3, \ldots . \tag{1}$$

Note that equation (1) when read aloud in a complete sentence actually reads the same as the boldface statement above. Note that this does not solve our problem, but restates it mathematically. To solve our problem, we need some method of finding the amount in our account at any time in the future.

One method for finding a 'solution' would be direct computation. Suppose we want to find $A(18)$. Since $A(0) = 1000$, by substitution we get that

$$A(1) = (1.1)A(0) = 1100.$$

Repeating this process, we get that

$$A(2) = 1.1A(1) = (1.1)1100 = 1210, \quad A(3) = (1.1)A(2) = 1331,$$

and so forth.

Before the days of computers, it would be tedious and time consuming to compute $A(18)$, but recursive tasks are what computers do best. Thus, after writing a simple program, we could compute $A(100)$ or $A(1000)$ quickly. Many of the results in this text were done on a computer. The programs are all easy to write in almost any computer language (and can also be written on a programmable/graphics calculator). Spreadsheets are also quite useful in performing recursive tasks. While you will not need access to a computer/calculator to follow this material, if you do use one you will have fun and learn a lot by computing answers to problems similar to the ones stated. For example, you could compute $A(1), A(2), \ldots$ when $A(0) = 100$ (or some other number of your choice).

In an effort to find a 'better' solution, that is, one that is easier to work with, we make the substitutions

$$A(2) = 1.1A(1) = 1.1(1.1A(0)) = (1.1)^2 A(0)$$

$$A(3) = 1.1A(2) = 1.1((1.1)^2 A(0)) = (1.1)^3 A(0), \ldots.$$

From this, it is not difficult to see that

$$A(k) = (1.1)^k A(0), \quad \text{for } k = 1, 2, \ldots. \tag{2}$$

Equation (2) is what we mean by a solution to our problem. We can use this equation and a calculator to compute easily the amount we have in our account at any future point in time.

The above example is indicative of the rest of this text, in the sense that we will use our knowledge of today to make predictions about tomorrow, then we will use our predictions about tomorrow to make predictions about the day after that, and so forth. Using this simple iterative idea, we will gain insight about the way the world operates. Particular examples will be from population growth, genetics, economics, and gambling, to name just a few.

Once we have analyzed a problem, the next step is to generalize. The reason for this is that generalizations are often as easy to study as the particular example while being far more widely applicable.

To generalize our savings problem, suppose the interest was not 10 per cent but some other per cent, say $100I$ per cent (where $I = 0.1$ in our previous discussion). The amount next year is the amount we have this year plus I times the amount we have this year. Written in the language of mathematics

$$A(n+1) = A(n) + IA(n) = (1+I)A(n), \quad \text{for } n = 0, 1, 2, \ldots. \tag{3}$$

Note that when $I = 0.1$, equation (3) is the same as equation (1).

Mathematicians prefer writing equations in more general forms, like equation (3), not because we like to confuse people, but because we are lazy (in the sense that we do not want to do work that is unnecessary). It actually happens that it is as easy to handle equation (3) as it is to handle equation (1). But once we have analyzed equation (3), if the bank changes its interest rate we will know what happens to our money **with no additional work**.

Similar to Example 1.1, the solution to equation (3) is

$$A(k) = (1 + I)^k A(0), \quad \text{for } k = 0, 1, 2, \ldots. \tag{4}$$

Equations that describe a relationship between one point in time and a previous point in time, such as equation (1) and equation (3), are called **discrete dynamical systems** or **difference equations**. Closed form, or explicit, expressions for the amount in any year, such as equation (2) and equation (4), are called **solutions** to the corresponding dynamical system. This will be stated more precisely in the next section.

1.1.1 Problems

1. Suppose a bank pays 5 per cent interest on its savings accounts, compounded annually.

   (a) Write down a dynamical system for the amount in the account in year $n + 1$ using the amount in the account in year n.

   (b) Given that the initial deposit is $A(0) = 200$, find the amount in the account after 1, 2, 3, and 4 years.

   (c) Give the solution to the dynamical system.

2. Suppose a broker charges a 2 per cent service charge on the money in your savings account each year.

   (a) Assuming your broker makes bad investments and that you do not earn any interest on your account, give a dynamical system for the amount in your account one year using the amount in the account the previous year.

   (b) Given that the initial deposit is 500 dollars, find the amount in your account after 1, 2, 3, and 4 years.

   (c) Give the solution to the dynamical system.

3. Suppose a bank pays 8 per cent interest each year on its checking accounts, but it also deducts 40 dollars per year as a service charge (after first adding on the interest).

   (a) If your initial deposit is 1000 dollars, what do you have in your account after 1 year, 2 years, and 3 years?

(b) Write a dynamical system to model this process.

4. Suppose that you borrow 2000 dollars from a friend. You agree to add 1 per cent interest each month to the amount of the loan that is still outstanding and also to pay your friend 150 dollars each month. Assume that the interest is first added on to what you owe and then your 150 dollar payment is subtracted.

    (a) Write a dynamical system to describe the amount $A(n)$ that you owe your friend after n months.

    (b) Using a calculator and the dynamical system, find how many months it will take you to pay off your loan and what the final payment will be.

5. Suppose your bank pays 8 per cent interest, compounded quarterly, and you initially deposit 100 dollars. Let $A(n)$ be the amount in your account after n quarters.

    (a) Develop a dynamical system to describe the amount in your account in one quarter in terms of the amount in the previous quarter.

    (b) Compute the amount in your account at the end of 1 year. Notice that you made more than 8 per cent interest for the year. (Remember that $A(1)$ is the amount after one quarter, not 1 year.)

    (c) Develop a closed form expression for the amount in your account after n quarters.

    (d) Develop a closed form expression for the amount in your account after t years.

6. Suppose your bank pays $100I$ per cent interest, compounded m times per year. Let $A(n)$ be the amount in your account after n compounding periods. For example, $A(m)$ represents the amount after 1 year.

    (a) Develop a dynamical system to describe the amount in your account in one compounding period in terms of the amount in the previous compounding period.

    (b) Develop a closed form expression for the amount in your account after n compounding periods in terms of I, $A(0)$, and m.

(c) Develop a closed form expression for the amount in your account after t years in terms of I, $A(0)$, and m.

1.2 Terminology

The dynamical systems we will consider come in many different forms but, as we will see, seemingly different types of equations can be handled similarly. Therefore we will divide these equations into large classes and study each class separately.

Informally, a discrete dynamical system is a sequence of numbers that are defined recursively, that is, there is a rule relating each number in the sequence to previous numbers in the sequence. One example is the sequence 0, 1, 2, ... Denoting each of these numbers by $A(k) = k$ for $k = 0, 1, 2, \ldots$, we note that the rule relating the numbers is $A(n+1) = A(n) + 1$. For the sequence 2, 4, 8, 16, ..., the rule is $A(n+1) = 2A(n)$, that is, each number is twice the previous number.

It is usually easier to give the rule and the first number, and then compute the sequence. Consider the rule

$$A(n+1) = 2A(n)(1 - A(n)),$$

with the first number being $A(0) = 0.1$. We then get the sequence

$$A(1) = 2A(0)(1 - A(0)) = 0.18, \quad A(2) = 0.2952, \quad A(3) = 0.416, \ldots .$$

Definition 1.2

*Suppose we have a function $y = f(x)$. A **first order discrete dynamical system** is a sequence of numbers $A(n)$ for $n = 0, \ldots$ such that each number after the first one is related to the previous number by the relation*

$$A(n+1) = f(A(n)).$$

The sequence of numbers given by the relationship

$$A(n+1) - A(n) = g(A(n))$$

*is called a **first order difference equation**. Note that by letting $f(x) = g(x) + x$, these two concepts are seen to be equivalent.*

From now on, we will often omit the term 'discrete' and just call such sequences **dynamical systems**. We will also equate a dynamical system with the rule that defines it. Three examples of dynamical systems are the relationships

$$A(n+1) = 3A(n), \quad A(n+1) = 2A(n) + 5, \quad A(n+1) = \frac{A(n)}{1 + A(n)}.$$

The functions are $f(x) = 3x$, $f(x) = 2x + 5$, and $f(x) = x/(1 + x)$, respectively.

When given a dynamical system, we are usually given what the values of the n variable can be (although sometimes it is obvious from the context of the problem). For example

$$A(n + 1) = 1 + 2A(n), \quad \text{for } n = 0, 1, 2, \ldots.$$

This dynamical system is in reality **an infinite collection of equations**. The above equation actually represents the equations

$$A(1) = 1 + 2A(0), \quad A(2) = 1 + 2A(1), \quad A(3) = 1 + 2A(2), \quad \ldots$$

Thus, if we are given the value of $A(0)$, we can substitute its value into the first of the above equations to find $A(1)$. We can then substitute the value of $A(1)$ into the second equation to find the value of $A(2)$, and so forth. Given that $A(0) = 5$, you should try finding $A(1)$ through $A(6)$.

When the function is linear and goes through the origin, that is, the graph of $y = f(x)$ is a straight line through the origin, the dynamical system is called **linear**. Thus, $A(n + 1) = 3A(n)$ is a linear dynamical system. When the function is 'linear' but does not go through the origin, that is, the graph of $y = f(x)$ is a straight line that does not go through the origin, it is called **affine**. Thus, $A(n + 1) = 2A(n) + 5$ is an affine dynamical system. We make a distinction between these similar types of dynamical systems because the method for finding solutions is slightly different.

If the function $f(x)$ is not linear, that is, the graph of $y = f(x)$ is not a straight line, the dynamical system is called **nonlinear**. Thus $A(n+1) = A(n)/(1+A(n))$ and $A(n+1) = 3A(n)(1-A(n))$ are nonlinear dynamical systems. These dynamical systems relate to selection in genetics and population growth, respectively, and will be studied in Chapter 3.

Linear equations are easy to work with, but nonlinear equations model real life better. The way we will resolve this dilemma is to learn as much about linear equations as possible, and then use as much of our linear analysis as possible on the nonlinear equations. We shall see that in some cases this works remarkably well, while in others, it is a complete disaster. We will learn to tell these two cases apart.

Our definition is not as general as it could be. The function f can also depend on n, that is,

$$A(n + 1) = f(n, A(n)).$$

For example

$$A(n + 1) = nA(n)$$

is such a dynamical system. When the coefficients of $A(n)$ depend on n, as in this case, we have what is called **a nonautonomous dynamical system**. Although nonautonomous dynamical systems are important in applications, they will rarely be considered in this text.

We could have a dynamical system defined as

$$A(n+1) = f(A(n)) + g(n).$$

Such a system is called **nonhomogeneous**. If $f(x) = ax$, as in

$$A(n+1) = 1.1A(n) + 1000n^2,$$

we will call the dynamical system **linear nonhomogeneous**. Otherwise, such as for

$$A(n+1) = A^2(n) + 2n + 1,$$

we will call the dynamical system **nonlinear nonhomogeneous**. Here, $A^2(n)$ means $[A(n)]^2$. Note that an affine dynamical system can be considered linear nonhomogeneous by letting $f(x) = ax$ and $g(x) = b$. Nonhomogeneous dynamical systems will be studied in Chapters 2 and 5.

The dynamical system $A(n+1) = f(A(n))$ is called **first order** since each number depends only on the previous number.

Definition 1.3

A dynamical system of the form

$$A(n+m) = f(A(n+m-1), A(n+m-2), \ldots, A(n))$$

*where m is a fixed positive integer is called a **higher order dynamical system**. In particular, this is said to be an m-th order dynamical system since each number depends on the previous m numbers.*

For example,
$$A(n+2) = 2A(n+1) - A(n)$$

is a second order (linear) dynamical system,

$$A(n+2) = 2A(n+1) - A(n) + 2n + 1$$

is a second order linear nonhomogeneous dynamical system, and

$$A(n+3) = A(n+1) - 5A(n)$$

is a third order linear dynamical system, even though the $A(n+2)$ term is missing. The important terms in computing the order are the first and last numbers used, that is, $A(n)$ and $A(n+3)$ in this case.

Consider the second order dynamical system

$$A(n+2) = 2A(n+1) - A(n) - (n-1)^2, \quad n = 0, 1, 2, \ldots$$

which is equivalent to the equations

$$A(2) = 2A(1) - A(0) - (-1)^2, \quad A(3) = 2A(2) - A(1) - (0)^2, \quad \ldots$$

Notice that we need to be given both $A(1)$ and $A(0)$ to find $A(2)$ in the first equation. Then we can use $A(1)$ and $A(2)$ to find $A(3)$ in the second equation, and so forth. Given that $A(0) = 2$ and $A(1) = 3$, you should try to find $A(2)$ through $A(6)$.

The values $A(1) = 3$ and $A(0) = 2$ are called the **initial values** for the corresponding dynamical system. To find the values $A(n)$ for all n, you need some initial values to get things started. This is because the first equation always has more than one unknown, so you must be given all but one of these unknowns. In particular, for an mth order dynamical system, we must be given m initial values (because there are usually $m+1$ unknowns in the first equation).

Another example to emphasize this is the second order dynamical system

$$A(n+2) = 2A(n) \quad \text{for } n = 0, 1, 2, \ldots,$$

which represents the equations

$$A(2) = 2A(0), \quad A(3) = 2A(1), \quad A(4) = 2A(2), \quad \ldots$$

Given $A(0) = 1$, we have $A(2) = 2$. But we cannot determine $A(3)$ in the second equation unless we are also given $A(1)$. Once you are given $A(1)$, you can then compute $A(n)$ for all n. So you need two initial values for this second order dynamical system.

If we have two (or more) sequences, say $A(n)$ and $B(n)$, $n = 0, 1, \ldots$, and each number in each sequence is related to previous numbers in both sequences, such as

$$A(n+1) = f(A(n), B(n)) \quad \text{and} \quad B(n+1) = g(A(n), B(n)),$$

we have a **dynamical system of 2 equations**. An example would be the system

$$A(n+1) = 2A(n)(1 - 0.1A(n) - 0.2B(n))$$
$$B(n+1) = 3B(n)(1 - 0.3A(n) - 0.1B(n))$$

which is developed in Chapter 7 in the study of competition between two species.

For a dynamical system of m equations, there must be one equation or relationship for each sequence, that is, if there are m sequences, we must have m equations relating those sequences.

It must be observed that quite often two seemingly different dynamical systems are actually the same. Consider the three dynamical systems

$$A(n + 2) = -2A(n + 1) + A(n), \quad \text{for } n = 0, 1, 2, \ldots,$$

$$A(n + 1) = -2A(n) + A(n - 1), \quad \text{for } n = 1, 2, 3, \ldots,$$

and
$$A(n) = -2A(n - 1) + A(n - 2), \quad \text{for } n = 2, 3, 4, \ldots.$$

If you substitute the corresponding integers for n into each of these three dynamical systems, you will get the equations

$$A(2) = -2A(1) + A(0), \quad A(3) = -2A(2) + A(1), \ldots.$$

Since these three dynamical systems represent the **same set of equations**, we will say that they are the same.

There is a simple way to see if two dynamical systems are the same. The trick is to use substitution, an idea that will be used often. Consider

$$A(n) = -2A(n - 1) + A(n - 5), \quad \text{for } n = 6, 7, 8, \ldots \tag{5}$$

and

$$B(k + 6) = -2B(k + 5) + B(k + 1), \quad \text{for } k = 0, 1, 2, \ldots. \tag{6}$$

Set the highest value of time (terms in parenthesis) in each equation equal to each other, that is,
$$n = k + 6.$$

Now, in equation (5), replace each n with $k+6$ (or in equation (6) replace k with $n - 6$). System equation (5) becomes

$$A(k + 6) = -2A(k + 6 - 1) + A(k + 6 - 5),$$

which is the same as equation (6) after simplifying. The conditions $n = 6$, 7, ... become $k + 6 = 6$, 7, ... Subtracting 6 from both sides gives $k = 6 - 6$, $7 - 6$, ... or $k = 0, 1, \ldots$. Thus equation (5) represents the same set of equations as equation (6) and so they are the same dynamical system.

Some authors write their dynamical systems so that the highest value of time is n, such as in equation (5). In this text, we tend to write dynamical systems so that the lowest value is n. It is important to be able to convert from one type to the other, so that you can read other articles involving dynamical systems.

In the rest of this text, we will see important applications of each of the types of systems discussed in this section. We will learn to analyse each type of dynamical system as well as possible and then apply this analysis to the applications. It will be seen that the behaviour of the solution to each of these types of dynamical systems can be quite strange and interesting, even for the simpler types.

1.2.1 Problems

1. Which of the following are dynamical systems? For those that are dynamical systems, classify as to linear, affine, linear nonhomogeneous, or nonlinear. Also give the order.

   (a) $A(n+3) = 2/A(n-1)$
   (b) $A(k) = A(k-1) + 1$
   (c) $A(n) = 4A(n) - 2$
   (d) $B(n) = 2A(n-1)$
   (e) $A(n+2) = A(n+1)/A(n)$
   (f) $A(n+5) = A(n+10) - 5$
   (g) $B(r+3) = 2B(r+1) - B(r-1)$
   (h) $A(n+5) = A(k) - A(n)$
   (i) $A(n+2) = A(n+1) + n^2 - 3$

2. Rewrite the following dynamical systems so that the lowest value of time is n. For example, rewrite

$$A(n+3) = 2A(n+1), \quad \text{for } n = 1, 2, \ldots$$

as

$$A(n+2) = 2A(n), \quad \text{for } n = 2, 3, \ldots.$$

   (a) $A(n+5) = A(n+4) - 2A(n+3), \quad \text{for } n = -2, -1, \ldots$
   (b) $A(n-3) = A(n-4) + 2n, \quad \text{for } n = 4, 5, \ldots$
   (c) $A(n+1) = A(n)A(n-1), \quad \text{for } n = 2, 3, \ldots$

3. Rewrite the dynamical systems in Problem 2 so that the highest value of time is n.

1.3 Deriving dynamical systems

In this section we will consider several situations and attempt to model them with dynamical systems. Let's start with a simple example. Suppose we draw n straight lines in a plane, such that every pair of lines intersects at one point but no three lines intersect at the same point. Let $A(n)$ be the number of regions into which these lines divide the plane. For example, $A(0) = 1$ (that one region being the whole plane), $A(1) = 2$, $A(2) = 4$, and $A(3) = 7$. You should draw these figures to see that these numbers are correct.

Suppose we know $A(n)$. (To follow this argument, draw three lines on a plane with $A(3) = 7$ regions.) We now draw the $(n + 1)$th line. It 'starts at infinity' and continues until it intersects one of the n lines. (Draw a fourth line on your figure, starting at the left and going on until it intersects one line.) When it intersects that line, it has divided one of the $A(n)$ regions into two parts, so we have increased the number of regions by 1. The line continues until it intersects a second line (continue drawing your fourth line until it intersects a second line), dividing another region into two parts and increasing our total by one more. Continuing in this manner, we add one region to our total every time we intersect a new line. Since we had n lines to begin with, and the new line can intersect each of the n lines once and no two lines simultaneously, we get n new regions. After we intersect the nth line, our new line goes to infinity, giving us one last new region for a total of $n + 1$ new regions (five new regions in the figure you are drawing).

Thus we find that $A(n + 1)$ is $A(n)$ plus $n + 1$ new regions, giving us the first order nonhomogeneous dynamical system

$$A(n + 1) = A(n) + n + 1.$$

Use this system to compute $A(10)$.

As a second example, let's consider an experiment originally performed by Galileo. Everyone remembers the story in which Galileo dropped objects off the Leaning Tower of Pisa to discover that objects of different weights fall at (approximately) the same speed. Most people are unfamiliar with Galileo's follow-up experiment in which he dropped his assistant off the tower. As his assistant fell, he made marks on the side of the tower every second. Later, Galileo measured the distance his assistant had fallen after 0, 1, 2, 3, 4, and 5 seconds. In feet, these numbers were $S(0) = 0$, $S(1) = 16$, $S(2) = 64$, $S(3) = 144$, $S(4) = 256$, and $S(5) = 400$. (Some people have doubts about this experiment since the Leaning Tower of Pisa is only 179 feet tall.)

Galileo then computed the average velocity during each second. Thus,

$$V(1) = \frac{S(1) - S(0)}{1} = 16$$

feet per second. Likewise, the average velocity during the nth second is $V(n) = (S(n) - S(n-1))/1$, so we get that $V(2) = 48$, $V(3) = 80$, $V(4) = 112$, and $V(5) = 144$. This did not tell him much, so he computed the average acceleration during each second, that is, $A(2) = (V(2) - V(1))/1 = V(2) - V(1) = 32$. Likewise, $A(n) = V(n) - V(n-1)$ so $A(3) = 32$, $A(4) = 32$, and $A(5) = 32$. From this, Galileo hypothesized that acceleration is a constant 32 feet per second squared, that is,

$$A(n) = 32.$$

Substituting $V(n) - V(n-1)$ for $A(n)$, we get the dynamical system

$$V(n) - V(n-1) = 32$$

describing the velocity of a falling object after n seconds. Substituting $S(n) - S(n-1)$ for $V(n)$, and $S(n-1) - S(n-2)$ for $V(n-1)$, we get the second order affine dynamical system

$$S(n) = 2S(n-1) - S(n-2) + 32$$

describing the distance traveled by a falling object. Note that this only give the distance traveled after an integer number of seconds.

As a third example, consider a container with fixed volume of $V = 500$ cubic centimetres. Suppose that this container is filled with pure water and that 5 grams of salt are added to the container and the water is then stirred thoroughly. Now we add ice cubes containing salt, each with volume $h = 2$ cubic centimetres, to the container. The concentration of salt in the ice cubes is $c = 0.07$ grams per cubic centimetre. We add the ice cubes, one at a time. Each time we add an ice cube, 2 cubic centimetres of water spills out of the container. We then let the ice cube melt and stir the water thoroughly before adding the next ice cube. We assume for the purposes of this model that the 2 cubic centimetres of ice contributes 2 cm^3 of water when it melts.

Let $A(n)$ be the amount (in grams) of salt in the container after we have added n ice cubes. So $A(0) = 5$. Then $A(n+1)$, the amount of salt after we add one more ice cube, is the amount we had before we added the ice cube ($A(n)$) minus the amount of salt that spills out plus the amount of salt in the ice cube added.

Since there are $A(n)$ grams of salt in the $V = 500$ cubic centimetres of water before adding the $(n+1)$th ice cube, the concentration is $A(n)/V = A(n)/500 = 0.002A(n)$. Since the volume of water spilling out is $h = 2$, the amount of salt spilling out is the product $hA(n)/V = 0.004A(n)$ grams.

Since the concentration of salt in the ice cube added is $c = 0.07$ and the volume is $h = 2$, the amount of salt added is $ch = 0.14$ grams. Combining this with the previous results, we get the first order affine dynamical system

$$A(n + 1) = A(n) - 0.002A(n) + 0.14, \quad \text{or} \quad A(n + 1) = 0.998A(n) + 0.14,$$

describing the amount of salt in the container after $n + 1$ ice cubes have been added. Given that $A(0) = 5$ grams, you should use this system to compute the amount of salt in the container after five ice cubes have been added.

Using the variables instead of the actual numbers for the volume of the container, the concentration of salt in the ice cubes, and the volume of each ice cube, the above dynamical system can be rewritten as

$$A(n + 1) = (1 - h/V)A(n) + hc.$$

We could then use this system in similar situations. One situation in which this model can be applied is in the application of medicines. The container can be a person and the liquid is the person's blood. Thus, V is the volume of blood in a person. Then the person can take pills containing P amount of a drug. The letter P represents the amount of drug added to the container, and is used in place of hc. Each time period, a certain **fraction** F of the drug is removed from the blood-stream. Thus, F represents h/V. The equation could then be rewritten as

$$A(n + 1) = (1 - F)A(n) + P.$$

This is only a beginning to modeling drugs in the body, since more complex interactions take place. As your understanding of the body and of dynamics increases, you can construct more accurate models of the bloodstream.

Another situation in which this model can be applied is in the study of pollution in ground water and lakes. A discussion of this will appear in Section 2.6.

1.3.1 Problems

1. Suppose it costs 120 dollars plus 20 cents a mile to rent a car for a week. Let $A(n)$ represent the total cost for renting the car if you

drive for a total of n miles. Develop a dynamical system for $A(n+1)$ in terms of $A(n)$.

2. To make a telephone call to New York City costs 45 cents for the first minute and 33 cents for each additional minute. Let $A(n)$ represent the cost of a call lasting for n minutes. Write a dynamical system relating $A(n+1)$ in terms of $A(n)$.

3. Let $A(n)$ be the number of gallons of gas left in a car after driving n miles. The car originally had $A(0) = 12$ gallons, and it goes 20 miles per gallon of gas. Write a dynamical system describing the amount of gas left after driving $n+1$ miles in terms of the amount of gas left after driving n miles.

4. Let $A(n)$ and $B(n)$ be the number of grams of radioactive materials A and B, respectively, after n years. Suppose that each year, 1 per cent of radioactive material A decays into radioactive material B, and that 3 per cent of radioactive material B decays into an inert material. Develop a dynamical system of 2 equations to describe the amounts $A(n)$ and $B(n)$ of each of the radioactive materials after n years. (This is called a radioactive chain.)

5. Suppose that a person takes a pill containing 200 milligrams of a drug every 4 hours, and assume that the drug goes into the bloodstream immediately. Also assume that every 4 hours the body eliminates 20 per cent of the drug that is in the bloodstream. Develop a dynamical system describing the amount $A(n)$ (in milligrams) of the drug in the bloodstream after taking the nth pill.

1.4 Equilibrium values

Suppose we borrow $A(0)$ dollars from a friend at 1 per cent per month interest, and that we pay our friend 20 dollars per month. The dynamical system that describes what we owe our friend each month is

$$A(n+1) = 1.01A(n) - 20.$$

Notice that if the original debt was $A(0) = 1000$, then $A(1) = 990$, $A(2) = 979.90$, and so forth. When we reach a point where $A(k)$ is negative, we will have paid off our loan. On the other hand, suppose that $A(0) = 3000$. Then $A(1) = 3010$, $A(2) = 3020.10$, and so forth. We now observe that we will never pay off our loan and that we will owe our friend more and more money as time goes on.

The problem is that if we restrict our payments to 20 dollars a month, then there is an upper limit to what we can borrow if we ever want to pay it back. This limit is 2000 dollars, the point at which our monthly payments equal our monthly interest charge. Notice that if $A(0) = 2000$, then $A(1) = 2000$, $A(2) = 2000$, and in fact

$$A(k) = 2000 \quad \text{for } k = 0, 1, 2, \ldots.$$

This is known as a constant solution and the number 2000 is called **an equilibrium value** or **a fixed point** for this dynamical system.

Constant solutions to a dynamical system are of extreme importance in that they often tell us what will eventually happen to our system. Recall the salt and water mixing example in the last section and consider the case of a container now with volume $V = 100$ to which we are adding ice cubes of volume $h = 2$ and salt concentration $c = 0.3$. If we add ice cubes, one at a time, the dynamical system that describes the amount of salt in the container after n ice cubes have been added is (see the previous derivation)

$$A(n + 1) = 0.98A(n) + 0.6.$$

Notice that if $A(0) = 30$, then $A(1) = A(2) = \ldots = 30$, and $A(k) = 30$ is a constant solution. If you pick any other starting value, such as $A(0) = 10$, and compute $A(1)$, $A(2)$, and so forth, you will observe that your values get close to 30, and in fact at the end of this section we will prove that

$$\lim_{k \to \infty} A(k) = 30$$

for this dynamical system.

Definition 1.4

Consider a first order dynamical system

$$A(n + 1) = f(A(n)).$$

A number a is called an **equilibrium value** *or* **fixed point** *for this dynamical system if $A(k) = a$ for all values of k when the initial value $A(0) = a$, that is,*

$$A(k) = a$$

is a constant solution to the dynamical system.

It is relatively easy to find equilibrium values a. If $A(n) = a$, it follows that $A(n+1) = a$ also. Thus, substitution of a into the dynamical system for $A(n)$ and $A(n + 1)$ gives equality. This proves the following theorem.

Theorem 1.5

The number a is an equilibrium value for the dynamical system

$$A(n + 1) = f(A(n))$$

if and only if a satisfies the equation

$$a = f(a).$$

The following examples should help you understand this definition and theorem.

Example 1.6

Consider the equation

$$A(n + 1) = 2A(n) - 3.$$

Note that $f(A(n)) = 2A(n) - 3$. The solution to

$$a = 2a - 3$$

is $a = 3$. Note that if $A(0) = 3$, then $A(1) = 2A(0) - 3 = 6 - 3 = 3$. By repeating this argument we see that $A(2) = 3$, $A(3) = 3$, and so on. Thus $a = 3$ is an equilibrium value for this dynamical system, and $A(k) = 3$ is a constant solution to this equation.

Theorem 1.7

Consider the general first order affine dynamical system

$$A(n + 1) = rA(n) + b.$$

The equilibrium value for this system is

$$a = \frac{b}{1 - r} \quad \text{if } r \neq 1.$$

If $r = 1$, there is no equilibrium value.

To prove this theorem, you only need to solve the equation $a = ra + b$ for a.

A dynamical system may have many equilibrium values. In general, the more nonlinear the dynamical system is, the more equilibrium values that system may have. For example, if there is an $A^2(n)$ term then there may be up to two equilibrium values, if there is an $A^3(n)$ term then there may be up to three equilibrium values, and so on. Also note that to find the equilibrium values, we often need to factorize a polynomial. Thus, while we can find the equilibrium values in theory, it may be difficult to find them in practice. In the discussion of Newton's method later in this text, we will see how nonlinear dynamical systems can be used to find the roots of these polynomials. Therefore, to study one dynamical system, you may need to develop a second dynamical system.

Table 1. $A(n)$ values for the dynamical system $A(n+1)=(A(n)+4)A(n)+2$ with different initial values.

$A(0) =$	-1.01	-0.99	-2.4
$A(1) =$	-1.0199	-0.9798999	-1.84
$A(2) =$	-1.039404	-0.9593959	-1.974
$A(3) =$	-1.077255	-0.9171431	-1.999345
$A(4) =$	-1.148541	-0.827421	-2
$A(5) =$	-1.275018	-0.6250584	-2
$A(6) =$	-1.474401	-0.1095357	-2
$A(7) =$	-1.723746	1.573855	-2
$A(8) =$	-1.923684	10.77244	-2
$A(9) =$	-1.994176	161.1353	-2
$A(10) =$	-1.999966	26611.12	-2
$A(11) =$	-2	708257900	-2

Example 1.8

Consider the nonlinear dynamical system

$$A(n + 1) = (A(n) + 4)A(n) + 2. \tag{7}$$

In this example, $f(A(n)) = (A(n) + 4)A(n) + 2$. Substituting a for $A(n)$ and $A(n + 1)$ gives

$$a = (a + 4)a + 2.$$

Simplification gives

$$0 = (a + 2)(a + 1).$$

Thus, the equilibrium values are the roots $a = -2$ and $a = -1$. Note that if $A(0) = -2$ then $A(1) = ((-2) + 4)(-2) + 2 = -2$, $A(2) = -2, \ldots$. Also, if $A(0) = -1$ then $A(1) = ((-1) + 4)(-1) + 2 = -1$. Likewise $A(2) = A(3) = \ldots = -1$. In this example we have **two** equilibrium values.

In the top row of Table 1 are three different initial values. The numbers under each value are the appropriate $A(1)$, $A(2)$, $\ldots$ values. In each case where $A(n) = -2$, it is actually equal to a number very close to -2, so it has been rounded off.

This is shown graphically in Figure 1. In this figure, we plot the points $(n, A(n))$ and connect corresponding points with straight lines. The lines between the points have no meaning, but make it easier to see the behaviour of the $A(n)$ values. Thus, the curves in that figure correspond to particular solutions to this dynamical system.

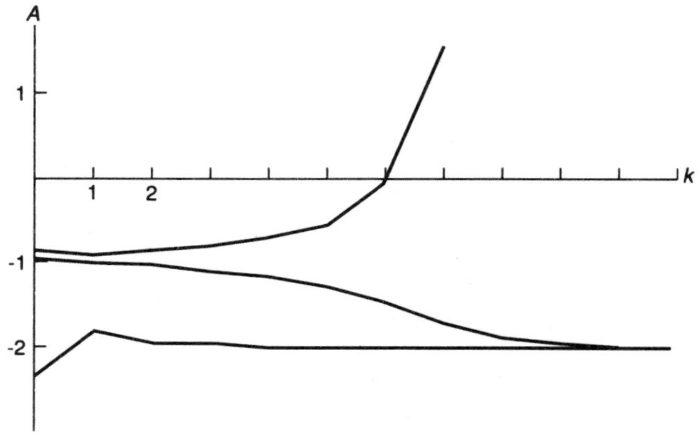

Fig. 1. Points $(k, A(k))$ satisfying the dynamical system $A(n+1) = (A(n) + 4)A(n) + 2$ with different initial values.

Notice that when $A(0)$ is close to -1, either -1.01 or -0.99, that $A(1)$ is further from -1, $A(2)$ is even further than $A(1)$, etc. But when $A(0)$ is 'close' to -2, -1.01 or -2.4, that $A(1)$ is closer to -2. In fact if $A(0)$ is close to -2, then

$$\lim_{k \to \infty} A(k) = -2.$$

Intuitively, $A(k)$ gets 'close' to -2 as k gets large.

The equilibrium value -1 is called an **unstable** equilibrium value or a **repelling** fixed point, and -2 is called a **stable** equilibrium value or **attracting** fixed point. Note that when $A(0) = -0.99$, then $A(k)$ goes to infinity. The problem is that -0.99 is not 'close enough' to -2.

Definition 1.9

*Suppose a first order dynamical system has an equilibrium value a. This equilibrium value is said to be **stable** or **attracting** if there is a number ϵ, unique to each system, such that, when*

$$|A(0) - a| < \epsilon, \quad then \quad \lim_{k \to \infty} A(k) = a.$$

*An equilibrium value is **unstable** or **repelling** if there is a number ϵ such that, when*

$$0 < |A(0) - a| < \epsilon, \quad then \quad |A(k) - a| > \epsilon$$

*for **some**, but not necessarily all, values of k.*

Note that $|A(k) - a|$ is a measure of the distance between the two values a and $A(k)$. Intuitively, the definition states that an equilibrium value is stable if whenever $A(0)$ is sufficiently close to a then $A(k)$ tends to a.   *asymptotically stable*

Similarly, an equilibrium value is **unstable** if, no matter how close $A(0)$ is to a, $A(k)$ eventually gets far, at least ϵ, from a. Usually, these $A(k)$ values stay away from a, going to infinity or to some other equilibrium value. But this does not preclude the possibility that the $A(k)$ values get close to a at a later point in time. We will see systems in Chapter 4 in which $A(k)$ keeps getting close to the unstable equilibrium value a, only to move away again and again.

Much of the analysis in this text will be devoted to determining when an equilibrium value is stable. For the moment, we shall deal with the stability of nonlinear dynamical systems in an intuitive manner.

In Example 1.6, the equilibrium value was $a = 3$. Letting $A(0)$ be close to 3, computation of $A(1)$, $A(2)$, and so forth, should convince you that $a = 3$ is unstable. On the other hand, if you pick $A(0)$ close to the equilibrium value $a = -10$ for the dynamical system

$$A(n + 1) = 0.8A(n) - 2$$

you will conclude that $a = -10$ is stable. In fact, for this dynamical system, no matter what value you pick for $A(0)$, you will find that $A(k)$ goes to -10.

While it is often difficult to determine if an equilibrium value is stable or unstable for nonlinear dynamical systems, it is easy for affine dynamical systems, such as the two studied above. For the general affine dynamical system

$$A(n + 1) = rA(n) + b,$$

where $r \neq 1$, we know that the equilibrium value is

$$a = \frac{b}{1 - r}.$$

The following theorem gives an easy criterion for determining the stability of a.

Theorem 1.10

The equilibrium value $a = b/(1 - r)$ for the dynamical system

$$A(n + 1) = rA(n) + b, \quad for \ r \neq 1$$

*is **stable** if $|r| < 1$, that is, if $-1 < r < 1$, and in fact $\lim_{k \to \infty} A(k) = a$ for any value of $A(0)$. Also, if $|r| > 1$, that is if $r < -1$ or $r > 1$, then a is unstable and $|A(k)|$ goes to infinity for any $A(0) \neq a$.*

*When $r = -1$, then $A(0) = A(2) = A(4) = \ldots$, and $A(1) = A(3) = A(5) = \ldots$. This is called a **2-cycle**. Since $A(k)$ doesn't go towards or away from the equilibrium value, the equilibrium value is neither stable nor unstable. Some people call this equilibrium value **neutral**.*

For the dynamical system $A(n+1) = 0.98A(n) + 0.6$ discussed at the beginning of this section, since $|0.98| < 1$, it follows that $A(k)$ goes to 30 as claimed.

Proof. We wish to study the distance from equilibrium, that is, $|A(n) - a|$. Notice that

$$
\begin{aligned}
|A(1) - a| &= \left| rA(0) + b - \frac{b}{1-r} \right| = \left| rA(0) + \frac{b - rb - b}{1-r} \right| \\
&= \left| rA(0) - \frac{rb}{1-r} \right| = |r|\,|A(0) - a|.
\end{aligned}
$$

Similarly,

$$
|A(2) - a| = |r|^2 |A(0) - a|.
$$

By induction, we get

$$
|A(k) - a| = |r|^k |A(0) - a|.
$$

Suppose that $|r| < 1$. Then

$$
\lim_{k \to \infty} |r|^k = 0 \quad \text{and} \quad \lim_{k \to \infty} |A(k) - a| = 0,
$$

so a is stable.

If $|r| > 1$, then $|r|^k$ goes to infinity, so $|A(k) - a|$ goes to infinity, meaning that $A(k)$ is going away from a (and in fact $|A(k)|$ is going to infinity). Thus, a is unstable.

If $r = -1$, then $A(n+2) = -A(n+1) + b = -(-A(n) + b) + b = A(n)$. Thus, every other value is equal; that is, $A(0) = A(2) = \ldots$, and $A(1) = A(3) = \ldots$. This completes the proof.

This theorem tells us immediately that the equilibrium value for: $A(n+1) = 2A(n) - 3$ is $a = 3$ and it is unstable; $A(n+1) = -3A(n) + 8$ is $a = 2$ and it is unstable; and $A(n+1) = 0.5A(n) + 3$ is $a = 6$ and it is stable.

For nonlinear dynamical systems, it is more difficult to prove the stability of equilibrium values, although computations can indicate what the stability is.

Example 1.11

Consider the dynamical system

$$A(n+1) = -0.1A^3(n) - 0.1A^2(n) + 1.2A(n).$$

The equilibrium values are the solutions to

$$a = -0.1a^3 - 0.1a^2 + 1.2a.$$

After collecting terms on the right and factoring, we get

$$0 = -0.1a(a+2)(a-1).$$

Thus the equilibrium values are $a = 0$, $a = 1$, and $a = -2$. You should pick several values for $A(0)$ and compute $A(1)$, $A(2)$, and so forth. You will find that when $A(0)$ is close to 1, the $A(k)$ values go to 1. Similarly, when $A(0)$ is close to -2, the $A(k)$ values go to -2. But when $A(0)$ is close to 0, the $A(k)$ values go away from 0. Thus $a = 1$ and $a = -2$ appear to be stable equilibrium values, while $a = 0$ appears to be an unstable equilibrium value.

An analogy for the above example is a coin. It has three equilibrium positions, heads up, tails up, and on its edge. Heads up (and likewise tails up) is a stable equilibrium position. If we set a coin close to heads up, $A(0)$, it will soon come to rest at heads up. If we place the coin close to on its edge, $A(0)$, it will soon be **further** from being on its edge (since it falls over), so the edge position is **unstable**.

In the following material, one major goal is to determine long term behaviour of physical systems. In other words, we want to determine what we expect to happen in the distant future. The term 'distant future' for many physical systems occurs fairly soon. If time units are in milliseconds, then 1 or 2 seconds may be the 'distant future'. If we have a stable equilibrium point a for our system, and our initial value is fairly close to a, then we expect to approach a. In mathematical terms we will never get to a, but in physical systems, we will be so close to a that, for all intents and purposes, we are at a. If we model the coin, the mathematical equation says the coin will be 'very close' to being at rest with heads up or tails up, since they are the stable equilibria. Physically we perceive it to be heads up or tails up.

1.4.1 Problems

1. Find the equilibrium values for the following dynamical systems (if any).

   (a) $A(n+1) = 2A(n) + 6$

    (b) $A(n + 1) = -4A(n) + 7$

    (c) $A(n + 1) = 2A(n) + n$

    (d) $A(n + 1) = A^2(n) - 2$

    (e) $A(n + 1) = 4A^3(n)$

2. Consider the dynamical system

$$A(n + 1) = 2A(n) - 3.$$

    (a) Find the equilibrium value, a.

    (b) Compute $A(1)$, $A(2)$, and $A(3)$ when $A(0) = a + 0.1$, that is, when $A(0)$ is slightly larger than the equilibrium value.

    (c) Compute $A(1)$, $A(2)$, and $A(3)$ when $A(0) = a - 0.1$, that is, when $A(0)$ is slightly smaller than the equilibrium value.

    (d) Does this confirm Theorem 1.10, that a is an unstable equilibrium value?

3. Consider the dynamical system

$$A(n + 1) = 2A(n) - 0.5A^2(n).$$

The two equilibrium values are $a = 0$ and $a = 2$ (you should check this).

    (a) Compute $A(1)$, $A(2)$, and $A(3)$ when $A(0) = 0.1$ and again when $A(0) = -0.1$. Do you think $a = 0$ is a stable equilibrium value?

    (b) Compute $A(1)$, $A(2)$, and $A(3)$ when $A(0) = 1.8$ and again when $A(0) = 2.2$. Do you think $a = 2$ is a stable equilibrium value?

4. Consider the dynamical system

$$A(n + 1) = 3A(n) - A^2(n) - 1.$$

    (a) Find its one equilibrium value, a.

    (b) Compute $A(1)$, $A(2)$, and $A(3)$ using $A(0) = a + 0.1$. Do you think a is a stable equilibrium value?

    (c) Compute $A(1)$, $A(2)$, and $A(3)$ using $A(0) = a - 0.1$. Do you still think $a = 1$ is a stable equilibrium value? (This equilibrium value does not satisfy the definition of stable or unstable, since for some $A(0)$ values sufficiently close to a, $A(k)$ tends towards a, while for others $A(k)$ goes away from a. This equilibrium value is called **semistable**.)

1.5 Cobwebs

We will now study a graphical technique that will lead to a better understanding of the dynamical systems and fixed points. This technique will help you 'see' what is going on for a particular equation.

Example 1.12

Consider the dynamical system

$$A(n+1) = 1.5A(n) - 1,$$

with $A(0) = 3$. We compute $A(1) = 1.5(3) - 1 = 3.5$. Let's denote the present value, $A(n)$, by x and the next value $A(n+1)$ by y. Then the above dynamical system becomes

$$y = 1.5x - 1.$$

Let $x = A(0) = 3$. Then $y = A(1) = 1.5(3) - 1 = 3.5$. We now let the present value be $A(1) = 3.5 = x$, so

$$y = 1.5x - 1 = 1.5(3.5) - 1 = 4.25 = A(2).$$

Now let $x = 4.25$ and compute a new value

$$y = 1.5x - 1 = 1.5(4.25) - 1 = 5.375 = A(3).$$

Thus we follow the following steps.

1. Let $x = 3$.

2. Let $y = 1.5x - 1$.

3. Replace the old x value with the new y value to get a new x value.

4. Go back to step 2 to compute a new y value.

These steps represent a **flow chart**. If you write a computer program that follows these steps, it will compute $A(k)$ for all values k. (There are two problems. These steps form an infinite loop and some procedure must be included to stop the program after enough $A(k)$ values have been computed. Also, a print statement needs to be included, so that you can obtain the results.)

Now let us follow this procedure graphically. First, draw a graph with the two lines

$$y = 1.5x - 1 \quad \text{and} \quad y = x.$$

The point at which these curves intersect is the point where both y values are the same. Thus we let the two y values be equal, giving

$$x = 1.5x - 1,$$

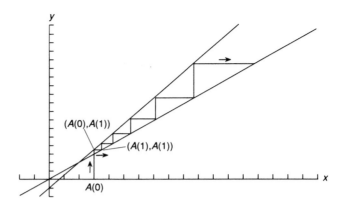

Fig. 2. Cobweb graph for $A(n+1) = 1.5A(n) - 1$. Points are $(A(k), A(k+1))$ for $k = 0, 1, \ldots$, on line $y = 1.5x - 1$. Points are $(A(k), A(k))$ on the line $y = x$.

or $x = 2$. Notice that the equilibrium value for the dynamical system $A(n+1) = 1.5A(n) - 1$ is $a = 2$. This was found by solving the equation $a = 1.5a - 1$, which is the same equation.

Graphically, step 2 says you should go vertically from $x = A(0) = 3$ to the line $y = 1.5x - 1$ to get the point $(A(0), A(1)) = (3, 3.5)$ (see Figure 2). Step 3 says you should now go horizontally to the line $y = x$ to get the point $(A(1), A(1)) = (3.5, 3.5)$ (which changes you from the old x value to the new x value). Now, returning to step 2, go vertically to $y = 1.5x - 1$ to get the point $(A(1), A(2))$.

Notice that the x coordinates of the points on the line $y = 1.5x - 1$ are the $A(k)$ values for the dynamical system. Remember that if $r > 1$, then the fixed point is **repelling** for the affine dynamical system. This can be seen visually in Figure 2 in that the cobweb moves (or is repelled) away from the point of intersection.

Also note that the statement that a fixed point for an affine dynamical system is repelling when $|r| > 1$ translates into the statement that since the slope of the line $y = 1.5x - 1$ is greater (in absolute value) than the slope of the line $y = x$, then the fixed point is repelling.

Definition 1.13

Suppose we have a dynamical system

$$A(n+1) = f(A(n)),$$

with $A(0)$ given. Draw a graph of the curve

$$y = f(x) \tag{8}$$

and the line

$$y = x. \tag{9}$$

Pick the first x value $A(0)$ and go vertically to a point on curve (8). Then go horizontally to a point on line (9). The x coordinate of the point on line (9) is $A(1)$. Repeat these steps to get $A(2)$, $A(3)$,.... The resulting figure is called a **cobweb** *for the given dynamical system.*

Recall from the last section that the equilibrium value for the first order affine dynamical system

$$A(n + 1) = rA(n) + b$$

is $a = b/(1 - r)$, and that a is stable if $|r| < 1$ and is unstable if $|r| > 1$. For cobwebs, this statement translates into the following theorem which is just a restatement of Theorem 1.10.

Theorem 1.14

Suppose a cobweb is drawn using the 'curve' $y = rx + b$ and the line $y = x$. These curves intersect at the point (a, a) where $a = b/(1 - r)$, and the sequence of points determined by the cobweb:

- *converges to (a, a) if $|r| < 1$,*

- *goes to positive and/or negative infinity if $|r| > 1$, and*

- *oscillates around a square centred at (a, a) if $r = -1$.*

For affine dynamical systems, when $r = 1$, there is no equilibrium value.

The following example helps demonstrate the above and also clarifies why these graphs are called cobwebs.

Example 1.15

Consider the dynamical system

$$A(n + 1) = -0.8A(n) + 3.6$$

with $A(0) = -4$. Here, the slope of the line

$$y = -0.8x + 3.6$$

is negative, but $|r| = 0.8 < 1$. The cobweb is given in Figure 3. Notice that the solution oscillates towards the attracting fixed point $a = 2$.

Example 1.16

Part 3 of Theorem 1.14 is demonstrated by the dynamical system

$$A(n + 1) = -A(n) + 4.$$

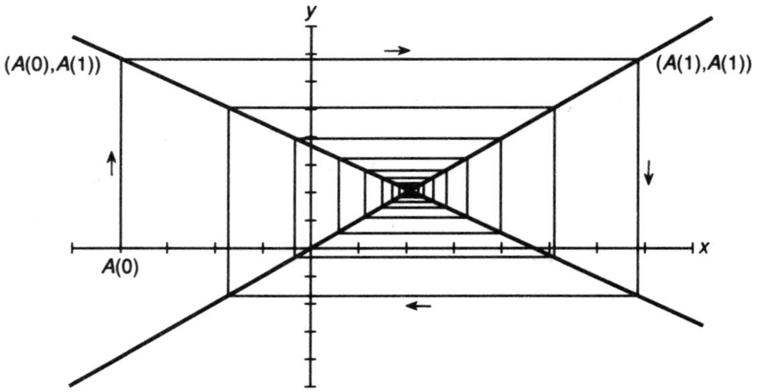

Fig. 3. Cobweb graph for the dynamical system $A(n+1) = -0.8A(n)+3.6$. With $A(0) = -4$, it is seen that the solution oscillates to the fixed point $a = 2$.

Letting $A(0) = 6$, we get a square when we follow the vertical and horizontal procedure for producing cobwebs (see Figure 4). (Note that because the scales are different for the x and y axes, the rectangle in Figure 4 does not 'appear' to be square.)

This means the solution is a 2-cycle. Whenever we get a closed curve as our cobweb, it means we have a cycle. This is important and will come up again in the study of nonlinear equations.

Let's now extend our concept of cobwebs to nonlinear dynamical systems to develop an intuitive idea for when a fixed point is attracting or repelling.

Example 1.17

Consider the dynamical system

$$A(n + 1) = 1.5A(n) - 0.5A^2(n).$$

The solutions to the equation

$$a = 1.5a - 0.5a^2$$

are the two fixed points, $a = 1$ and $a = 0$.

If we substitute x for $A(n)$ and y for $A(n+1)$ in the above dynamical system, we then have the equation

$$y = 1.5x - 0.5x^2,$$

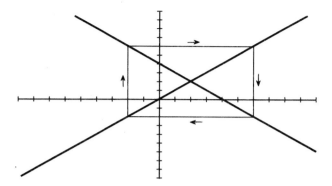

Fig. 4. Cobweb graph for the dynamical system $A(n + 1) = -A(n) + 4$. Notice that the solution forms a 2-cycle, oscillating between $x = -2$ and $x = 6$. The fixed point $a = 2$ is neutral.

which is the equation of the parabola shown in Figure 5, along with the line $y = x$. Notice that the equilibrium values correspond to the points of intersection of the two curves, that is, the points $(0, 0)$ and $(1, 1)$.

In the same manner as for affine dynamical systems, we pick a point on the x axis, which we call $A(0)$. To find $A(1)$ algebraically, we substitute $A(0)$ for x in the equation of the parabola. To find $A(1)$ graphically, we go vertically from the $A(0)$ value to the graph of the parabola. This point on the parabola corresponds to $(x, y) = (A(0), A(1))$. In Figure 5, we do this for the value $A(0) = 0.2$. Proceeding as before, we see that the cobweb goes towards $a = 1$.

If you construct cobwebs using other values for $A(0)$, you should get that when $A(0)$ is reasonably close to 1, then the cobweb is attracted to 1, while if $A(0)$ is near 0, then the cobweb is repelled away from 0, although not necessarily to infinity.

Let's examine the equilibrium value $a = 1$ closer. Figure 6 is a magnification of the part of the graph of Figure 5 which is close to the point $(1, 1)$, that is, the horizontal and vertical axes go from 0.9 to 1.1 on this graph. The curve $y = 1.5x - 0.5x^2$ appears to be 'almost' a straight line under this magnification, which is easy to see when it is compared with the **tangent line** to the parabola at the point $(1, 1)$, that is, the line

$$y = 0.5x + 0.5,$$

which is also shown in Figure 5. (Since the derivative of $f(x) = 1.5x - 0.5x^2$ is $f'(x) = 1.5 - x$, the slope of the tangent line to the parabola at

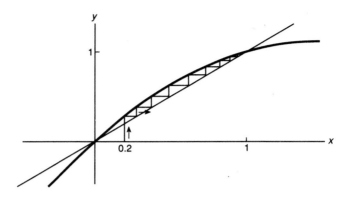

Fig. 5. Cobweb graph using the curve $y = 1.5x - 0.5x^2$. Notice that $x = 1$ appears to be attracting or stable, and that $x = 0$ appears to be repelling or unstable.

$(1,1)$ is 0.5, giving the above equation for the tangent line using the point slope formula for the equation of a line.)

Notice that the cobweb using the parabola is essentially the same as the cobweb using the tangent line. The cobwebs move towards the point $(1,1)$, that is, the equilibrium value $a = 1$ is stable. We knew the point $(1,1)$ was stable for the line $y = 0.5x + 0.5$ since the slope of this line, 0.5, is less than 1.

Let's learn how to determine the stability of the equilibrium values without graphing the curve $y = f(x)$.

The equilibrium values for the nonlinear dynamical system

$$A(n+1) = f(A(n))$$

are also the coordinates of the points of intersection of the curves $y = f(x)$ and $y = x$, that is, points (a, a) for which a satisfies the equation

$$a = f(a).$$

These points of intersection are called **equilibrium points**.

Remember that the cobweb for a first order affine dynamical system $A(n+1) = rA(n) + b$ is constructed using the line $y = rx + b$. Also recall that if $|r| < 1$ then the equilibrium value is stable, while if $|r| > 1$ then the equilibrium value is unstable.

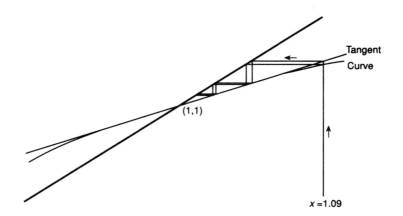

Fig. 6. Magnification of cobweb graph for the parabola $y = 1.5x - 0.5x^2$. A cobweb is also drawn using the tangent line to the parabola at $(1, 1)$. Notice both cobwebs are essentially the same.

Suppose the number a is an equilibrium value for the nonlinear dynamical system

$$A(n + 1) = f(A(n)).$$

Then the tangent line to the curve $y = f(x)$ at the equilibrium point has slope $f'(a)$ and goes through the point (a, a). The tangent line at the equilibrium point is therefore

$$(y - a) = f'(a)(x - a),$$

or, after simplification,

$$y = rx + b,$$

where

$$r = f'(a) \quad \text{and} \quad b = a[1 - f'(a)].$$

This tangent line corresponds to the first order affine dynamical system

$$A(n + 1) = rA(n) + b,$$

where $r = f'(a)$ and the equilibrium value is a.

In Example 1.17, we have that $f(x) = 1.5x - 0.5x^2$ so that $f'(x) = 1.5 - x$. Considering the fixed point $a = 1$, we find that $f'(1) = 0.5$. Thus, the equation of the tangent line is

$$y = 0.5x + (1 - 0.5) \times 1 = 0.5x + 0.5,$$

which has $a = 1$ as a stable equilibrium value. The other fixed point for that dynamical system is $a = 0$. Since $f'(0) = 1.5$, the tangent line is $y = 1.5x$, which has $a = 0$ as an unstable equilibrium value.

From Figure 5, it appears that cobwebs for a nonlinear dynamical system

$$A(n + 1) = f(A(n))$$

and cobwebs using the tangent line at an equilibrium point of the nonlinear dynamical system,

$$y = rx + b, \quad \text{where} \quad r = f'(a),$$

are essentially the same when $A(0)$ is close enough to the equilibrium point (a, a). But the equilibrium value a is stable for the affine equation if $|r| < 1$, and unstable if $|r| > 1$. This inspires the following theorem.

Theorem 1.18

Suppose a is an equilibrium value for the dynamical system

$$A(n + 1) = f(A(n)).$$

The equilibrium value a is stable or attracting if

$$|f'(a)| < 1,$$

and is unstable or repelling if

$$|f'(a)| > 1.$$

If $|f'(a)| = 1$, our work is inconclusive.

The derivative of a curve at a point is, in some sense, **the best linear approximation** of the curve at that point. One of the reasons that the derivative is important is that in many cases this linear approximation gives us all the information we need. In particular, suppose that a is an equilibrium value and $|f'(a)| < 1$. Then we know that, if $A(0)$ is close enough to a, then

$$\lim_{k \to \infty} A(k) = a.$$

This is often all we need to know.

In our later studies of nonlinear dynamical systems, we will find that when $f'(a) = \pm 1$, the derivative does not give us enough information, but higher derivatives do.

The above discussion indicates that Theorem 1.18 is true, but it is not a proof. The actual proof of this theorem is based on the mean value theorem and will be given later in this text.

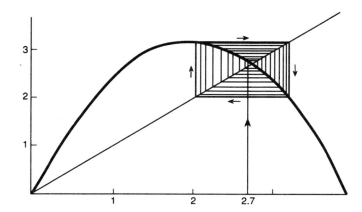

Fig. 7. Cobweb using the parabola $y = 3.2x - 0.8x^2$ and the starting value of $A(0) = 2.7$. Notice the cobweb oscillates away from the fixed point $(2.75, 2.75)$, and towards a 2-cycle.

Example 1.19

Consider the dynamical system

$$A(n + 1) = 3.2A(n) - 0.8A^2(n).$$

After making the substitutions $A(n + 1) = y$ and $A(n) = x$, we consider the curve

$$y = 3.2x - 0.8x^2.$$

The equilibrium values, which are the solutions of the equation $a = 3.2a - 0.8a^2$ are $a = 0$ and $a = 2.75$. Since $f(x) = 3.2x - 0.8x^2$, we have

$$f'(x) = 3.2 - 1.6x.$$

Since $f'(2.75) = -1.2$ and $|-1.2| > 1$, it follows that 2.75 is unstable. In Figure 7 it is seen that if $A(0)$ is close to 2.75 ($A(0) = 2.7$), then the solution $A(k)$ is repelled away from 2.75, and in fact appears to become a 2-cycle. Notice that although the derivative tells us that $a = 2.75$ is unstable, it does not tell us what eventually happens to $A(k)$.

Likewise $a = 0$ is unstable since $f'(0) = 3.2 > 1$. If you were to construct a cobweb starting with a small positive initial value $A(0)$ (say $A(0) = 0.1$), you would find that the solution $A(k)$ would be repelled from $a = 0$, and would eventually go to the same 2-cycle as seen in Figure 7.

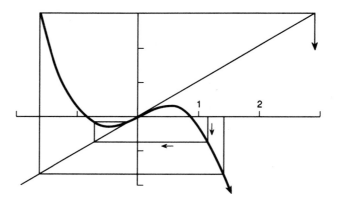

Fig. 8. Cobweb using the curve $y = 0.8x - x^3$. Note that when $A(0) = 1.2$ the cobweb is attracted to 0, but if $A(0) = 1.4$ then the cobweb is repelled from 0.

Example 1.20

Consider the dynamical system

$$A(n + 1) = 0.8A(n) - A^3(n).$$

The only real equilibrium value is $a = 0$, and it is stable since $f'(0) = 0.8 - 3(0)^2 = 0.8$. In Figure 8, we can see that for $A(0)$ near 0 ($A(0) = 1.2$ in this case) the points $(A(k), A(k))$ are attracted to the origin, but that for $A(0)$ far away from 0 ($A(0) = 1.4$ in this case), the points $(A(k), A(k))$ cycle outwards corresponding to $|A(k)|$ going to infinity.

When an equilibrium value a is stable, an interesting and often difficult problem is to determine the maximum interval (c, d) about a such that if $A(0)$ is in that interval then $\lim_{k \to \infty} A(k) = a$. Using graphical techniques, these intervals can sometimes be determined exactly; for example, in Figure 5 it can be seen that if $A(0)$ is in the interval $(0, 3)$ then $A(k)$ goes to 1, but if $A(0)$ is outside that interval then $|A(k)|$ goes to infinity. At other times, computer experiments can help estimate that interval; for example, in Figure 8 it can be seen that the interval is larger than $(-1.2, 1.2)$, but smaller than $(-1.4, 1.4)$. By experimenting with $A(0)$ values between 1.2 and 1.4, we could give the interval as accurately as we wish.

Example 1.21

Consider the dynamical system

$$A(n + 1) = A^3(n) - A^2(n) + 1.$$

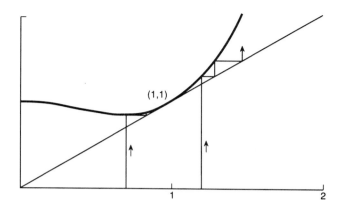

Fig. 9. Cobweb using the curve $y = x^3 - x^2 + 1$. It indicates that the equilibrium value $a = 1$ is semistable.

The two equilibrium values are $a = -1$ and $a = 1$. Since $f'(-1) = 3(-1)^2 - 2(-1) = 5 > 1$, then $a = -1$ is unstable.

But notice that $f'(1) = 3 \times 1^2 - 2 \times 1 = 1$. So far we have no rule when $|f'(a)| = 1$. Notice in Figure 9 that $a = 1$ is attracting on the left and repelling on the right. We call such a point **semistable**.

In the case that an equilibrium value a satisfies

$$|f'(a)| = 1,$$

the equilibrium value may be stable, unstable, or semistable. In such cases, other methods must be used. These methods will be discussed later in this text.

We end this section with a discussion of our terminology. Suppose we are studying a dynamical system that models the real world, say the price of a product under the pressures of supply and demand. Then an equilibrium value for the dynamical system corresponds to an equilibrium price; that is, a price which, once reached, remains there for a long time (assuming no other outside influences). Thus, the term 'equilibrium value' seems to fit better than the term 'fixed point'. Suppose we are considering a dynamical system without being concerned about its real world applications (such as we did earlier in this section). Then if a cobweb is started at a point of intersection, the cobweb doesn't move; that is, we have a 'fixed point'.

Similarly, if an equilibrium value relates to the real world, say an equilibrium price, then it makes more sense to say the price is 'stable' or 'unstable'. But if we are drawing cobwebs of the dynamical system, then the cobwebs make the intersection point appear to be 'attracting' or 'repelling'. Thus, the best terminology to use seems to depend on what we are doing. For this reason, we will refer to 'equilibrium value' and 'fixed point' interchangeably throughout this text, and similarly for the terms 'stable' and 'attracting', and 'unstable' and 'repelling'.

1.5.1 Problems

1. Sketch a cobweb for the dynamical system

$$A(n + 1) = -1.5A(n) + 5,$$

with $A(0) = 3$. Also find the equilibrium point and note from the cobweb that it is unstable.

2. For each part, sketch the cobweb, find the equilibrium value if there is one, and use the cobweb to determine the stability of the equilibrium value.

   (a) $A(n + 1) = -A(n) + 3, \quad A(0) = 1$

   (b) $A(n + 1) = 1.5A(n) - 5, \quad A(0) = 9$

   (c) $A(n + 1) = A(n) + 3, \quad A(0) = 0$

3. Suppose for the dynamical system

$$A(n + 1) = 2A(n) - 1,$$

you are given that $A(3) = 9$. Sketch a cobweb starting at $y = A(3) = 9$ to find $A(0)$. This can be done by reversing the cobweb procedure.

4. Consider the dynamical system

$$A(n + 1) = 3A(n) - A^2(n) + 3.$$

   (a) Find the equilibrium values for this dynamical system.

   (b) Draw the graph of the curve $y = 3x - x^2 + 3$ and determine the stability of the equilibrium values using cobwebs.

   (c) Determine the stability of the equilibrium values by using $f'(x)$.

5. Consider the dynamical system

$$A(n+1) = 1.4A(n) - 0.2A^2(n) + 3.$$

   (a) Find the equilibrium values for this equation.
   (b) Determine the stability of the fixed points using cobwebs.
   (c) Determine the stability of the fixed points using derivatives.

6. For the dynamical system

$$A(n+1) = A(n) - A^3(n),$$

   the only equilibrium value is $a = 0$. Since $f'(0) = 1$, Theorem 1.18 does not help in determining the stability. Draw a cobweb for this curve and use it to find if $a = 0$ is stable, unstable, or semistable.

7. Consider the dynamical system

$$A(n+1) = 2A(n) - 0.25A^2(n) - 0.75.$$

   The two equilibrium values are $a = 1$, which is unstable, and $a = 3$, which is stable. Sketch a cobweb for this equation and use it to determine the maximum interval containing $a = 3$ such that if $A(0)$ is in that interval, then $\lim_{k \to \infty} A(k) = 3$.

1.6 Deriving differential equations

The purpose of this section is to connect discrete dynamical systems with continuous phenomena by way of differential equations (or continuous dynamical systems). In particular, it shows how discrete dynamical systems can be used to develop the differential equations that many readers will have studied in calculus courses.

In a discrete problem, such as the study of compound interest, we have a function, $A(n)$, which gives the amount in our account after n compounding periods. The way we found this function was to derive an equation that relates the value of this function at one point in time to its value at a previous point in time. For compound interest, this relationship gave us the dynamical system

$$A(n+1) = (1 + I/m)A(n),$$

where I is the yearly interest rate as a decimal, m is the number of compounding periods in a year, and $A(n)$ is the amount in the account after n compounding periods.

In this section we will study continuous phenomena, that is, problems in which the amount we are observing changes continuously instead of in discrete jumps. Stairs are discrete, while a ramp is continuous. Suppose a boat has a hole in the bottom. The water flows in continuously. If we have a bucket, then we bail out the water in discrete amounts (one bucketful at a time).

Suppose we have something that grows continuously. Then we have a continuous function $f(t)$ that gives the amount present at time t. Thus, one difference between discrete and continuous models is that in the discrete model time n must be an integer value, while in the continuous model time t can be **any** real value.

The way we will study continuous models is to derive an equation, called a **differential equation**, that gives a relationship between the function $f(t)$ and its derivative $f'(t)$. We will derive this equation in a similar manner to the way we derived discrete dynamical systems. It is assumed that the reader has learned methods in other courses for studying these derived differential equations.

Let's now learn how to develop a differential equation from a real world problem. Suppose we have a bank account that has an annual interest rate of $100I$ per cent, compounded continuously. If we initially deposit 1000 dollars, how much will we have in 2 years? In fact, what does it mean to say our money is compounded continuously?

Before studying this question, let's again consider a bank account that compounds our money m times per year, but let's use a different terminology. Let $f(t)$ be our principal after t years (instead of using $A(n)$ for the principal after n compounding periods). Let $h = 1/m$ be the fraction of a year consisting of one compounding period; for example, if the money is compounded quarterly, then $m = 4$ and $h = 1/4 = 0.25$. Thus, n compounding periods correspond to $t = hn$ years. For example, if the money is compounded quarterly, then $n = 12$ compounding periods correspond to $t = 12 \times 0.25 = 3$ years. If $f(t)$ is the principal at time t, then $f(t + h)$ is the principal one compounding period later.

Using this terminology, the change in our principal from one compound period to the next is

$$f(t + h) - f(t).$$

The interest earned in one compounding period is the annual interest rate times the fraction of a year consisting of one compounding period times the principal at the beginning of the compounding period. Translated into our terminology, the interest earned in one compounding period is $Ihf(t)$. Since the change in our money equals the interest earned, we have the equation

$$f(t + h) - f(t) = Ihf(t).$$

This equation is the same as the discrete dynamical system

$$A(n+1) - A(n) = \frac{I}{m} A(n)$$

but in our new terminology. Now $f(0)$ is the initial deposit instead of $A(0)$.

This equation will be easier to study if we divide both sides by h giving

$$\frac{f(t+h) - f(t)}{h} = If(t). \tag{10}$$

We can now describe what we mean by 'continuous compounding'. Interest is compounded continuously if the **length** of the compounding period goes to zero. Thus, we let h go to zero in equation (10) giving

$$\lim_{h \to 0} \frac{f(t+h) - f(t)}{h} = \lim_{h \to 0} If(t)$$

or,

$$f'(t) = If(t).$$

If we have an account that pays 7 per cent interest, compounded continuously, then the principal $f(t)$ satisfies the equation

$$f'(t) = 0.07 f(t).$$

We have thus derived a differential equation that models the continuous compounding of interest. As with discrete dynamical systems, this equation does not give the answer to our problem, but instead it translates our problem into the language of mathematics.

While you can now use your calculus techniques to find a solution to the above differential equation, often discrete dynamical systems can help in finding solutions. Remember that equation (10) is the same as the discrete dynamical system

$$A(n+1) = (1 + I/m) \, A(n)$$

which has the solution

$$A(k) = (1 + I/m)^k \, A(0).$$

Translating to the new terminology, we get that the solution to equation (10) is

$$f(t) = (1 + I/m)^{mt} \, f(0).$$

Substitute $M = m/I$ to get

$$f(t) = (1 + 1/M)^{MIt} f(0).$$

Recalling that the number e is defined by

$$e = \lim_{M \to \infty} (1 + 1/M)^M$$

and that the differential equation was derived by letting h go to zero (and consequently letting M go to infinity) gives the solution to the differential equation as

$$f(t) = e^{It} f(0).$$

This solution will then tell you what you have in your account at any time t.

Principle for deriving differential equations: Suppose you are studying the amount $f(t)$ of something which changes continuously as t changes. Pretend instead that what you are studying changes during discrete intervals of length h, where h is a fraction of one unit of t. Develop a discrete dynamical system for $f(t + h)$ in terms of $f(t)$ (instead of $A(n + 1)$ in terms of $A(n)$), and then subtract $f(t)$ from both sides. You should be able to factor an h out of the right side of the equation. This is because the right side, which equals the change in the amount of $f(t)$, is usually proportional to h (and often proportional to $f(t)$ also). Dividing both sides by h and taking the limit as h goes to zero gives the corresponding differential equation.

Let's consider a model related to advertising. Now t will represent money, not time. Suppose we wish to compute the number $f(t)$ of coat hangers our company will sell if we spend t dollars in advertising. Thus, while sales must be integers and advertising is given to 2 decimal places (hundredths of a dollar), we assume they are continuous.

Our first step is to assume that the problem is discrete. Pretend we know how many coat hangers we will sell if we spend t dollars, that is, we know $f(t)$. Then how many coat hangers will we sell if we spend $t + h$ dollars in advertising, that is, what is $f(t + h)$? We are pretending that we increase our advertising budget in increments of h dollars.

To develop a discrete dynamical system to model this, we need to make some assumptions. First, we will assume that there is some upper limit L on the number of coat hangers the public will buy, that is, no matter how much we spend in advertising, we cannot sell more than L coat hangers.

Let's make up some numbers to get a feel for this problem. Suppose that $L = 1000$ and $h = 10$. We wish to know what happens if we increase our advertising by 10 dollars. Suppose that $f(100) = 200$, that is, if we spend 100 dollars in advertising, we can sell 200 coat hangers. We now have a potential market of 800 more coat hangers. Also suppose that $f(500) = 900$, and we then have a potential market of 100 more coat hangers. It should be clear that a 10 dollar increase in advertising should have more effect in the first case than the second, because we have a larger potential market in the first case (800 versus 100).

We are trying to compute the change in sales $f(t + h) - f(t)$ which results from an increase of h dollars in advertising. It should be clear that the change should depend on both the potential sales $L - f(t)$, and on the additional amount of advertising h. Thus, a second possible assumption is that the change in sales is proportional both to the change in advertising and to the potential sales, that is,

$$f(t + h) - f(t) = rh(L - f(t)).$$

This corresponds to the affine dynamical system

$$A(n + 1) - A(n) = rh(L - A(n)).$$

Now that we have developed a dynamical system to model our problem in advertising, we divide both sides by h and then let h go to zero, that is,

$$\lim_{h \to 0} \left(\frac{f(t + h) - f(t)}{h} = r(L - f(t)) \right)$$

or

$$f'(t) = rL - rf(t).$$

Let's review several important points in developing dynamic mathematical models. First, it is usually easier to model a problem if we assume that change occurs in small jumps. Second, it is also often easier to study how the amount changes, that is, to find out what $f(t + h) - f(t)$ equals. Third, you need to make simplifying assumptions. These assumptions are often of the form 'the change is proportional to h and to ...'.

An important application that occurs in many different areas is the problem of dilution of liquids that was considered in Section 1.3. These problems are often of the following form. A container with volume V is filled with salt water at a dilution of d grams of salt per unit volume. Salt water with a dilution of c grams per unit volume is being poured continuously into the container, and a corresponding amount of the water in the container spills out. How much salt remains in the container after x units of water are poured into it?

This type of problem can occur in studying pollution. The container can be a lake and salt can be replaced by a chemical pollutant. Or the container can be the human body, and the liquid is blood instead of water, into which a medicine or chemical is introduced instead of salt. Because of the importance of these and other variations of this problem in the real world, let's develop a differential equation to model a simple form of this problem.

Before studying this problem, let's recall a simple fact. If water has a concentration of d grams of salt per litre, then a bucket containing h litres of water contains hd grams of salt.

In Section 1.3, we considered a similar problem in which $A(n)$ was the amount of salt after adding n ice cubes of volume h and concentration c. The discrete dynamical system we developed was

$$A(n + 1) - A(n) = -\frac{hA(n)}{V} + ch.$$

The only differences now are that: a) instead of counting the number of ice cubes n, we want to consider the total amount of water added $x = nh$; and b) instead of using $A(n)$ for the amount of salt, we use $f(x)$ for the amount of salt. Using these changes, the above equation translates into the equation

$$f(x + h) - f(x) = -\frac{hf(x)}{V} + ch.$$

Dividing both sides by h and letting h go to zero gives

$$f'(x) = -\frac{1}{V} f(x) + c$$

as the differential equation modeling the change in the amount of salt when salt water is being added continuously to the container. Notice that if pure water is being added, then $c = 0$ and the equation becomes

$$f'(x) = -\frac{1}{V} f(x).$$

A few comments about this model are in order. Inherent in our assumptions is that when an ice cube containing h litres of salt water is added to the container, the water is well mixed before the next ice cube is added. By letting h go to zero, we are assuming that the water is added continuously and it is instantaneously being mixed with the water already in the container. In reality this is impossible, so our model is only an approximation. It requires additional mathematical techniques to include in our model the assumption that the dilution of salt in the water varies throughout the container.

This brings up another point of mathematical modeling. Many people make the mistake of initially trying to develop models that take into account too many factors. The correct method of modeling is to consider only the barest essentials of the problem. After you develop and understand this model, you then attempt to introduce other aspects of the problem (by way of additional assumptions) into your equation. Also you should realize that the more elements you introduce into your model, the more mathematics you will need to be able to analyse the associated equation.

You may now have a question about which model to use, discrete or continuous. There is no clear cut answer. Most real world situations are a combination of discrete and continuous phenomena. You then need to consider which phenomena you consider the most important. Often the model you pick is the one that is the easiest to analyse mathematically. Depending on the model, sometimes the discrete model is easiest and at other times the continuous model is easiest.

Sometimes the type of model you choose is irrelevant in the sense that the discrete and continuous models will result in the same conclusions about reality. But there are situations (such as the population growth models considered later in this text) in which the model makes an important difference, that is, the discrete model leads to one conclusion while the continuous model leads to another conclusion. Therefore, you should be careful in choosing the appropriate approach, that is, discrete or continuous.

1.6.1 Problems

1. Suppose you have a savings account that pays 8 per cent interest, compounded continuously. Suppose you decide to add 1000 dollars a year to your account, but you add it continuously (this is often called a revenue stream). Let $f(t)$ represent the amount in your account after t years. Derive a differential equation to model this account. (It is technically impossible to add money continuously, but many companies assume they earn and spend money continuously because it gives a good approximation of the actual earnings and the associated differential equation is easy to study.)

2. Suppose a population has a fixed birth rate of b per $100\,000$ per year and a fixed death rate of d per $100\,000$ per year, but that the population is changing continuously. Let $f(t)$ represent the size of the population after t years.

   (a) Derive a differential equation to model this population.

   (b) Suppose in addition that there are a immigrants per year, but that they immigrate continuously. Derive a differential equation to model this situation.

First order linear dynamical systems

2.1 Solutions to linear and affine dynamical systems

When modeling the real world, we first consider only the most basic assumptions. This usually leads to a linear (possibly nonhomogeneous) dynamical system. The good news is that in general we can find solutions to these linear dynamical systems. These solutions often lead us to a better understanding of the situation we are modeling. We then try to make our model more realistic by adding secondary assumptions. These assumptions often lead to nonlinear dynamical systems. Unfortunately, we can rarely find solutions to nonlinear dynamical systems. We will find in the next chapter that while we cannot find solutions, we can determine the long term behavior of many nonlinear systems using the techniques we develop in studying linear systems. We will then find that there are still a great many types of nonlinear systems for which the behavior is still not understood. To understand the world better, mathematicians need to develop means for understanding these equations better.

A major part of this book will be devoted to finding solutions to linear systems. This is not because linear systems are more important or more common than nonlinear systems, but because we know more about linear systems. Similarly, a great many of the applications in this text will lead to linear dynamical systems. This does not mean that most applications are linear, but that the first step to most applications is linear.

The most general form of a first order linear dynamical system is

$$A(n + 1) = rA(n), \quad \text{for } n = 0, 1, \ldots, \tag{1}$$

where r is a constant. One example derived in Chapter 1 was the model of compound interest

$$A(n + 1) = (1 + I)A(n), \quad \text{for } n = 0, 1, \ldots.$$

A **solution** to a dynamical system is a function $A(k)$ defined for all integers $k \geq 0$ that satisfies the dynamical system. One solution to the dynamical system (1) is

$$A(k) = 3\,r^k, \quad \text{for } k = 0, 1, 2, \ldots.$$

Note that this means $A(0) = 3$, $A(1) = 3\,r$, $A(2) = 3\,r^2$, $A(n) = 3\,r^n$, and $A(n + 1) = 3\,r^{n+1}$. Substituting into the dynamical system (1) gives

$$3\,r^{n+1} = r(3r^n),$$

which is a balanced equation. Thus the above is a solution to the dynamical system (1).

Likewise $A(k) = (-2)r^k$ is a solution. In fact the discrete function

$$A(k) = c\,r^k \tag{2}$$

is a solution where c is any constant. The function (2) is called **the general solution** to the dynamical system (1). This means that every solution to the dynamical system (1) is of the form of function (2). If we are given an initial value such as $A(0) = 5$, then by letting $k = 0$ in equation (2) we get $A(0) = c\,r^0 = c$. Since $c = A(0) = 5$, we know $c = 5$ and that the **particular solution** to the first order linear dynamical system (1) with initial value $A(0) = 5$ is

$$A(k) = 5\,r^k.$$

Definition 2.1

The **general solution** *to a first order dynamical system*

$$A(n + 1) = f(A(n)), \quad for\ n = 0,\ \ldots$$

is a function $A(k)$, with domain $k = 0,\ \ldots,$ which

- *satisfies the dynamical system when substituted in for $A(n)$ and $A(n + 1)$, and*

- *involves a constant c which can be determined once an initial value is given.*

The **particular solution** *to a first order dynamical system*

$$A(n + 1) = f(A(n)), \quad for\ n = 0,\ \ldots$$

with an initial value given, say $A(0) = a_0$, is a function $A(k)$, with domain $k = 0,\ \ldots,$ which

- *satisfies the dynamical system when substituted in for $A(n)$ and $A(n + 1)$, and*

- *when $k = 0$, satisfies the equation $A(0) = a_0$.*

For the first order dynamical system (1), if you are given that $A(0) = a_0$, then simple computations and substitutions give that $A(1) = ra_0$, $A(2) = rA(1) = r^2 a_0$, $\ldots$, $A(k) = rA(k - 1) = r(r^{k-1}a_0) = r^k a_0$. This leads us to believe that the particular solution to the dynamical system (1) is

$$A(k) = a_0 r^k.$$

Simple substitution of $A(k)$ into the dynamical system (1) shows that it does satisfy the system and is therefore the particular solution. Furthermore, if we define

$$A(k) = c\,r^k,$$

then $A(k)$ satisfies the dynamical system (1) and we can solve the equation $A(0) = cr^0 = a_0$ for c, that is, $c = a_0$. We have thus proved the following theorem.

Theorem 2.2

The general solution to the first order linear dynamical system

$$A(n+1) = rA(n), \quad for\ n = 0, \ldots$$

is

$$A(k) = c\,r^k, \quad for\ k = 0, \ldots.$$

The particular solution to this dynamical system given that $A(0) = a_0$ is

$$A(k) = a_0\,r^k, \quad for\ k = 0, \ldots.$$

Example 2.3

What is the general solution to

$$A(n+1) = -3A(n), \quad for\ n = 0, 1, \ldots ?$$

Since $r = -3$, the general solution is

$$A(k) = c(-3)^k.$$

What is the particular solution to the above dynamical system with $a_0 = -3$? By the above we see that $c = A(0) = -3$ and thus the particular solution is

$$A(k) = (-3)(-3)^k = (-3)^{k+1}.$$

Substituting $A(n+1) = (-3)^{n+2}$ and $A(n) = (-3)^{n+1}$ into the dynamical system gives

$$(-3)^{n+2} = (-3)(-3)^{n+1}$$

which is a balanced equation, verifying this theorem.

If $A(1) = a_1$ were given instead of $A(0)$, we could find the particular solution by solving

$$A(1) = c\,r^1 = a_1$$

for the unknown c. In this case, $c = a_1 r^{-1}$ and the particular solution is

$$A(k) = a_1 r^{-1} r^k = a_1 r^{k-1}.$$

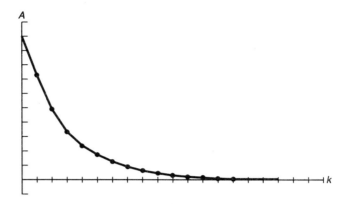

Fig. 10. The points $(k, A(k))$ for the dynamical system $A(n+1) = 0.7A(n)$ with $A(0) = 10$.

We already know from the previous chapter that if $|r| < 1$ then $A(k)$ goes to zero, if $|r| > 1$ then $|A(k)|$ goes to infinity, and if $r = -1$ then $A(k)$ forms a 2-cycle. Let's look at two figures that tell us how $A(k)$ goes to zero. Similar figures can be constructed to show how $|A(k)|$ goes to infinity when $|r| > 1$.

When $0 < r < 1$, the solution $A(k)$ goes to zero exponentially. If $a_0 > 0$ it decreases to zero (as in Figure 1 in which $r = 0.7$ and $a_0 = 10$) and if $a_0 < 0$ it increases to zero. When $-1 < r < 0$, the solution oscillates to zero. This can be seen in Figure 2, where $r = -0.8$ and $a_0 = 10$. When $|r| > 1$, the solution goes exponentially to either positive or negative infinity, and when $r < -1$, the solution oscillates to infinity with increasing amplitude.

Definition 2.4

A solution $A(k)$ is **periodic** *if*

$$A(k + m) = A(k)$$

for some fixed integer m and all k. The smallest integer, m, for which this holds is called the **period** *of the solution.*

For the dynamical system $A(n + 1) = -A(n)$ with $a_0 = -6$, the particular solution is $A(k) = -6(-1)^k$ and thus

$$A(k + 2) = -6(-1)^{k+2} = -6(-1)^k(-1)^2 = -6(-1)^k = A(k).$$

So this solution is periodic with period 2. In particular $A(0) = A(2) = A(4) = \ldots = -6$ and $A(1) = A(3) = A(5) = \ldots = 6$. Notice that

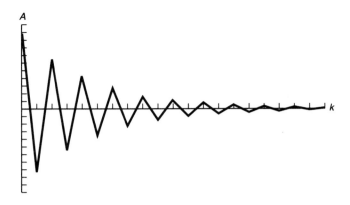

Fig. 11. The points $(k, A(k))$ for the dynamical system $A(n + 1) = -0.8A(n)$ with $A(0) = 10$.

$A(k + 4) = A(k)$, $A(k + 6) = A(k)$, etc. But since 2 is the smallest number that works, this solution has period 2.

We will see examples with very large periods later in the text. Cyclic behavior occurs in nature in the periodic attacks of locusts and in planetary motion such as the return of Halley's comet. I'm sure you can come up with many other examples.

It is interesting to note the many different types of behavior exhibited by the solutions to the simple equation

$$A(n + 1) = rA(n)$$

for different values of r and a_0. Note that the equation

$$A(n + 1) = (1 + I)A(n),$$

which gives the amount in a savings account, is first order linear with $r = 1 + I$, $I > 0$. Thus the money in our account increases exponentially (to infinity). We could be very rich if we could wait long enough.

We now turn our attention to the analysis of first order affine dynamical systems, that is, equations of the form

$$A(n + 1) = rA(n) + b,$$

where r and b are constants.

Example 2.5

Let's again consider a savings account that receives $100I$ per cent yearly interest rate, compounded m times a year. To make this account more realistic, let's assume that at the beginning of each compounding period, we make an additional deposit of b dollars. Let $A(n)$ represent the amount we have in our account after n compounding periods (and immediately following our deposit of b dollars).

For example, suppose we make an initial deposit of $a_0 = 1000$ dollars, and we collect 8 per cent interest, compounded quarterly. At the beginning of each compounding period, we make an additional deposit of 100 dollars. Thus, the amount we have after the $(n+1)$th quarter $A(n+1)$ is our principal from the nth quarter $A(n)$, the quarterly interest on our principal $0.02A(n)$, plus the 100 deposit we make. Notice that the deposit is made at the beginning of the next quarter, so we don't receive any interest on it, yet. In summary,

$$A(n+1) = 1.02A(n) + 100,$$

with $a_0 = 1000$. We wish to find the particular solution to this dynamical system. (You could use this equation to compute what you have at the beginning of, say, the second year, that is, $A(4)$.)

Our goal now is to find the general and the particular solution to first order affine dynamical systems, that is, to dynamical systems of the form

$$A(n+1) = rA(n) + b, \tag{3}$$

where r and b are two constants. We will develop the solution using a technique similar to the one we used in proving Theorem 1.10. To do this, we first observe that the equilibrium point for the dynamical system (3) is

$$a = \frac{b}{1-r}.$$

We then make the substitution

$$A(k) = E(k) + \frac{b}{1-r} = E(k) + a.$$

Substituting $A(n+1) = E(n+1) + b/(1-r)$ and $A(n) = E(n) + b/(1-r)$ into the dynamical system (3) gives

$$E(n+1) + \frac{b}{1-r} = r\left(E(n) + \frac{b}{1-r}\right) + b,$$

or, after simplifying,

$$E(n+1) = rE(n).$$

We know by Theorem 2.2 that the general solution to this linear dynamical system is $E(k) = cr^k$, so by substituting back, we get

$$A(k) = E(k) + \frac{b}{1-r} = cr^k + \frac{b}{1-r},$$

when $r \neq 1$. It therefore follows that the general solution to the first order affine dynamical system (3), when $r \neq 1$, is

$$A(k) = cr^k + a = cr^k + \frac{b}{1-r}, \qquad (4)$$

where $a = b/(1-r)$ is the equilibrium value.

What is the particular solution when $A(0) = a_0$ is given, that is, what is c in terms of r, b, and a_0? Substitution of $k = 0$ into the general solution gives

$$A(0) = cr^0 + \frac{b}{1-r} = c + \frac{b}{1-r} = a_0.$$

Equating the two forms of $A(0)$ and solving for the unknown c gives

$$c = a_0 - \frac{b}{1-r}.$$

Thus, the particular solution to the first order affine dynamical system (3), when $r \neq 1$, is

$$A(k) = r^k \left(a_0 - \frac{b}{1-r} \right) + \frac{b}{1-r}.$$

Example 2.6

Let's consider the dynamical system

$$A(n+1) = 2A(n) + 5$$

with initial value $a_0 = 3$. We compute $b/(1-r) = 5/(1-2) = -5$. Thus the general solution to this dynamical system is

$$A(k) = c2^k - 5.$$

Since $a_0 - b/(1-r) = 3 - (-5) = 8$, the particular solution is

$$A(k) = 8(2^k) - 5.$$

We can use this solution to find $A(k)$ at any future point in time, say $A(5) = 8(2^5) - 5 = 251$. Note that this is simpler than iterating the dynamical system five times.

Observe that if we are given that $A(3) = 4$, then we can still use the general solution to find the particular solution. In this case, we have $A(3) = c2^3 - 5 = 4$ or $8c - 5 = 4$, so that $c = 9/8$ and the particular solution is

$$A(k) = (9/8)(2^k) - 5 = 9(2^{k-3}) - 5.$$

What about the case in which $r = 1$, that is, the dynamical system

$$A(n + 1) = A(n) + b?$$

Suppose that $A(0) = a_0$. Then we have $A(1) = a_0 + b$ and, by substitution, $A(2) = A(1) + b = a_0 + 2b$, $A(3) = a_0 + 3b$, and so forth. Thus, the particular solution appears to be

$$A(k) = a_0 + k\,b.$$

From this, you should conclude that the general solution is

$$A(k) = c + k\,b.$$

Substitution of $A(n) = n\,b + c$ and $A(n + 1) = (n + 1)\,b + c$ into this affine dynamical system gives

$$(n + 1)\,b + c = n\,b + c + b.$$

We have equality, so this is the correct form of the general solution.

Given that $A(0) = a_0$, substitution of $k = 0$ into the general solution gives

$$A(0) = (0)\,b + c = a_0,$$

so $a_0 = c$ and the particular solution is

$$A(k) = b\,k + a_0.$$

Example 2.7

Find the particular solution to

$$A(n + 1) = A(n) - 2$$

with $a_0 = 9$. Since $b = -2$, the solution is

$$A(k) = -2k + 9.$$

Notice that there is no equilibrium value. The graph of this solution is given in Figure 3.

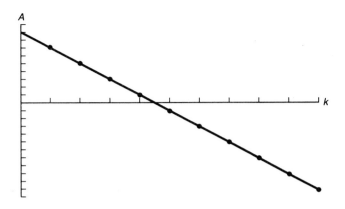

Fig. 12. The points $(k, A(k))$ for the dynamical system $A(n+1) = A(n) - 2$ with $A(0) = 9$. Observe the linear relationship.

Note that $r = 1$ corresponds to the equation

$$A(n + 1) - A(n) = b,$$

that is, we have constant differences. When we have constant differences or constant change, then the solution is given by $A(k) = c + bk$, that is, the points $(k, A(k))$ lie on a straight line. Thus, constant change results in a linear relationship between amount $A(k)$ and time k.

We summarize our results as a theorem.

Theorem 2.8

Suppose we are given the first order linear dynamical system

$$A(n + 1) = rA(n) + b.$$

*For simplicity, let $a = b/(1 - r)$. Then the **general solution** to this dynamical system is*

$$A(k) = cr^k + a, \quad if \quad r \neq 1,$$

and

$$A(k) = bk + c, \quad if \quad r = 1.$$

*If $A(0) = a_0$ is given, then the **particular solution** is*

$$A(k) = (a_0 - a)r^k + a, \quad if \quad r \neq 1,$$

and

$$A(k) = bk + a_0, \quad if \quad r = 1.$$

Notice that when $r \neq 1$ and $a_0 = b/(1-r)$, then the particular solution to the first order affine dynamical system is

$$A(k) = \frac{b}{1-r},$$

that is, we have a constant solution (which should be no surprise since the initial value equals the equilibrium value).

We could have used Theorem 2.8 to prove Theorem 1.10, that is, to prove that if $|r| < 1$, then $\lim_{k \to \infty} A(k) = b/(1-r)$. The proof is as follows:

$$\lim_{k \to \infty} A(k) = \lim_{k \to \infty} \left(c\, r^k + \frac{b}{1-r} \right) = \frac{b}{1-r},$$

since r^k goes to zero.

2.1.1 Problems

1. For the following dynamical systems, find $A(1)$ through $A(5)$, give the particular solution, describe the long term behavior (that is, increasing to infinity, oscillating to zero, etc.), and draw a graph of the points $(k, A(k))$.

   (a) $A(n+1) = -1.1A(n), \quad A(0) = 2$

   (b) $A(n+1) = 1.1A(n), \quad A(0) = -1$

   (c) $A(n+1) = -0.2A(n), \quad A(0) = 1000$

   (d) $A(n+1) = 0.2A(n), \quad A(0) = -1000$

   (e) $A(n+1) = 0.8A(n) - 1, \quad A(0) = 3$

   (f) $A(n+1) = -A(n) + 3, \quad A(0) = 5$

   (g) $A(n+1) = -1.5A(n) + 5, \quad A(0) = 3$

2. For the following dynamical systems, give the general solution and the equilibrium value, if any.

   (a) $A(n+1) = 3A(n)$

   (b) $A(n+1) = -0.5A(n)$

   (c) $A(n+1) = -1A(n)$

   (d) $A(n+1) = A(n) + 3$

   (e) $A(n+1) = 1.5A(n) - 5$

   (f) $A(n+1) = -0.9A(n) + 3.8$

3. For the dynamical systems in Problem 2, give the particular solution for $A(0) = 4$.

4. For the dynamical systems in Problem 2, give the particular solution for $A(2) = 0$.

5. For what value of b is the equilibrium value of the dynamical system

$$A(n + 1) = -0.3A(n) + b$$

equal to 5?

6. For what value of b is the equilibrium value of the dynamical system

$$A(n + 1) = 2A(n) + b$$

equal to -8?

7. For what value of r is the equilibrium value of

$$A(n + 1) = rA(n) - 2$$

equal to 0.5?

8. For what value of r is the equilibrium value of

$$A(n + 1) = rA(n) + 3$$

equal to 4?

9. For what value of r is the equilibrium value of

$$A(n + 1) = rA(n) + 2r$$

equal to 2?

10. Consider the dynamical system $A(n + 1) = 3A(n) - 4$.

    (a) Given that $A(0) = 3$, for what value of k does $A(k) = 245$?
    (b) Given that $A(6) = -1456$, find $A(0)$.

11. Find the general solution to the dynamical system

$$3A(n + 1) + 1 = 2A(n) - 4.$$

12. Find the general solution to the dynamical system

$$2A(n + 1) - 3A(n) = 8.$$

2.2 Applications to finance

Consider this general situation. Suppose we have an account that contains $A(n)$ dollars after n compounding periods. Suppose that account is collecting $100I$ per cent annual interest, compounded m times per year. In addition, assume a constant amount b is added to the account at the end of each compounding period (or taken from the account if $b < 0$). Let a_0 be the initial amount in the account, that is, $A(0) = a_0$. You should see that the dynamical system

$$A(n + 1) = \left(1 + \frac{I}{m}\right) A(n) + b \tag{5}$$

describes the relationship between the amount in the account at the end of $n+1$ compounding periods and the amount after n compounding periods. As we will see in this section, this simple model applies to a wide range of financial applications.

First, we recall that the solution to the affine dynamical system $A(n + 1) = rA(n) + b$ (when $r \neq 1$) is

$$A(k) = r^k \left(a_0 - \frac{b}{1 - r}\right) + \frac{b}{1 - r}.$$

This is exactly dynamical system (5) with $r = 1 + I/m$. Thus, the solution to dynamical system (5) is, after substitution and simplification,

$$A(k) = \left(1 + \frac{I}{m}\right)^k \left(a_0 + \frac{mb}{I}\right) - \frac{mb}{I}. \tag{6}$$

When $b = 0$, this formula simplifies to

$$A(k) = \left(1 + \frac{I}{m}\right)^k a_0.$$

The idea in the following is to study a situation similar to the one described above. Note that there are six constants in dynamical system (5), that is, k, $A(k)$, a_0, I, m, and b. In most applications, real numbers will be given for five of these constants. Once we have identified the situation as being modeled by dynamical system (5), we can immediately write down the solution (6) using the given numbers where possible. There will then be one unknown left in equation (6), for which we solve. That number will answer our original question.

To start with, we will consider situations in which $A(k)$ is the unknown, and no work is necessary to solve for it.

Let's consider a savings account in which we add b dollars each compounding period. We collect $100I$ per cent annual interest, compounded m times per year. Then dynamical system (5) models our savings where $A(n)$ is the amount after n compounding periods.

Example 2.9

For example, suppose we initially deposit $a_0 = 100$, plus an additional deposit of $b = 100$ every year thereafter, into a savings account that pays 10 per cent interest, compounded annually. Then $A(n + 1) = 1.1A(n) + 100$, and $mb/I = 100/0.1 = 1000$, so

$$A(k) = (1.1)^k (1100) - 1000.$$

In particular $A(40) = 48\,785.17$. A total of $48\,785.17$ dollars in our account after 40 years is quite amazing when we realize that our total deposits have been only 4100 dollars. But our interest totals $44\,685.17$ dollars.

Suppose you have an account in which the advertised annual interest rate is $100I$ per cent, compounded m times a year. The **effective interest rate** is the per cent increase in your principal if left in the account for 1 year.

We model this with an account in which we make no deposit except for the initial deposit of a_0 dollars. This is just dynamical system (5) with $b = 0$. The solution is $A(k) = (1 + I/m)^k a_0$, and the amount we have at the end of 1 year is

$$A(m) = \left(1 + \frac{I}{m}\right)^m a_0.$$

We have made $A(m) - A(0)$ dollars in interest, so the effective annual interest rate, denoted here by I' (where the interest rate is given as a decimal), is the total interest at the end of 1 year divided by the initial deposit, that is,

$$I' = \frac{A(m) - A(0)}{a_0} = \frac{(1 + I/m)^m a_0 - a_0}{a_0} = \left(1 + \frac{I}{m}\right)^m - 1.$$

Example 2.10

Suppose we have an account that advertises an annual interest rate of 10 per cent, compounded monthly. The effective annual interest rate is then

$$I' = \left(1 + \frac{0.1}{12}\right)^{12} - 1 = 0.104\,712.$$

or 10.4712 per cent interest.

Note that the more frequent the compounding period, the higher the effective yield, that is, the more interest we earn.

Let's see how we can use this material to develop an intelligent retirement program.

Example 2.11

When you retire in 30 years, how much per year will you need to live? Suppose you could live comfortably on 20 000 dollars a year today. Assuming an average of 5 per cent inflation (5 per cent was chosen arbitrarily) you would need 5 per cent more next year, etc. The amount you would need each year is modeled by

$$A(n+1) = (1.05)A(n).$$

Since $a_0 = 20\,000$, you can use this dynamical system to determine what you would need per year when you retire, 30 years hence. Thus you would need

$$A(30) = (1.05)^{30}20\,000 = 86\,438.74$$

dollars per year. (This neglects the fact that inflation will continue after you retire.)

Later in this section we will discuss how you can accomplish the task of saving enough money to retire on.

Often, we are given the amount we have at some future point in time $A(k)$ for some fixed value of k, and wish to know what the initial amount a_0 was. This is relatively simple if $b = 0$. In this case, we solve

$$A(k) = \left(1 + \frac{I}{m}\right)^k a_0,$$

for a_0, that is,

$$a_0 = \left(1 + \frac{I}{m}\right)^{-k} A(k).$$

Example 2.12

Suppose you wish to make an investment that will pay for your child's college education. You figure you will need 20 000 dollars when your child starts college, 15 years from now. (That's optimistic.) You can buy a long term certificate of deposit or CD that pays an 8.5 per cent annual interest rate, compounded quarterly. What size CD should you buy?

If we let $A(n)$ be the value of our CD after n compounding periods, then $A(n)$ satisfies the dynamical system

$$A(n+1) = \left(1 + \frac{0.085}{4}\right) A(n).$$

Here, you are given that in 15 years or $k = 4(15) = 60$ quarters, you will need $A(60) = 20\,000$. Thus,

$$a_0 = 20\,000 \left(1 + \frac{0.085}{4}\right)^{-60} = 5663.77.$$

So if you invest 5663.77 dollars in these CDs, you will have 20 000 dollars in 15 years.

Definition 2.13

*When you are given $A(k)$ and want to find $A(0) = a_0$, you are finding the **present value** of some future amount of money. This present value is given by*

$$a_0 = \left(1 + \frac{I}{m}\right)^{-k} A(k),$$

where k is the number of compounding periods and not the number of years. If $100I$ is the effective annual interest rate, then we assume $m = 1$ and k is the number of years. In this case

$$a_0 = (1 + I)^{-k} A(k).$$

Example 2.14

Suppose a number of years ago we purchased a savings bond that will be worth 200 dollars in 5 years. Suppose also that we have the opportunity to make an investment that will pay an effective yearly interest rate of 8 per cent. What is our savings bond presently worth to us, that is, what present amount of money, invested at 8 per cent interest, would yield 200 dollars in 5 years? Here, $k = 5$, $A(5) = 200$, $I = 0.08$, and

$$a_0 = (1.08)^{-5} 200 = 136.12.$$

Thus, if someone would pay us more than 136.12 dollars for our savings bond, we should sell it. Notice that the actual value of the bond today is irrelevant.

Often people will make a long term investment at a certain interest rate. After a while, interest rates change. People then determine, not the actual value of their original investment, but the present value (or present worth) of this investment given the new interest rate. This is one of the causes of changes in the bond market.

Suppose we want to know a_0 for an account in which fixed amounts b are added each compounding period. If the relationship between compounding periods is described by the dynamical system (5), then we know that a_0 satisfies solution (6),

$$A(k) = \left(1 + \frac{I}{m}\right)^k \left(a_0 + \frac{mb}{I}\right) - \frac{mb}{I}.$$

Solving for a_0 gives

$$a_0 = \left(A(k) + \frac{mb}{I}\right)\left(1 + \frac{I}{m}\right)^{-k} - \frac{mb}{I}. \tag{7}$$

In the last example, you paid a certain amount for a bond, received no interest in the interim, and then received a lump sum at the termination date. We then learned to compute the present value of that future payment at any time before maturity. In the next example, you buy a bond for P dollars, receive periodic interest payments (say each year), and then receive your payment of P dollars back at maturity.

Example 2.15

Suppose several years ago you paid 1000 dollars for a bond which pays you 100 dollars a year, and that when the bond matures 10 years from now, you get your 1000 dollars back. The **coupon value** of this bond is said to be 10 per cent, since you receive 10 per cent interest on your 1000 dollars each year.

If you sell the bond to someone else today, you can invest the proceeds at an effective yearly interest of 9 per cent. How much is this bond worth to you now, that is, what is its **present value**?

The trick is to rephrase this question in terms we are more familiar with. Suppose you sold your bond today for a_0 dollars and invested that money in a bank account paying 9 per cent interest per year, compounded annually. Assume that at the end of each year, for the next 10 years, you withdraw 100 dollars from this account, and that at the end of 10 years, there was 1000 dollars in this account. What is a_0?

The dynamical system that models the last paragraph (and which answers our original question) is

$$A(n+1) = (1.09)A(n) - 100,$$

with A(10) = 1000. Using equation (7) with $m = 1$, $I = 0.09$, $b = -100$, and $k = 10$, gives

$$a_0 = \left(1000 + \frac{(-100)}{0.09}\right)(1.09)^{-10} - \frac{(-100)}{0.09} = 1064.18,$$

which is the present value of your bond.

A similar application of present value is to **annuities**. In an annuity, you receive a fixed payment over some period of time. The question is, what are all these payments worth today, that is, what is the annuity's present value? One particular example of this is the true value of winning 1 000 000 dollars in a lottery.

Example 2.16

Suppose you win 1 000 000 dollars in a lottery in the sense that you will receive 50 000 dollars a year for the next 20 years. How much did you **actually** win?

Let's rephrase this problem. Suppose the lottery commission deposits a_0 dollars into a bank account paying $100I$ per cent interest, compounded annually. Let $A(n)$ represent the amount in this bank account after you have received your nth payment of 50 000 dollars (and for simplicity, assume you receive your first payment after 1 year). Thus, $A(1) = (1 + I)A(0) - 50\,000$, and

$$A(n + 1) = (1 + I)A(n) - 50\,000.$$

Also, $A(20) = 0$. The amount, a_0, is the present value of your lottery win which is how much you **actually won**.

Suppose the money is put into an account paying an effective annual interest rate of 8 per cent. Using equation (7), with $m = 1$ and $I = 0.08$, we get that

$$a_0 = -500\,000(1.08)^{-20} + 500\,000 = 392\,725.90,$$

that is, your 1 000 000 dollars paid over 20 years is equivalent to winning, approximately, 400 000 dollars, assuming you can invest at 8 per cent interest.

Normally, you would be paid your first 50 000 dollars today, and would receive 19, not 20, additional payments. In this case, your winnings will be $a_0 + 50\,000$, where

$$a_0 = -500\,000(1.08)^{-19} + 500\,000 = 384\,143.97,$$

so your winnings are $384\,143.97 + 50\,000 = 434\,143.97$ dollars. The moral of this is that the present value of most lottery winnings is far less than the advertised winnings.

The next example applies to anyone who might purchase a home.

Example 2.17

Suppose we can get a 30 year mortgage at 10 per cent interest. We can afford to make monthly payments of 800 dollars. How much can we afford to borrow? Let a_0 be the amount we borrow and $A(n)$ the amount we owe the bank after n months. Then the amount we owe satisfies the dynamical system

$$A(n+1) = \left(1 + \tfrac{0.1}{12}\right) A(n) - 800.$$

Notice that we add on the interest each month, then subtract our payment. Also note that a 30 year mortgage means that $A(360) = 0$, that is, we pay off the loan in 360 months.

Using equation (7) with $m = 12$, $b = -800$, $k = 360$, $I = 0.1$, and $A(k) = 0$ gives

$$\frac{mb}{I} = -96\,000$$

and therefore

$$a_0 = -96\,000 \left(1 + \tfrac{0.1}{12}\right)^{-360} + 96\,000 = 91\,160.$$

Thus, we can afford to borrow about 90 000 dollars. Add our down payment to that, and we know what price range to consider in looking for our house.

Remember that, in reality, you will also have to consider insurance and property taxes in your monthly payment.

As our last application of equation (7), let's continue exploring the retirement plan we started discussing in Example 2.11.

Example 2.18

In Example 2.11, we concluded that when we retire, we need to have an amount a_0 in our savings, so that we can withdraw approximately 87 000 dollars each year. One answer would be: a_0 is the amount needed such that the yearly interest is $0.1a_0 = 87\,000$. In this case, $a_0 = 870\,000$ dollars. This way, we could afford to live for ever.

Let's say instead that we plan for our savings to last 25 years. In other words, what should a_0 be if, when we start retirement (year 0) with a_0 dollars invested at 10 per cent interest, compounded annually, we can withdraw 87 000 dollars per year for 25 years and $A(25) = 0$? The dynamical system for this annuity is the first order affine dynamical system

$$A(n+1) = 1.1A(n) - 87\,000.$$

Using equation (7) to find a_0, we get

$$a_0 = -870\,000(1.1)^{-25} + 870\,000 = 789\,702.39.$$

This says that when we retire in 30 years, we need to have about 800 000 dollars in our savings. Shortly we will discuss one method for saving this amount of money.

In some applications of the dynamical system (5), the unknown quantity is the deposit (or withdrawal) b. Solving equation (6)

$$A(k) = \left(1 + \frac{I}{m}\right)^k \left(a_0 + \frac{mb}{I}\right) - \frac{mb}{I}$$

for b gives

$$b = \frac{I}{m}\left(\frac{A(k) - r^k a_0}{r^k - 1}\right) \tag{8}$$

where $r = 1 + I/m$. As our first application of this equation, let's complete our retirement plan.

Example 2.19

Referring to Example 2.18, how do we save 800 000 dollars over the next 30 years, assuming we collect 10 per cent interest, compounded annually? To rephrase, suppose we have a savings account that pays 10 per cent annual effective interest, and that we make an additional deposit of b dollars each year. This is modeled by dynamical system (5), that is,

$$A(n + 1) = 1.1\, A(n) + b,$$

with $A(30) = 800\,000$. Equation (8) gives

$$b = 0.1 \left(\frac{800\,000 - (1.1)^{30} a_0}{(1.1)^{30} - 1}\right).$$

The answer depends on the amount we can initially put into savings. For this example, let $a_0 = 0$. Then

$$b = \frac{80\,000}{(1.1)^{30} - 1} = 4863.40.$$

To review, if we deposit 4900 dollars in a savings account each year for the next 30 years earning 10 per cent interest, compounded annually (this is called a **sinking fund**), then when we retire, our account will have 800 000 dollars in it. This will allow us to withdraw 87 000 dollars per year for the next 25 years.

Example 2.20

Let's consider an example similar to the previous example. Suppose we were not able to save as much as we wanted, and when we retired, we only had $a_0 = 700\,000$ dollars in our savings account collecting 10 per cent interest, compounded annually. We want our savings to last for 25 years. The question is now, how much can we withdraw from savings each year so that our savings last for 25 years ($A(25) = 0$)?

The dynamical system that models this problem is

$$A(n+1) = (1.1)A(n) + b,$$

where b is the amount we withdraw (and is therefore a negative number). Using equation (8) we get

$$b = \frac{-70\,000(1.1)^{25}}{(1.1)^{25} - 1} = -77\,117.65,$$

that is, we must live on about 77 000 dollars a year instead of 80 000.

One more application of equation (8) is another problem dealing with amortization of loans. Suppose we borrow a_0 dollars at $100I$ per cent per year, compounded monthly. What are our monthly payments if there are to be k equal payments, that is, $A(k) = 0$? This situation is modeled by the dynamical system

$$A(n+1) = \left(1 + \frac{I}{12}\right)A(n) + b,$$

where $A(n)$ is the amount we owe after n months and b is the monthly payment, which is a negative number. Since the monthly payment b is the only unknown in the problem, by equation (8) we get

$$b = \frac{-Ia_0\,(1 + I/12)^k}{12\left[(1 + I/12)^k - 1\right]}.$$

Table 1 gives a comparison of mortgage payments (computed using the above equation) for different length loans at different interest rates. The amount borrowed is fixed at $a_0 = 50\,000$.

There are several observations that can be made. The first is that if you double the length of time you take to pay the loan, you **do not** cut your payments in half. Going from 10 to 20 years at 10 per cent, your payments are still 73 per cent of the original amount. Going from 10 to 30 years, your payments are still two-thirds of the original amount. In fact, the amount of interest you pay goes from 29 291.20 dollars for the 10 year loan to 107 964.40 dollars for the 30 year loan. It's even worse for the higher interest loans. At 15 per cent interest, the payment for a 30 year loan is almost 80 per cent of the payment for a 10 year loan. This is a small reduction in payments for three times the number of mortgage payments. The difference between a 20 year mortgage payment and a 30 year mortgage payment at 15 per cent is only 26.17 dollars. Personally,

Table 2. Relationship between interest rates, length of loans, and monthly payments on 50 000 dollar loan.

Interest rate	Term	Monthly payment	Total payment
10	10	660.76	79 291.20
10	15	537.30	96 714.00
10	20	482.51	115 802.40
10	30	438.79	157 964.40
11	10	688.75	82 650.00
11	15	568.30	102 294.00
11	20	516.09	123 861.60
11	30	476.16	171 417.60
15	10	806.67	96 800.40
15	20	658.39	158 013.60
15	30	632.22	227 599.20

I would try to come up with the extra 26.17 dollars a month in order to save the 69 585.60 dollars in extra interest.

The reason for the discrepancy is that for a 10 per cent, 10 year loan, your first monthly payment is 416.66 dollars interest and 244.10 dollars principal. But at 10 per cent for 30 years, the first payment is still 416.66 dollars interest and only 22.13 dollars principal. For the long term loan, you are paying interest, almost entirely.

Another observation is about the effect of interest rates. For shorter term loans, say 10 years, the 15 per cent loan has payments 22 per cent higher than the 10 per cent loan, although the interest rate is 50 per cent higher. But for longer term loans, say 30 years, the 15 per cent loan has payments 44 per cent higher than the 10 per cent loan. That is, the per cent increase in payments is almost the same as the per cent increase in the interest rate. The 11 per cent loan has payments 8.5 per cent higher than the 10 per cent loan. Again, this is because the monthly payments are, initially, nearly all interest and the principal is (almost) irrelevant.

Most people take long term loans in order to have lower monthly payments. But the moral of the above discussion is that this course of action can be a mistake, especially at high interest rates. Loans longer than 15 or 20 years do not appreciably cut monthly payments, that is, you can afford to buy the same size house with a 20 year loan as you can with a 30 year loan. The decision on the length of loan depends on the present interest rate and possible alternate investments.

Suppose we are given a_0, $A(k)$, and k, and we wish to determine I. For simplicity, let's assume $m = 1$ and $b = 0$, and that we wish to determine the effective yearly interest rate. Solving for I in the equation

$$A(k) = (1 + I)^k a_0,$$

gives

$$(1 + I)^k = \frac{A(k)}{a_0}.$$

Taking kth roots gives

$$I = \left(\frac{A(k)}{a_0} \right)^{\frac{1}{k}} - 1.$$

Example 2.21

Suppose you have a savings bond (in which the interest is given to you at maturity) that is worth 1000 dollars at its maturity, in 10 years. Someone will give you 500 dollars for your bond today. Thus your bond is worth $a_0 = 500$ today and is worth $A(10) = 1000$ in 10 years. The effective interest on this bond is

$$I = \left(\tfrac{1000}{500} \right)^{0.1} - 1 = 0.0718,$$

that is, this 500 dollar offer is equivalent to a 7.18 per cent interest rate. If you can find an investment that pays more than 7.18 per cent, take the person up on their offer.

If we need to solve for I in the case when $b \neq 0$, it is necessary for us to find a root of the polynomial

$$0 = \left(1 + \frac{I}{m} \right)^k \left(a_0 + \frac{mb}{I} \right) - \frac{mb}{I} - A(k).$$

In general, this is impossible to factorize, but there are computer techniques for estimating the solution I as accurately as we wish (see Section 3.4 on Newton's method for one approach). Let's see an example which shows that this problem does occur.

Example 2.22

Suppose we wish to get a 100 000 dollar mortgage on our home. We can get a 9 per cent, 30 year loan. Many mortgage companies require the borrower to pay **points**. For example, suppose we must pay 2 points on our loan. What this means is that we must pay 2 per cent of the loan at settlement, that is, 2000 dollars. So essentially, we borrow 102 000 dollars, but we only get 100 000 dollars to buy our home. The monthly payments on 102 000 dollars are (using our previous methods) 820.72 dollars.

But since we've only seen 100 000 dollars of the borrowed money, as far as we are concerned we are making monthly payments of 820.72 dollars on a 100 000 dollar loan. What is the **effective interest** on this loan, that is, what interest rate I would cause us to make monthly payments of 820.72 dollars for 360 months on a loan of 100 000 dollars? To find this, we need to solve the equation

$$0 = \left(1 + \frac{I}{12}\right)^{360}\left(100\,000 - \frac{9848.64}{I}\right) + \frac{9848.64}{I}$$

for I. To make things easier, multiply by I, giving the 361th order polynomial

$$0 = \left(1 + \frac{I}{12}\right)^{360}(100\,000I - 9848.64) + 9848.64.$$

There may be many solutions, so when we find one we have to make sure it is the correct one.

The solution, that is, the **effective interest** on this loan, is slightly more than 9.2 per cent. One method is to 'guess' at I: try I values slightly more than 0.09 until you have a reasonably correct answer, in other words an I value that makes the above expression close to zero. (In calculus, this is known as the bisection method.) There are computer programs that do this.

Finally, let's consider the case in which we know $A(k)$, a_0, and I, and we wish to find k. Again, let's assume I is the effective annual interest rate and so $m = 1$. We need to solve equation (6)

$$A(k) = \left(1 + \frac{I}{m}\right)^k\left(a_0 + \frac{mb}{I}\right) - \frac{mb}{I}$$

for k. Solving for k consists of adding mb/I to both sides, dividing both sides by $a_0 + mb/I$, taking the natural logarithm of both sides, and finally dividing both sides by $\ln(1 + I/m)$. This gives, after simplifying by using the rules of logarithms,

$$k = \frac{\ln(A(k) + mb/I) - \ln(a_0 + mb/I)}{\ln(1 + I/m)}. \tag{9}$$

Let's first consider some situations in which we want to find k, but with $b = 0$. In such cases, equation (9) simplifies to

$$k = \frac{\ln(A(k)/a_0)}{\ln(1 + I/m)}.$$

**Example
2.23**

Suppose you invest 1000 dollars at 7 per cent effective annual interest. How many years will it take for your investment to double, that is, for what value of k will $A(k) = 200$? Here, $I = 0.07$, $a_0 = 100$, and $m = 1$. Then

$$k = \frac{\ln 2}{\ln 1.07} = 10.24.$$

So in 11 years you will have more than doubled your money.

Notice that when $b = 0$ you do not need to know a_0 and $A(k)$. Instead you only need to know $A(k)/a_0$. For example, how long will it take to triple your money, that is, for what value of k is $A(k)/a_0 = 3$?

$$k = \frac{\ln 3}{\ln 1.07} = 16.24.$$

**Example
2.24**

Suppose you deposit 10 000 dollars into a bank account paying 8 per cent interest, compounded annually. Suppose that in each of the following years, you deposit an additional 5000 dollars. How long will it take for you to have a million dollars, that is, for what value of k is $A(k) = 1\,000\,000$? Here, $mb/I = 62\,500$, so

$$k = \frac{\ln 1\,062\,500 - \ln 72\,500}{\ln 1.08} = 34.9.$$

Since k must be an integer, if $k = 35$, you will have more than a million dollars in your account.

2.2.1 Problems

1. Set up the dynamical system and compute the amount in your savings account after

   (a) 1 year with an initial deposit of 1000 dollars at 8 per cent interest, compounded quarterly.

   (b) 5 years with an initial deposit of 200 dollars at 5 per cent interest, compounded semi-annually.

2. Suppose you start a savings account which pays 8 per cent interest a year compounded monthly. You initially deposit 1000 dollars and decide to add an additional 100 dollars each month thereafter. How much is in your account after 5 years?

3. Suppose, due to inflation, the value of your money is decreasing at the rate of 0.5 per cent per month. This is equivalent to an interest rate of −6 per cent per year, compounded monthly.

(a) Model this with a dynamical system and give its solution.

(b) If you now have 1000 dollars hidden under your bed, use the dynamical system from part (a) to find what it will be worth in 10 years.

4. Suppose you wish to buy a house, but can only afford 800 dollars a month.

(a) If you can get a loan at 9 per cent (compounded monthly) for 30 years, how large can your loan be?

(b) How large can your loan be if you amortize your loan in 20 years?

5. Suppose you inherit a trust fund that pays you 500 dollars a month for the next 10 years. How much is that trust worth to you if you can invest your money at 8 per cent interest compounded monthly?

6. Suppose you have a 5000 dollar, 20 year bond, with a coupon value of 11 per cent, that is, it pays you 550 dollars each year for the next 20 years, at which time you get your 5000 dollars back. What is the present value of this bond if your alternate investment is a savings account paying 7 per cent interest compounded annually?

7. At retirement, your savings account has 300 000 dollars which is collecting 6 per cent interest, compounded monthly. How much money can you withdraw each month so that your savings will last 20 years?

8. Suppose you borrow 6000 dollars at 10 per cent per year, compounded monthly, in order to buy a car. If the loan is to be paid back in 5 years, what is your monthly payment?

9. Suppose you borrow 2000 dollars at 8 per cent interest, compounded quarterly, to take a vacation. If the loan is to be paid back in eight equal quarterly payments, how much should these payments be?

10. How much is the monthly payment on a 100 000 dollar loan at 12 per cent interest (compounded monthly) which must be amortized in

(a) 10 years?

(b) 20 years?

(c) 30 years?

11. Consider the following retirement problem.

    (a) Suppose you presently need 2000 dollars a month to live comfortably, and that inflation is 0.5 per cent per month. In 40 years, how much will you need each month to live comfortably?

    (b) Using your answer to part (a), how much savings should you have (in 40 years) so that you can live comfortably for the next 30 years? Your savings are collecting 12 per cent interest compounded monthly.

    (c) How much money should you put in your savings account (collecting 12 per cent interest compounded monthly) each month in order to have the savings computed in part (b)? Remember you are saving for 40 years.

12. Suppose you buy a painting for 200 dollars. Five years from now, someone offers you 300 dollars for your painting. What is the effective yearly interest on this investment?

13. You buy stocks for 1000 dollars. After 3 years, you sell them for 1500 dollars. What is your effective yearly yield? Note that it's actually higher since you have also (probably) received dividends on the stocks.

14. What effective yearly interest rate would you need on an investment in order to double your money in 8 years?

15. How many years would it take to double your money if you invested at

    (a) 5 per cent effective yearly interest rate?

    (b) 9 per cent effective yearly interest rate?

16. Suppose you have 100 000 dollars in a savings account that pays 8 per cent interest, compounded quarterly. Suppose each quarter you withdraw 3000 dollars from your account.

    (a) How many quarters will it take for you to deplete your account to only 50 000 dollars?

    (b) How many quarters will it take for you to deplete your entire savings account?

2.3 Applications to the social sciences

In the previous section, we studied quantitative properties of a dynamical system, that is, we were interested in the numerical values of quantities such as monthly loan payments. Often, numerical answers are not important. What is important is the qualitative properties of the model; for example, for large values of k, what is happening to the solution $A(k)$? We will see this in the first two applications of this section, an investigation of the law of supply and demand and Richardson's model of an arms race.

2.3.1 Supply and demand

Let's consider supply and demand as it relates to a product that takes one unit of time to produce. This model was developed to study the farming industry where the product (a crop) is produced once each year, and the farmer has to plan next year's crops using information about prices this year.

Suppose we own a farm and want to decide how much acreage to devote to corn. If the price of corn is high after this year's harvest, then we will plant a large amount of corn next year. With a large harvest of corn next year, the price of corn will have to drop in order to create enough demand to sell the entire harvest. With the price dropping next year, people will not plant much corn the year after. With a small harvest that year, the price will rise since not much demand is needed to sell the entire crop. The price is then high that year and this entire process repeats itself.

Notice that this is a recursive process and that the price oscillates between high and low values. But does it oscillate to equilibrium or with increasing magnitude (or does it exhibit some other type of behavior)? Let's develop a dynamical model of this supply and demand process and see if we can find the answer.

To develop our model, we need to consider three quantities, the supply $S(n)$ of our product, the demand $D(n)$ for our product, and the price $P(n)$ of one unit of our product, all in year n. Since there are three quantities or unknowns, we need to develop three equations relating them. This corresponds to three assumptions. One reasonable set of assumptions is the following.

1. The supply of the product in any year depends positively on the price of the product the previous year.

2. The demand for the product in any year depends negatively on the present price of the product.

3. Each year, the price of the product is adjusted so that the demand equals the supply.

Let's study the third assumption in more detail. Suppose we have a certain supply of a product this year and we wish to sell the entire supply. Our goal is to sell at a high price. The consumers' goal is to buy at a low price. The consumers offer to buy a large amount of the product at a low price. If we do not have that much of the product, we hold out for a higher price. The consumers then offer a higher price, but decrease the amount they are willing to buy. This process continues until the consumers reach a price at which they are willing to buy exactly what the producer has to sell. This is the price implied by the third assumption.

Example 2.25

Let's put these assumptions together. Let $S(n)$ represent the supply of rutabagas, let $D(n)$ represent the demand (the amount the consumers buy) for rutabagas, and let $P(n)$ represent the price per bushel of rutabagas, all in year n.

The first assumption states that the supply in year $n + 1$ depends positively on the price in year n, that is, the higher the price in year n, the larger the supply in year $n + 1$. Let's assume that the relationship is given by the **supply equation**

$$S(n + 1) = 0.8P(n).$$

Thus, if the price is 6 dollars per bushel this year, the producers will grow 4.8 units of rutabagas next year, but if the price is 12 dollars per bushel this year, they will produce 9.6 units of rutabagas next year. The higher the price this year, the more rutabagas next year. This can be seen in that the slope of the line $S = 0.8P$ is positive.

The second assumption states that the demand this year depends negatively on the price this year, that is, the higher the price, the lower the demand. Let's assume that this relationship is given by the **demand equation**

$$D(n) = -1.2P(n) + 20.$$

In this case, if the price is 6 dollars per bushel, the consumers are willing to buy 12.8 units of rutabagas, while if the price is 12 dollars per bushel, the consumers are only willing to buy 5.6 units of rutabagas. Notice that the higher the price, the lower the demand. This is reflected in the negative slope of the line $D = -1.2P + 20$.

We now use the third assumption to determine the price of rutabagas for next year. This assumption states that the price next year will be adjusted so that the supply equals the demand, that is,

$$S(n + 1) = D(n + 1).$$

But since $D(n + 1) = -1.2P(n + 1) + 20$ and $S(n + 1) = 0.8P(n)$, substitution gives

$$-1.2P(n+1) + 20 = 0.8P(n).$$

Solving for $P(n+1)$ gives the first order affine dynamical system

$$P(n+1) = -\tfrac{2}{3}P(n) + \tfrac{50}{3}.$$

From this first order affine dynamical system, it is easy to see that if the price this year is 7 dollars, then the price next year is $P(n+1) = -(2/3) \times 7 + 50/3 = 12$ dollars.

If we apply our knowledge of first order affine equations to this dynamical system, we see that $p = 10$ is the equilibrium value (or equilibrium price) for this equation, and that $r = -2/3$, so that the general solution is

$$P(k) = (-\tfrac{2}{3})^k c + 10,$$

which oscillates to equilibrium. Thus, the price of rutabagas will fluctuate above and below 10 dollars per bushel, but will also become closer to that price over time.

Let us analyze this process more abstractly. From our first assumption, the supply next year $S(n+1)$ depends on the price this year. Let us suppose that the relationship is 'linear', so that the **supply equation** will be

$$S(n+1) = s\,P(n) + a,$$

where s and a are two fixed constants. (While this seems to be a bit restrictive, in real life this usually models the behavior quite well.) Since the supply is positively related to price, we also assume that $s > 0$. The number s measures the **sensitivity of the producers to price**.

From the second assumption, demand in year $n+1$ depends on the price in year $n+1$. Again we assume this relationship is linear, so that the **demand equation** is

$$D(n+1) = -d\,P(n+1) + b,$$

where d and b are two fixed constants. Since demand is negatively related to price, we assume that $d > 0$ so that the coefficient $-d$ of $P(n+1)$ is negative. The number d measures the **sensitivity of consumers to price**.

From the third assumption, we want the demand in year $n+1$ to equal the supply in year $n+1$, that is,

$$S(n+1) = D(n+1).$$

Remember that through bargaining, the producers and consumers will come to an agreement on price that is as advantageous as possible to both. From this equation, we can substitute in for both $S(n+1)$ and $D(n+1)$, just as we did in the previous example, to get

$$-d\,P(n+1) + b = s\,P(n) + a.$$

Subtracting b from both sides, then dividing by $-d$ gives the first order affine dynamical system

$$P(n+1) = -\left(\frac{s}{d}\right)P(n) + \frac{b-a}{d}.$$

The equilibrium value for this dynamical system is

$$p = \frac{(b-a)/d}{1+s/d} \quad \text{or} \quad p = \frac{b-a}{s+d},$$

after simplification. The general solution is then

$$P(k) = c\left(-\frac{s}{d}\right)^k + p.$$

We know that if

$$-1 < -\frac{s}{d} < 1,$$

the equilibrium value is stable, that is, $P(k)$ oscillates to p as k goes to infinity. This means we have a stable price structure for this product.

Since $-s/d < 0 < 1$, the equilibrium value is stable if $-1 < -s/d$, that is, if $d > s$. Likewise, the equilibrium value is unstable if $d < s$, and the price will fluctuate with increasing amplitude until something drastic happens. This can be stated formally in what is known as the **cobweb theorem of economics**.

Theorem 2.26

*Suppose we have a product whose price satisfies the three assumptions given earlier. Then the equilibrium price is **stable** and we have a stable market if*

$$s < d,$$

*that is, if the consumers are more sensitive to price than the producers. Likewise, the price is **unstable** and we have an unstable market if*

$$s > d,$$

that is, if the producers are more sensitive to price than the consumers.

When studying the market for a particular product, how can we use this model, that is, how can we find the constants, s, a, d, and b? First, we aren't interested in the actual equilibrium price, but only whether that price is stable or not. Therefore, we only need the constants s and d. In fact, to determine the stability, we don't even need s and d. What we need to know is how s and d compare. By observing consumers' and suppliers' habits at different prices, it can usually be determined who is the more sensitive.

Remark: In reality, the supply and demand relationships are nonlinear and difficult to discover. When studying these relationships, the 'changes' in producer and consumer behavior (relative to a change in price) are approximated. These changes are derivatives and approximate s and d. Thus, the equations $S = sP + a$ and $D = dP + b$ are 'tangent line' approximations to the nonlinear functions for supply and demand.

Consider the oil industry. When the price of oil went up in the 1970s, the oil industry greatly expanded their search for, and consequently their production of, oil (with a few years' delay). Thus, their sensitivity, s, was large. But the consumers had somewhat fixed oil requirements, and consumption dropped only slightly as the price rose. So the consumers' sensitivity to price d was relatively small. Since $s > d$, we predict an unstable cyclic situation in the oil industry, which seems to be the case.

Suppose that for a certain product, say corn, it has been determined that $s > d$, and the market is unstable. What can be done? One solution is that the government can enter the picture as a consumer and make d larger. This can be done by price supports. Another solution is to pay farmers not to grow corn. Paying not to grow the crop is almost the same as buying the corn that would have been grown, and again increases d.

As we see from this discussion, mathematics can, not only explain the reasons for certain problems, but also often help suggest solutions to the problem.

Suppose that it is determined that $s = d$, that is,

$$P(k) = c(-1)^k + p.$$

Then the price oscillates with constant amplitude. But in reality, can we be sure $s = d$, or are they only close to each other? Unless they are **exactly** equal, we cannot be sure if the price is stable or unstable. You should be uncomfortable making a prediction in this case.

2.3.2 A model of an arms race

We will now develop a dynamical model of a two nation arms race. A variation of this model was originally developed by Lewis Fry Richardson in the 1930s. Let's assume that we have two countries, A and B. Let $A(n)$ and $B(n)$ represent the amount (in some common monetary unit) spent on armaments (defense?) by the corresponding countries in year n. We also assume that each country has a fixed amount of distrust of the other country, causing it to retain arms. We will now develop equations that relate the amount each country spends on arms in one year in terms of what they **both** spent the previous year.

First we look at the **increase** in expenditures by country A, that is, $A(n+1) - A(n)$. We wish to have an equation that takes into account that if B spends a lot on defense in one year, then A spends more on defense the next year. Also, since large expenditures will deplete a country's treasury, our equation should indicate that large expenditures by A one year will cause smaller expenditures the next year. A simple equation that satisfies the assumptions above is the dynamical system

$$A(n+1) - A(n) = -r\,A(n) + s\,B(n) + a,$$

where r, s, and a are given constants, with r and s both being positive. The constant s measures country A's distrust of country B in that it reacts to the way B arms itself. The constant r is a measure of country A's own economy.

Similar assumptions for country B lead to the dynamical system

$$B(n+1) - B(n) = -R\,B(n) + S\,A(n) + b,$$

with S measuring B's distrust of A and R measuring country B's economy.

We now have a dynamical system of two equations, which we will learn to deal with later in this text. For the present, we will make simplifying assumptions. Assume that the two countries have an equal amount of distrust of each other, that is, $s = S$. Also assume that the two countries' economies are about the same, that is, $r = R$. We now have

$$A(n+1) - A(n) = -rA(n) + sB(n) + a$$

and

$$B(n+1) - B(n) = -rB(n) + sA(n) + b.$$

Add the two equations, giving

$$[A(n+1) + B(n+1)] - [A(n) + B(n)] = (-r+s)[A(n) + B(n)] + c,$$

where $c = a + b$.

The idea is to look at the total expenditures of the two countries, that is, $T(n) = A(n) + B(n)$. Making this substitution in the previous equation gives $T(n+1) - T(n) = (s-r)T(n) + c$ or

$$T(n+1) = (1 - r + s)T(n) + c.$$

The equilibrium value for this first order affine dynamical system is $c/(r-s)$, and the particular solution is

$$T(k) = (1 - r + s)^k \left(T_0 - \frac{c}{r-s}\right) + \frac{c}{r-s}, \tag{10}$$

where $T_0 = T(0)$. We know that if $-1 < 1 - r + s < 1$, that is, if $-2 < -r + s < 0$, then the equilibrium value $c/(r-s)$ is stable.

In particular, looking at the right side of this inequality, we see that if $s < r$, then $T(k)$ approaches $c/(r-s)$, and we have a **stable arms race**. In other words, if a country's restraint r caused by its economy is greater then its distrust s of the other country, there will eventually be a constant expenditure on arms each year.

But if the distrust is too great, then $s > r$ and $(1 - r + s)^k$ goes to positive infinity. In the solution (10), if $T_0 - c/(r-s) < 0$, then $T(k)$ goes to negative infinity (or zero, whichever comes first); but if $T_0 - c/(r-s) > 0$, then $T(k)$ goes to positive infinity. The conclusion in this case is that if the initial total expenditure T_0 of the two countries is small enough (less than $c/(r-s)$), and the countries have a large amount of mutual distrust ($s > r$), then the arms race will die out. But if T_0 is large, then we have an escalating arms race. Since no two countries can sustain exponentially increasing expenditures on arms, the alternative is war or negotiations.

Example 2.27

Before World War I, there were two alliances, France and Russia being one, and Germany and Austria-Hungary being the other. Thus, the total expenditures on arms by these two alliances would satisfy a dynamical system of the form

$$T(n+1) = RT(n) + c,$$

where $R = 1 - r + s$. In Richardson (1960), we find that the estimated total expenditures of these two alliances were (in millions of pounds sterling): 199 in 1909, 205 in 1910, and 215 in year 1911. Letting 1909 be year 0, we have $T(0) = 199$, $T(1) = 205$, and $T(2) = 215$. Since, from the dynamical system, we have

$$T(1) = RT(0) + c \quad \text{and} \quad T(2) = RT(1) + c,$$

substitution gives the two equations

$$205 = 199R + c \quad \text{and} \quad 215 = 205R + c.$$

Solving these two equations gives $R = 5/3$ and $c = -380/3$. Thus, the dynamical system becomes

$$T(n + 1) = \tfrac{5}{3}T(n) - \tfrac{38}{3}$$

and the solution is

$$T(k) = (\tfrac{5}{3})^k(T_0 - 190) + 190.$$

The values we computed for R and c are only approximate. There are techniques for finding better estimates of R and c by using more years, and in some sense, averaging all the R and c values we find. But this is a different topic.

Note that $1 - r + s = 5/3$, so that $s - r = 2/3$. Although we do not know r or s, we do know that $s > r$. From the solution $T(k)$, we see that if $T_0 < 190$, then the countries would have disarmed. But, since $T_0 = 199$, $T(k)$ grew exponentially leading to an accelerating arms race, which led to **war**. This, Richardson claimed, could be one of the causes of World War I.

While this is an over-simplification of the causes of war, it could help us understand the reasons behind escalations in arms races and might possibly help in ending them.

2.3.3 Radioactive decay

We now come to the first of two quantitative applications, that is, applications in which we are interested in numerical values instead of limits.

Suppose we want to find the half-life of a radioactive substance. Suppose $A(n)$ is the amount of a radioactive material remaining after n years. For any radioactive material, there is a certain fixed probability that in any given time period any one atom of that material will decay during that period. Assume that in 1 year there is a 10 per cent chance that any one atom decays. Since each atom acts independently of all the others, it follows that 10 per cent of the material will decay in 1 year.

For any time period, let p equal the probability that any atom decays during that time period, and let $A(n)$ be the amount of material we have after n time periods. Then the amount of material left after $n + 1$ time periods is proportional to the amount left after n time periods, that is,

$$A(n + 1) = (1 - p)\,A(n) = r\,A(n),$$

where $0 < r = 1 - p < 1$. It is relatively easy to get a good approximation for r. For example, suppose that at time $n = 0$ you have $A(0) = a_0 = 10$ grams of the material, but that after 1 year you have 9.9 grams. Then

$$A(1) = rA(0) \quad \text{or} \quad 9.9 = 10\,r,$$

so $r = 0.99$.

The dynamical system for the decay of this radioactive substance is then

$$A(n + 1) = 0.99A(n).$$

What is the half-life of this substance, that is, in how many years, k, will $A(k) = 0.5a_0$? Since the solution is $A(k) = (0.99)^k a_0$, we need to solve for k in the equation

$$0.5a_0 = (0.99)^k a_0.$$

Dividing both sides by a_0 and taking natural logarithms gives

$$k = \frac{\ln 0.5}{\ln 0.99} = 68.97 \text{ years.}$$

This is a much better approach than waiting for 69 years to find 5 grams remaining.

It must be stated that r is the effective yearly change in the radioactive substance, but that actually it is decaying continuously. Using techniques similar to those discussed in Section 1.6, a continuous model (differential equation) can be developed to model this situation. It must also be noted that this is not the method normally used for computing the half-life of radioactive materials.

An important application of radioactive decay is to **carbon dating**. A certain proportion of the carbon in the atmosphere is radioactive carbon-14. Thus, the proportion of carbon-14 in plants and animals is the same as in the atmosphere. It is assumed that this proportion remains constant over time, so that we know what per cent of the carbon in a plant or animal was carbon-14 when the plant or animal died.

When an animal or plant dies, the carbon-14 in their tissue starts decaying and is not replaced with new carbon-14. The half-life of carbon-14 is approximately 5700 years, so that $A(5700) = 0.5A(0)$. Solving for r in the solution

$$A(5700) = 0.5A(0) = r^{5700}A(0)$$

gives

$$r = (0.5)^{\frac{1}{5700}}.$$

Suppose we find a bone of some animal in which only 83 per cent of the original amount of carbon-14 is present. How old is this bone? If the animal died in year 0, then the amount left after k years is, from our solution,

$$A(k) = (0.5)^{\frac{k}{5700}} A(0).$$

If today is year k, then we know that $A(k) = 0.83 A(0)$. Substitution into the above equation, canceling the $A(0)$'s, and taking natural logarithms gives that

$$\frac{\ln 0.83}{\ln 0.5} = \frac{k}{5700}$$

or that $k = 1532$. Thus this animal lived about 1500 years ago.

2.3.4 Glottochronology

The last application of this section is the study of **glottochronology**. The term, glottochronology, is a combination of Greek words meaning, essentially, language dating. Mathematicians and linguists have worked together to develop a theory for studying the changes in languages.

We all know that, over time, certain words disappear from usage and new words appear. Suppose that, at a certain point in time, we look at a list of L words (say $L = 250$). At a later point in time, we study that same list of words and determine what per cent of the original list of words are still in use.

Let one unit of time be 1 year. Thus, time n will be n years. Let $A(n)$ represent the per cent of the original list of words still in use n years later, given as a decimal. The basic assumption is that the per cent $A(n+1)$ of the original list of words in use at time $n+1$ is proportional to the per cent of the original list of words in use at time n, that is,

$$A(n + 1) = r\, A(n),$$

where r is a positive constant less than one. At time 0, all of the original list of words is in use, so $A(0) = 1$. Therefore, at time k, $A(k) = r^k(1) = r^k$ is the per cent of the original list of words still in use, as a decimal.

Since languages change slowly, r should be close to 1 and would probably be hard to estimate on a year by year comparison. By comparing a written language today with the same language a millennium ago, glottochronologists can estimate r^{1000}. This number r also depends on the particular language. But glottochronologists have found that the number r^{1000} is usually close to 0.805. So for languages with no written history, that is, for languages in which we cannot estimate r, we will assume that

$$r^{1000} = 0.805.$$

Thus, the per cent of the original list of words that are still in use k years later is $r^k = (0.805)^{0.001k}$.

Before proceeding with our discussion of languages, we need to review some aspects of probability. We will do this through an example.

Example 2.28

Suppose two people each 'know' a certain per cent of a list of words. For example, suppose Frank knows 70 per cent of list L and Sue knows 80 per cent of list L, where L contains 100 words. Given any random sublist of words from list L, we would expect Frank to know 70 per cent of them and Sue to know 80 per cent of them.

Frank knows 70 of the original 100 words. We would expect Sue to know 80 per cent of Frank's 70 words, that is, 56 of Frank's words. Thus, Sue and Frank know 56 words in common, that is, the per cent of the 100 words that Frank and Sue both know is $(0.80)(0.70) = 0.56$ or 56 per cent.

Multiplication principle: suppose person A knows P per cent of a list of L words and person B knows Q per cent of the same list of L words (where P and Q are given as decimals). Given no additional information, we would expect A and B to both know PQ per cent of the words.

Suppose at time 0, a group of people separate themselves from their culture. A group of American Indians leaves the tribe and forms its own tribe, or a group sails to a deserted island and starts its own culture. We then have two cultures, A and B. At time 0, they have the same language, so that for a given list of L words, $A(0) = B(0) = 1$ is the per cent of the words they both know (and have in common).

If we contact each of these cultures k years later, culture A will know $A(k) = (0.805)^{0.001k}$ per cent of the original list and culture B will also know $B(k) = (0.805)^{0.001k}$ per cent of the original list. Thus the per cent of the words that both cultures know is, by the multiplication principle,

$$Q = (0.805)^{0.001k}(0.805)^{0.001k} = (0.805)^{0.002k}.$$

What the glottochronologist does now is to construct a list of words. From that list of words, the two cultures are studied and it is determined what per cent Q of this list of words is known by both cultures. Thus in the equation for Q above, Q is known, but k, the number of years since the two cultures separated, is unknown. Solving for k gives

$$k = \frac{500 \ln Q}{\ln 0.805}.$$

**Example
2.29**

Suppose that the natives of two islands have similar languages. From a list of 300 words, 180 words are understood by both groups, that is, $Q = 180/300 = 0.6$. Then

$$k = \frac{500 \ln 0.6}{\ln 0.805} = 1177.5.$$

We then conclude that the natives of these two islands came from a common ancestry, approximately 1200 years ago.

Suppose a collection of tribes with a similar language is considered. First, group the tribes into geographical regions. Then date the time separation n for pairs of tribes in each geographical region. It can be argued that the region with the pair of tribes with the largest time separation is the homeland of the tribes. The reason for this conclusion is as follows. Suppose one tribe separates into three tribes. One tribe might move away while the other two remain in the same general region. The tribe that moved away may split again in its geographical location, but the largest time separation will always be the two that remained in the original area.

Glottochronology was popular for some time, but there are now some doubts about its accuracy. This could be from, among other things, problems with measurement and assumptions that are not realistic. For example, how do you determine if a word is the same for two cultures? If the spelling of a word or the pronunciation of a word changes 'slightly', we will still count it as being on the list. If the **meaning** of a word changes 'significantly', we will delete it from the list. Thus, there is some subjectivity in determining Q which could drastically change the results. Also, some words are more likely to change than others. But in the multiplication principle, we tacitly **assumed** that all words were equally likely to change. This can also throw the results off.

The moral of this is that you need to be careful not to make more claims about your model than are justified. Most of the models in this text are only first approximations at modeling a situation.

2.3.5 Problems

1. Consider the supply and demand equations

$$S(n + 1) = 0.8P(n) \quad \text{and} \quad D(n + 1) = -0.6P(n + 1) + 7.$$

   (a) Find the first order affine dynamical system relating $P(n + 1)$ to $P(n)$.

   (b) Find the equilibrium value for this equation.

   (c) Discuss the behavior of $P(k)$, that is, is it stable or unstable?

2. Determine the dynamical system for $P(n+1)$ in terms of $P(n)$, find the equilibrium value, and classify it as stable, unstable, or unsure, if

$$S(n+1) = 1.2P(n) - 1 \quad \text{and} \quad D(n+1) = -0.8P(n+1) + 7.$$

3. Consider the supply and demand equations

$$S(n+1) = 0.3P(n) - 4 \quad \text{and} \quad D(n+1) = -0.4P(n+1) + 10.$$

   (a) Repeat Problem 2 for these equations.

   (b) Use these equations to develop a first order affine dynamical system relating $S(n)$ to $S(n+1)$.

   (c) Use these equations to develop a first order affine dynamical system relating $D(n)$ to $D(n+1)$.

4. Consider the supply and demand equations

$$S(n+1) = P^2(n) \quad \text{and} \quad D(n+1) = -3P(n+1) + 4.$$

   (a) Assuming supply equals demand, find a first order nonlinear dynamical system relating $P(n+1)$ to $P(n)$.

   (b) Find the two equilibrium values for this equation.

   (c) By constructing a cobweb close to the positive equilibrium value, do you think this equilibrium value is stable or unstable?

5. Suppose we have followed the price of a product for several years. We observed that when the price was 8 dollars per bushel in one year, the demand that year was 6000 bushels and the supply was 12 000 bushels the next year. We also observed that when the price was 5 dollars per bushel in one year, the demand that year was 9000 bushels and the supply was 10 000 bushels the next year.

   (a) From this information, determine the constants s and a in the supply equation $S(n+1) = sP(n) + a$.

   (b) From this information, determine the constants d and b in the demand equation $D(n+1) = -dP(n) + b$.

   (c) Determine the equilibrium price and its stability.

6. Consider Harrod's model of an economy. Suppose we have an economy where $S(n)$ is the amount of savings, $I(n)$ is the amount of investment, and $T(n)$ is the total income (public and private) of the economy, all in year n. Suppose it is assumed that (1) savings in any year are proportional to income that year (savings assumption), (2) investment in any year is proportional to the change in total income between that year and the previous year (acceleration principle), and (3) each year savings (which is actual investment) equal investment (which is the desired investment). Model these three assumptions with three dynamical systems, use substitution to develop a first order affine dynamical system for $T(n)$, and make predictions on the growth of $T(n)$ in a healthy economy.

7. Suppose an arms race between two countries is given by the dynamical system

$$T(n+1) = 1.2T(n) - 40,$$

where $T(n)$ is the total amount spent by the two countries in year n. The arms race will die out if the initial total arms expenditures is below what number?

8. Suppose the arms race between two countries is described by the equations

$$
\begin{aligned}
A(n+1) - A(n) &= -2A(n) + 1.5B(n) + 30 \\
B(n+1) - B(n) &= 1.5A(n) - 2B(n) + 70.
\end{aligned}
$$

What are the long range projections for the total expenditures by the two countries in this arms race?

9. Suppose the total expenditures by two countries are 75, 80, and 84 billion dollars in three consecutive years. Derive the dynamical system for $T(n)$ and make your predictions about this arms race.

10. Two groups of people have a common language. From a list of 250 words, the two groups have 220 in common. How long ago did these two groups split from one?

11. Consider the model of glottochronology. Assume a language is given today.

    (a) How long will it take for 1/4 of the words to change?

    (b) How long will it take for 10 per cent of the words to change?

12. Suppose that person A knows 60 per cent of a list of 1000 words, person B knows 70 per cent of that list, and person C knows 30 per cent of that list.

  (a) How many words do you expect all three people know?

  (b) What per cent of the words is known by A and B but not by C?

13. Suppose that you presently have 15 grams of a radioactive material. In a year, you have 14.7 grams remaining. What is the half-life of this material?

14. Suppose the half-life of a radioactive material is 100 years. If you presently have 1 gram of the material, how much will you have in 1 year?

15. Suppose that a piece of wood is discovered at an archaeological dig which has 30 per cent of its original amount of carbon-14. Approximate the age of this wood.

16. Radium decreases at the rate of 0.0428 per cent per year. What is its half-life?

17. Radioactive beryllium, with a half-life of 4.6 million years, is used to date fossils in deep-sea sediment. If a fossil is found with 99 per cent of its original amount of radioactive beryllium, then how old is this fossil?

2.4   An introduction to Markov chains

In this section we will study a type of probability problem which is indicative of a large class of problems. Let's start with a simple example. Consider two bags containing marbles. The first bag contains 3 red marbles and 2 blue marbles. The second bag contains 3 red marbles and 7 blue marbles. A marble is drawn from the first bag, its color is recorded, and it is returned to the bag from which it was drawn. If the first marble drawn was **red**, we draw the second marble from **bag 1**. If the first marble drawn was **blue**, we draw the second marble from **bag 2**.

We now repeat the entire process with the second marble, the third marble, and so forth. Thus, we draw the nth marble, record its color, and return it to the bag from which it was drawn. If the nth marble is **red**, we draw the $(n + 1)$th marble from **bag 1**, but if the nth marble is **blue**, we draw the $(n + 1)$th marble from **bag 2**. What is the probability that the nth marble drawn will be red? This process is called a Markov chain.

A **Markov chain** is a sequence of experiments (drawing a marble), in which the same results (red or blue) are possible after each experiment (draw). The probability of each result (red or blue) on the $(n + 1)$th experiment depends only on the result of the nth experiment. For the above problem, this means that we know the probability of getting a red or blue marble on the $(n+1)$th draw once we are told the color of the nth marble drawn. For example, if the nth marble is red, we draw the $(n+1)$th marble from bag 1 and so the probability it is red is $3/5 = 0.6$, while if the nth marble is blue, we draw the $n + $1st marble from bag 2 and so the probability it is red is $3/10 = 0.3$.

To solve our problem, let $p(n)$ be the probability that the nth marble is red, and let $q(n) = 1 - p(n)$ be the probability that the nth marble is blue. Since the first marble is being drawn from bag 1, we know that $p(1) = 0.6$ and $q(1) = 0.4$.

What is $p(2)$? That is, what is the probability that the second marble drawn is red? There are two cases or ways in which a red marble can be drawn on the second draw. The first case is that the first marble is red and the second marble is red, denoted rr and its probability of happening is $p(rr)$, while the second case is that the first marble is blue and the second marble is red, denoted br with probability $p(br)$. To compute $p(2)$, we need to compute the probability of each of the two cases and then add them together, that is,

$$p(2) = p(rr) + p(br).$$

(This is an example of the **addition principle** in probability.)

What is the probability of getting rr? This is a two-stage process. The first stage is to get a red on draw 1 and the probability of this happening is $p(1) = 0.6$. The second stage is to get a red on draw 2 **given that we got a red on draw 1**, that is, given that we are drawing from bag 1. The probability of this happening is 0.6. The probability of getting a red on the first and second draw is then the product of the individual probabilities, that is,

$$p(rr) = 0.6p(1) = (0.6)^2.$$

(This is a variation of the **multiplication principle**, discussed in the previous section.)

What is the probability of getting br? This is a two-stage process, also. The first stage is to get a blue on draw 1, and the probability of this happening is $q(1) = 0.4$. The second stage is to get a red on draw 2 **given that we got a blue on draw 1**, that is, given that we are drawing from bag 2. The probability of this happening is 0.3. Again by the multiplication principle, the probability of case 2 is

$$p(br) = 0.3q(1) = (0.3)(0.4) = 0.12.$$

Adding these together, we get

$$p(2) = 0.6p(1) + 0.3q(1) = 0.36 + 0.12 = 0.48.$$

We could use the same logic to compute $q(2)$, the probability of getting a blue marble on the second draw, but there is a simpler method. Since we must get a red or a blue marble on draw 2 and we know the probability that it is red equals 0.48, then the probability it is blue must equal $1 - 0.48 = 0.52$, that is,

$$q(2) = 1 - p(2) = 0.52.$$

What is $p(n + 1)$, that is, what is the probability that the $(n + 1)$th marble drawn is red? There are two cases. Case 1 is that the nth marble is red and the $(n+1)$th marble is red, denoted rr; while case 2 is that the nth marble is blue and the $(n+1)$th marble is red, denoted br. (Note that we are listing only the **last two** marbles drawn.) To compute $p(n+1)$, we need to compute the probability of each of the two cases and then add them together, that is,

$$p(n + 1) = p(rr) + p(br).$$

What is the probability of getting rr? This is a two-stage process. The first stage is to get a red on draw n, and the probability of this happening is $p(n)$. The second stage is to get a red on draw $n + 1$ **given that we got a red on draw** n, that is, given that we are drawing from bag 1. The probability of this happening is 0.6. Thus, the probability of case 1 is, using the multiplication principle,

$$p(rr) = 0.6p(n).$$

Similarly, the probability of getting br, again by the multiplication principle, is

$$p(br) = 0.3q(n).$$

Adding these together, we get

$$p(n + 1) = 0.6p(n) + 0.3q(n).$$

Since we must get a red or blue marble on the nth draw, we must have

$$p(n) + q(n) = 1, \quad \text{or} \quad q(n) = 1 - p(n).$$

Substitution into the above equation gives the first order affine dynamical system

$$p(n + 1) = 0.6p(n) + 0.3(1 - p(n)) = 0.3p(n) + 0.3.$$

The equilibrium value for this equation is $p = 3/7$, so the general solution is

$$p(k) = c\,(0.3)^k + \tfrac{3}{7}.$$

Using the fact that $p(1) = 0.6 = 0.3c + 3/7$, we get $c = 4/7$ and the particular solution is

$$p(k) = \tfrac{4}{7}(0.3)^k + \tfrac{3}{7}.$$

Alternatively, since the first marble is drawn from bag 1, this means marble 0 'was red', that is, $p(0) = 1$. This also gives $c = 4/7$.

Observe that

$$\lim_{k \to \infty} p(k) = \tfrac{3}{7},$$

that is, the probability that the 1000th marble is red is essentially $3/7$. Thus, the probability that the 1000th marble is blue is $4/7$. In effect, this says that approximately three-sevenths of the marbles drawn will be red and four-sevenths blue.

Suppose we keep all the rules the same for our marble drawing problem, except that we draw the first marble from bag 2 instead of bag 1, that is, $p(0) = 0$. Then the particular solution is

$$p(k) = -\tfrac{3}{7}(0.3)^k + \tfrac{3}{7},$$

but we still have that

$$\lim_{k \to \infty} p(k) = \tfrac{3}{7}.$$

Observe that the initial condition does not affect the **long range probabilities**, which seems to make sense, that is, getting a red marble on the first draw should have little effect on our getting a red marble on the 1000th draw. To see this mathematically, we consider the general solution. In particular, we note that

$$\lim_{k \to \infty} p(k) = \lim_{k \to \infty} \left[c(0.3)^k + \tfrac{3}{7}\right] = \tfrac{3}{7}.$$

Also $\lim_{k \to \infty} q(k) = \lim_{k \to \infty}[1 - p(k)] = 4/7$. We also see that, for this example, the initial value $p(0)$ plays no part in determining the long term probabilities $p(k)$ and $q(k)$.

This example is called a **regular Markov chain** with two states, red and blue. Later in this text we will consider the general theory of Markov chains in which there may be more than two states, that is, our bags may contain marbles of more than two colors.

2.4.1 Problems

1. Suppose we play our marble drawing game, but the first bag contains 4 red and 2 blue marbles and the second bag contains 3 red and 5 blue marbles.

    (a) Find the affine dynamical system that models this situation.

    (b) Find the general solution and the long term probabilities for $p(k)$ and $q(k)$, that is, the limit as k goes to infinity. (Note that although half the marbles are red, the long range probability of drawing a red marble is slightly greater than one-half.)

    (c) Find the probability that the fourth marble is red given that we draw the first marble from the first bag.

    (d) Suppose we flip a fair coin and if we get heads we draw our first marble from the first bag, but if we get tails, we draw our first marble from the second bag. Find the particular solution and $p(4)$.

2. Suppose there are two competing hamburger chains, A and B. Suppose a research firm has determined that if a customer eats a hamburger from chain A, then the probability they will buy their next hamburger from chain A is 0.7 while the probability they buy their next hamburger from chain B is 0.3. Similarly, they have determined that if a customer eats a hamburger from chain B, then the probability they will buy their next hamburger from chain B is 0.6 while the probability they buy their next hamburger from chain A is 0.4. Determine the market share of each chain, that is, determine the fraction of hamburgers bought from chain A and the fraction bought from chain B.

2.5   An introduction to genetics

Many traits of individuals of a species are determined by genes inherited from each of the parents of the individual. Let's consider a gene $\mathcal{A}$ that determines a certain trait. The simplest case is when gene $\mathcal{A}$ has two forms or alleles, allele A and allele a. Suppose the individual inherits one allele from each parent and the trait is determined by the particular allelic pair (A, A), (A, a), (a, A), or (a, a).

    Individuals with allelic pairs (A, A) or (a, a) are called homozygotes. Individuals with allelic pairs (A, a) or (a, A) are called heterozygotes. In this section we will consider traits in which the order of the alleles on the chromosome is unimportant in determining the trait. Thus, we will always list the allelic pair for heterozygotes as (A, a), meaning that they have exactly one allele of each type. These three types are called the genotypes of the individuals. In the rest of this section, 'gene' will mean 'gene $\mathcal{A}$'.

Let us initially assume that mating among our species is random and there are no outside forces, such as mutation, acting on the species. We also assume that the fitness of the three genotypes is the same, that is, none of the genotypes has an environmental advantage.

Suppose that the size of the initial population, which we will call generation 0, is T. Since each individual has two genes, there are $2T$ genes in our initial population. Of these genes, assume that the proportion that are alleles A is $p(0)$, and that the rest are alleles a. Note that the proportion that are a must be $1 - p(0)$ which, for simplicity, we will call $q(0)$. Therefore

$$p(0) + q(0) = 1.$$

For simplicity, we will also assume that the proportion of A alleles is the same for males as it is for females.

The total number of alleles of the form A is the total number of genes $2T$ times the proportion $p(0)$ of alleles of the form A, that is, there are $2p(0)T$ A-alleles. Likewise, the total number of a-alleles is $2q(0)T$.

An individual in the next generation, that is, generation 1, receives two genes, one from each parent. Since mating is random, it is equally likely that the individual will be the offspring of any two parents, and so the alleles that this individual receives are essentially drawn at random from the total pool of genes.

To model this selection process, consider two bowls, one containing all of the females' genes and the other containing all of the males' genes. If the females have a total of W genes, then $p(0)W$ of them are A-alleles and $q(0)W$ are a-alleles. If the males have a total of M genes, then $p(0)M$ of them are A and $q(0)M$ are a. The number of ways we can draw a gene from the females' bowl is W. For each of these ways, there are M ways to draw a gene from the males' bowl. Thus, there are (again by the multiplication principle) WM equally likely ways to draw an individual's two genes, one for each sex.

The number of ways in which an individual can be an A-homozygote is the number of ways $p(0)W$ in which we can draw an A-allele from the females' bowl times the number of ways $p(0)M$ we can draw an A-allele from the males' bowl, that is, $p^2(0)WM$. Thus the proportion of A-homozygotes in generation 1, which we will call u, is the number of ways of getting two A-alleles divided by the total number of ways of selecting two genes, that is,

$$u = \frac{p^2(0)MW}{MW} = p^2(0).$$

Similarly, the proportion, w, of a-homozygotes is

$$w = q^2(0).$$

The number of ways in which an individual can get an A-allele from a female and an a-allele from a male is $p(0)Wq(0)M$. The number of ways in which an individual can get an a-allele from a female and an A-allele from a male is $q(0)Wp(0)M$. The number of ways of getting an A-allele from one bowl and an a-allele from the other is the sum of these two totals, that is, $2p(0)q(0)MW$. So the proportion of heterozygotes is

$$v = \frac{2p(0)q(0)MW}{MW} = 2p(0)q(0).$$

Example 2.30

Suppose that gene $\mathcal{A}$ determines the color of a particular kind of flower and that it comes in two forms, allele A which gives these flowers the color red, and allele a which gives these flowers the color white. Each flower has a pair of the color genes. Suppose that initially, the proportion of A-alleles is $p(0) = 0.3$, and the proportion of a-alleles is $q(0) = 0.7$. Then the proportion of flowers of each genotype in the next generation is

$$u = (0.3)^2 = 0.09, \quad v = 2(0.3)(0.7) = 0.42, \quad w = (0.7)^2 = 0.49.$$

Notice that $u + v + w = 1$. This is always true, since each individual must be one of these three types.

As an aside, if A is a dominant allele and a is a recessive allele, that is, if the heterozygotes are also red, then there are two phenotypes, red and white. In this case, the proportion of red flowers is the proportion of (dominant) A-homozygotes plus the proportion of heterozygotes, that is, 0.51 of the flowers. Then 49 per cent of the flowers will be white.

In this example, suppose that the total number of flowers in generation 1 is T. Since each individual has two genes, the total number of genes in generation 1 is $2T$. The total number of plants of each genotype is

$$U = 0.09T, \qquad V = 0.42T, \qquad W = 0.49T,$$

respectively. Since each A-homozygote has two A-alleles, and each heterozygote has one A-allele, the total number of A-alleles in generation 1 is

$$2U + V = 0.18T + 0.42T = 0.6T.$$

To get $p(1)$, the proportion of A-alleles in generation 1, we divide the total number of A-alleles by the total number of genes to get

$$p(1) = \frac{0.6T}{2T} = 0.3.$$

Thus, $q(1) = 1 - p(1) = 0.7$.

Notice that the proportion of A- and a-alleles in generation 1 is the same as it was in generation 0. By induction, we see that the proportion of A- and a-alleles remains fixed at $p(n) = 0.3$ and $q(n) = 0.7$ for every generation n. Therefore, the proportions of A-homozygotes, heterozygotes, and a-homozygotes remain fixed at 0.09, 0.42, and 0.49, respectively, for every generation. Again, if A is dominant, then the per cent of red and white flowers remains fixed at 51 per cent and 49 per cent, respectively, from the first generation on.

The above example is a demonstration of the Hardy-Weinberg law.

Theorem 2.31

The Hardy-Weinberg law: *Suppose a parent population has random mating with an initial proportion, $p(0) = p$ of A-alleles, and $q(0) = q$ of a-alleles but the proportion of the three genotypes is unknown. If there are no outside influences such as mutation or selection due to fitness, then the population will be in equilibrium starting with the next generation, that is*

$$p(n) = p \quad and \quad q(n) = q$$

for all n. The proportions of A-homozygotes, heterozygotes, and a-homozygotes will be

$$u = p^2, \qquad v = 2pq, \qquad w = q^2,$$

respectively, starting with generation 1.

Proof: Suppose $p(n)$ and $q(n) = 1 - p(n)$ are known. Let's write a first order dynamical system for $p(n + 1)$ in terms of $p(n)$. To do this, we first compute u, v, and w, the proportions for generation $n + 1$ of A-homozygotes, heterozygotes, and a-homozygotes, respectively.

Let T be the total number of individuals in generation $n + 1$. To be an A-homozygote, an individual must draw (inherit) two A-alleles from parents in generation n. Since it is unknown to us who these parents are, the individual is equally likely to inherit any one of the W females' genes and any one of the M males' genes for a total of WM ways of selecting two genes. To be an A-homozygote, one of the $p(n)W$ females' A-alleles and one of the $p(n)M$ males' A-alleles must be inherited. Thus, as in the above example, the proportion of A-homozygotes is

$$u = \frac{p(n)Wp(n)M}{WM} = p^2(n).$$

The total number of A-homozygotes in generation $n + 1$ will be the proportion of A-homozygotes, u, times the total number T of individuals in generation $n + 1$. Since each of these individuals has two A-alleles, the total number of A-alleles contributed by A-homozygotes in generation $n + 1$ is

$$2Tu = 2Tp^2(n).$$

Likewise, the number of ways of getting a heterozygote in generation $n+1$ is the number of ways of getting an A-allele from a female and an a-allele from a male, or an a-allele from a female and an A-allele from a male, that is, $2p(n)q(n)WM$. Thus, the proportion of heterozygotes is

$$v = \frac{2p(n)q(n)WM}{WM} = 2p(n)q(n).$$

Thus, there are $2p(n)q(n)T$ heterozygotes in generation $n+1$, and since each of these individuals contributes one A-allele, the total number of A-alleles contributed by the heterozygotes is $2Tp(n)q(n)$.

The a-homozygotes contribute no A-alleles, so the total number of A-alleles in generation $n+1$ is the total of the A-alleles computed above, that is,

$$2Tp^2(n) + 2Tp(n)q(n) = 2Tp(n)[p(n) + q(n)] = 2Tp(n)$$

since $p(n)+q(n) = 1$. The total number of genes in generation $n+1$ is $2T$, thus the proportion $p(n+1)$ of A-alleles in generation $n+1$ is the quotient of these two numbers, that is,

$$p(n+1) = \frac{2Tp(n)}{2T} = p(n).$$

The particular solution is easily seen to be

$$p(k) = p(0)1^k = p.$$

Thus, $q(k) = 1 - p(k) = 1 - p = q$.

Knowing $p(n) = p$ and $q(n) = q$, substitution into the above formulas gives $u = p^2$, $v = 2pq$, and $w = q^2$, from the first generation on, which completes the proof.

The above theorem implies that even when A is a dominant gene and a is a recessive gene, if there is no selective advantage to any of the genotypes, then the recessive trait will not tend to die out, but will remain fixed at q^2 of the population. This goes counter to the intuition of many people. In fact, Hardy and Weinberg discovered this theorem independently in an effort to show that recessive traits need not die out, and in fact that the recessive trait may even be the most common trait.

Next we consider the effect of selection. We now assume that A is a dominant allele and a is a recessive allele. In this case, genotype (A, A) is called a dominant homozygote, while genotype (a, a) is called a recessive homozygote.

Suppose there **is** an outside factor affecting the recessive trait. In fact, let's consider a genetic defect that causes recessive homozygotes to be sterile or to die before reproductive age. Allele a is said to be a **lethal allele** and allele A is said to have a **selective advantage**.

Again, we let $p(n)$ and $q(n)$ be the proportion of A- and a-alleles in the reproductive population of generation n. As above, the proportions of the three genotypes in generation $n + 1$ are

$$u = p^2(n), \qquad v = 2p(n)q(n), \qquad w = q^2(n).$$

We let T be the total number of individuals born into generation $n + 1$.

What we would like to do is to compute the proportion of recessive a-alleles in the adult (reproductive) population of generation $n + 1$. To do this, we must compute the total number of **adults** in generation $n + 1$. Our assumption is that all of the dominant homozygotes and heterozygotes reach reproductive age or adulthood, while **none of the recessive homozygotes reaches reproductive age**. Thus, the total number of individuals that reach adulthood in generation $n + 1$ is

$$T(u+v) = T[p^2(n) + 2p(n)q(n)] = Tp(n)[p(n) + 2q(n)] = Tp(n)[1 + q(n)],$$

since $p(n) = 1 - q(n)$. Since each of these individuals has two genes, the total number of genes in the adult population of generation $n + 1$ is

$$2Tp(n)[1 + q(n)].$$

Since none of the dominant homozygotes have an a-allele, each heterozygote has one a-allele, and none of the recessive homozygotes reaches adulthood, the total number of a-alleles in the adult population of generation $n + 1$ equals the number of heterozygotes in that generation, that is,

$$Tv = T2p(n)q(n).$$

Since the proportion $q(n + 1)$ of a-alleles in the adult population of generation $n+1$ is the ratio of the number of a-alleles to the total number of genes, we have

$$q(n + 1) = \frac{2Tp(n)q(n)}{2Tp(n)[1 + q(n)]} = \frac{q(n)}{1 + q(n)}.$$

This is a first order nonlinear dynamical system.

There is a clever trick for solving this particular nonlinear dynamical system, and that is to make the substitutions

$$q(n) = \frac{1}{Q(n)} \quad \text{and} \quad q(n + 1) = \frac{1}{Q(n + 1)}.$$

This gives

$$\frac{1}{Q(n+1)} = \frac{1/Q(n)}{1 + 1/Q(n)}.$$

Simplifying the right hand side of this equation gives

$$\frac{1}{Q(n+1)} = \frac{1}{1 + Q(n)}.$$

Cross multiplying gives the first order affine dynamical system (where $r = 1$)

$$Q(n+1) = Q(n) + 1.$$

The particular solution is then

$$Q(k) = k + Q_0.$$

Thus, substituting $1/q(k)$ back for $Q(k)$ gives

$$q(k) = \frac{1}{k + Q_0} = \frac{1}{k + 1/q_0} = \frac{q_0}{kq_0 + 1}.$$

Let's summarize.

Theorem 2.32

Principle of selection: *Suppose that individuals with a lethal recessive trait determined by allele a do not reproduce, but that dominant homozygotes and heterozygotes reproduce normally. Then the proportion of a-alleles in the population in generation k is given by*

$$q(k) = \frac{q_0}{kq_0 + 1},$$

where q_0 is the initial proportion of a-alleles.

Notice that $q(k)$ goes to zero as k goes to infinity. But it goes to zero very slowly. Suppose there is a lethal trait, or, as was advocated in the early 1900s, negative eugenics (in which all people with a certain undesirable trait are sterilized) is practiced. Since the trait is deleterious, we will assume that, initially, the proportion of these a-alleles in the population is small, say $q(0) = 0.02$. Notice that, after one generation, the proportion is $q(1) = 0.02/(0.02 + 1) = 1/(51)$, which is not much of a change.

How long will it take to cut the initial proportion in half, that is, for what value of k is $q(k) = 0.01$? To answer this question, we need to solve

$$0.01 = q(k) = \frac{q(0)}{q(0)k + 1} = \frac{0.02}{0.02k + 1}$$

for k. This equation simplifies to

$$0.02k + 1 = \frac{0.02}{0.01} = 2, \quad \text{or} \quad k = 50.$$

Thus, it takes 50 generations (which would be approximately 1250 years for humans) for the proportion of a-alleles to be cut in half, that is, to be cut to

$$q(50) = \frac{0.02}{50(0.02) + 1} = 0.01.$$

Similarly, it will take 100 more generations to cut this proportion in half again, that is, to 0.005.

A Supreme Court decision in the first part of the twentieth century allowed a mentally retarded woman to be sterilized so that she wouldn't produce retarded children. Assuming retardation to be a recessive genetic trait (a poor assumption), we see that sterilizing all such people would not significantly reduce this trait in society. This slow reduction in the proportion of deleterious alleles explains why negative eugenics would be ineffective for humans.

Next we will consider the effects of mutation with no selective advantage. We do not assume that either allele is dominant, but we do assume that all genotypes have the same fitness.

In mutation, a certain proportion of the genes spontaneously change from A-alleles to a-alleles or vice versa. Let $P(n)$ and $Q(n)$ be the proportions of A- and a-alleles, respectively, in generation n just before mutation. Let $p(n)$ and $q(n)$ be the proportions of A- and a-alleles, respectively, in generation n just after mutation.

To simplify matters, we will consider the following series of events. We know that the proportions of A- and a-alleles in generation n just prior to reproduction are $p(n)$ and $q(n)$, respectively. We then draw genes for generation $n + 1$ as before. Thus, the proportions of A- and a-alleles in the children of generation $n + 1$ are, by the Hardy-Weinberg law, $P(n + 1) = p(n)$ and $Q(n + 1) = q(n)$.

Then we assume that a certain proportion μ of the A-alleles mutate to a-alleles. (Alternatively, we could have assumed the genes mutated first, then the children were born.) If a proportion μ of the A-alleles mutate to a-alleles, then the proportion of A-alleles in generation $n + 1$ after mutation is

$$p(n + 1) = P(n + 1) - \mu P(n + 1) = p(n) - \mu p(n) = (1 - \mu)p(n).$$

We know that the solution to this dynamical system is

$$p(k) = (1 - \mu)^k p(0).$$

Thus we get the following theorem.

Theorem 2.33

Principle of mutation: *Suppose that the proportion of alleles that mutate from A to a is μ. In the absence of other influences, the proportion of A-alleles present in generation k is*

$$p(k) = (1 - \mu)^k p(0),$$

and thus goes to zero.

Usually the mutation rate is small, say $\mu = 10^{-5}$. This means that $p(k)$ goes to zero slowly. In fact, with μ as above, after $10\,000$ generations,

$$p(10\,000) = 0.9047 p(0).$$

Thus, you can see that even after long periods of time, the proportion of A-alleles has decreased by only a small amount. This and the previous example of selection help explain why evolution sometimes takes so long. If we observe certain species for a short (say several hundred years) period of time, the characteristics of that species will not appear to be changing. In these cases it may take several thousand years for the effects of evolution to have an observable affect.

For some species the effects of evolution may be much quicker, as in the rapid evolution of resistant bacteria. One explanation for this is the short time span between generations. There are other reasons, but these are not relevant to this discussion.

We have seen that selection by itself causes a trait to die out. Similarly, mutation in one direction also causes a trait to die out. Why then are there traits in which the proportions of A- and a-alleles are both relatively large?

Let's consider two possible explanations. First, selection may act in one direction while mutation acts in the other direction. This will be discussed later in this section. A second possible explanation is that mutation occurs in both directions, that is, μ of the A-alleles mutate to a-alleles and ν of the a-alleles mutate to A-alleles. In this case, let $p(n)$, $q(n)$, $P(n)$, and $Q(n)$ have the same meanings as above. Also, for the same reasons,

$$P(n + 1) = p(n) \quad \text{and} \quad Q(n + 1) = q(n).$$

Now mutation from a to A will increase the proportion of A-alleles by $\nu Q(n + 1)$, while mutation from A to a will decrease the proportion of A-alleles by $\mu P(n + 1)$. This gives

$$p(n + 1) = P(n + 1) - \mu P(n + 1) + \nu Q(n + 1) = (1 - \mu)p(n) + \nu q(n)$$

after substitution. Since $q(n) + p(n) = 1$, we have

$$p(n+1) = (1-\mu)p(n) + \nu[1 - p(n)] = (1 - \mu - \nu)p(n) + \nu.$$

The general solution to this dynamical system, with $r = (1 - \mu - \nu)$ and $b = \nu$, is

$$p(k) = c\,(1 - \mu - \nu)^k + \frac{\nu}{\mu + \nu}$$

after simplification. Since μ and ν are small, $|1 - \mu - \nu| < 1$ so that

$$\lim_{k \to \infty} p(k) = \frac{\nu}{\mu + \nu}.$$

To rephrase, the proportion of A-alleles in the population should be close to the (equilibrium) value, $p = \nu/(\mu + \nu)$. Therefore the proportion of a-alleles should be close to $q = 1 - p = \mu/(\mu + \nu)$.

Example 2.34

Suppose that A is a dominant allele. Then the proportion of recessive homozygotes equals q^2. In this case, it is possible to estimate the proportion of recessive homozygotes, and suppose this equals 0.04. Then the proportion of a-alleles is $q = \sqrt{0.04} = 0.2$ and the proportion of A-alleles is then $p = 0.8$.

Suppose that neither trait has a selective advantage, and that A-alleles mutate to a-alleles and vice versa. Then

$$\frac{p}{q} = \frac{0.8}{0.2} = 4.$$

But

$$\frac{p}{q} = \frac{\nu/(\mu + \nu)}{\mu/(\mu + \nu)} = \frac{\nu}{\mu}.$$

Thus, while we cannot compute ν and μ, we do know the ratio $\nu/\mu = 4$, that is, alleles mutate from a to A at four times the rate that they mutate from A to a.

Now we will study the combined effects of mutation and selection. **Galactosaemia is a lethal genetic disease** caused by a recessive allele, a. It also happens that normal (dominant) A-alleles mutate to a-alleles at the rate μ. We will model this disease.

Let $P(n)$ and $Q(n)$ be the proportions of A- and a-alleles in adults of generation n before mutation and let $p(n)$ and $q(n)$ be the proportions of A- and a-alleles in adults of generation n after mutation. Let u, v, and w be the proportions of dominant homozygotes, heterozygotes, and recessive homozygotes, respectively, among the children of generation $n + 1$. As before

$$u = p^2(n), \qquad v = 2p(n)q(n), \qquad w = q^2(n).$$

Let T be the total number of children born to generation $n+1$. Since all of the recessive homozygotes die before reaching adulthood, the total number of adult dominant homozygotes, heterozygotes, and recessive homozygotes are

$$U = Tp^2(n), \qquad V = T2p(n)q(n), \qquad W = 0.$$

Thus, the proportion of a-alleles in the adults before mutation is

$$Q(n+1) = \frac{\cdot \ T2p(n)q(n)}{2Tp^2(n) + 4Tp(n)q(n)} = \frac{q(n)}{1+q(n)}$$

as before. Therefore

$$P(n+1) = 1 - Q(n+1) = \frac{1}{1+q(n)}.$$

Now μ of the A-alleles mutate to a-alleles, giving

$$q(n+1) = Q(n+1) + \mu P(n+1) = \frac{q(n)}{1+q(n)} + \mu \frac{1}{1+q(n)},$$

or

$$q(n+1) = \frac{q(n)+\mu}{1+q(n)}. \tag{11}$$

A trick for solving this nonlinear dynamical system is the following. First, find the equilibrium value to this dynamical system, that is, find a number q such that $q(k) = q$ satisfies the equation. The number q can be found by substituting q for $q(n+1)$ and $q(n)$ giving

$$q = \frac{q+\mu}{1+q}, \quad \text{or} \quad q^2 = \mu.$$

We will use the root $q = -\sqrt{\mu}$ (although either root will work).
Next, make the substitution

$$q(n) = q + \frac{1}{a(n)} = -\sqrt{\mu} + \frac{1}{a(n)} = \frac{-\sqrt{\mu}a(n)+1}{a(n)}$$

into the dynamical system (11). Collecting all terms except $1/a(n+1)$ on the right, finding a common denominator, and simplifying gives the first order affine dynamical system

$$a(n+1) = \left(\frac{1-\sqrt{\mu}}{1+\sqrt{\mu}}\right) a(n) + \frac{1}{1+\sqrt{\mu}}.$$

With

$$r = \left(\frac{1 - \sqrt{\mu}}{1 + \sqrt{\mu}}\right) \quad \text{and} \quad b = \frac{1}{1 + \sqrt{\mu}},$$

we get the general solution

$$a(k) = c \left(\frac{1 - \sqrt{\mu}}{1 + \sqrt{\mu}}\right)^k + \frac{1}{2\sqrt{\mu}},$$

after simplification. Again, c depends on $q(0) = q_0$.

Since

$$\left|\frac{1 - \sqrt{\mu}}{1 + \sqrt{\mu}}\right| < 1,$$

it follows that

$$\lim_{k \to \infty} a(k) = \frac{1}{2\sqrt{\mu}}.$$

Thus,

$$\lim_{k \to \infty} q(k) = -\sqrt{\mu} + \lim_{k \to \infty} \frac{1}{a(k)} = -\sqrt{\mu} + 2\sqrt{\mu} = \sqrt{\mu},$$

and so

$$q = \lim_{k \to \infty} q(k) = \sqrt{\mu}$$

is the stable equilibrium proportion of a-alleles when balancing selection and mutation.

The above analysis tells us that the proportion of recessive homozygotes should be approximately $w = q^2 = \mu$. It has been observed that the frequency of galactosaemia in the general population is $w = 5.6 \times 10^{-5}$, thus, this should also be (approximately) the mutation rate.

2.5.1 Problems

1. Suppose that a certain bug has either red or black eyes, determined by a pair of genes. Suppose that the dominant allele A gives red eyes while the recessive allele a gives black eyes.

   (a) Suppose that, initially, $p(0) = 0.4$ and $q(0) = 0.6$. Use the Hardy–Weinberg law to find the proportion of dominant homozygotes, heterozygotes, and recessive homozygotes in generation n, where $n > 0$.

   (b) Suppose we observe that 16 per cent of the bugs have black eyes while 84 per cent have red eyes. What proportion, $q(n)$, of the genes are a-alleles and what proportion of the individuals are dominant homozygotes?

(c) Suppose that, initially, $p(0) = 0.2$ and $q(0) = 0.8$. Suppose that 10 000 bugs are born to this generation of bugs. How many homozygotes, heterozygotes, and recessive homozygotes do you expect in this generation? How many A-alleles do you then expect in generation 1? From this, what proportion of the genes in this generation are A-alleles ?

2. Assume that alleles A and a are additive in the sense that A- and a-homozygotes appear to be identical, but the heterozygotes are differ-ent from the homozygotes. Suppose the proportion of heterozygotes is 0.32 while the proportion of the homozygotes (combined) is 0.68. Determine the proportion of A- and a-alleles in the population.

3. Suppose that we have a trait in which the recessive homozygotes do not reach adulthood so that the **principle of selection** applies. Suppose that, initially, $q(0) = 0.06$, that is 6 per cent of the genes are of type a.

   (a) How many generations will it take to cut the proportion to one-fourth of the initial amount?

   (b) How many generations will it take to cut the proportion of a-alleles to 1 per cent?

   (c) How many generations will it take to cut the proportion of recessive homozygotes to 0.09 per cent of the population?

4. Suppose that the mutation rate from A-alleles to a-alleles is $\mu = 0.0001$. Also suppose that $p(0) = 0.9$. How many generations will it take so that $p(k) = 0.5$?

5. Find the solution to dynamical system (11) by making the substi-tution

$$q(n) = \sqrt{\mu} + \frac{1}{a(n)}.$$

After finding the solution, show that $\lim_{k \to \infty} q(k) = \sqrt{\mu}$, as before.

6. Using methods similar to those in this section, find the general solu-tion to the following dynamical systems, and find $\lim_{k \to \infty} A(k)$.

   (a) $A(n+1) = 3A(n)/(2 - A(n))$
   (b) $A(n+1) = (4 + 5A(n))/(-1 - 2A(n))$
   (c) $A(n+1) = (-12 + 5A(n))/(-2 + A(n))$

7. Suppose that the mutation rate from A- to a-alleles is 10^{-4} and that the mutation rate from a to A-alleles is 4×10^{-5}. After a long period of time, what per cent of the genes are A, what per cent are a, and what per cent of the individuals exhibit the dominant trait?

8. Suppose that the mutation rate from A-alleles to a-alleles is 0.01, but that **all** recessive homozygotes die before reaching adulthood. Find a dynamical system for $p(n+1)$ in terms of $p(n)$, find the equilibrium value, and determine its stability by solving the dynamical system.

9. Suppose that there is a partially lethal trait in that only half of the recessive homozygotes die before reaching adulthood, while the dominant homozygotes and heterozygotes are normal. (The fitness of a genotype is the relative proportion of that genotype which survives to adulthood. In this problem, the fitness of the dominant homozygotes is 1, the fitness of the heterozygotes is 1, and the fitness of the recessive homozygotes is 0.5.)

   (a) Assuming there is no mutation, develop a nonlinear dynamical system for $q(n)$, the proportion of a-alleles in the adult population. You will not be able to solve this dynamical system.

   (b) Assuming in addition that a-alleles mutate to A-alleles at the rate μ, again develop a nonlinear dynamical system for $q(n)$.

2.6 Nonhomogeneous dynamical systems

Let's reconsider our study of savings accounts. We had originally developed the dynamical system

$$A(n + 1) = (1 + I)A(n) + b$$

for a savings account paying $100I$ per cent interest, compounded annually, in which we added a fixed amount b each year. In reality, our salary will (hopefully) be increasing, so each year we will be able to add more money to our savings account than we did the previous year. To study this, we need to consider dynamical systems in which we do not add a constant b, but instead add an amount that is a function of time, that is, dynamical systems of the form

$$A(n + 1) = rA(n) + g(n).$$

This is called a **first order nonhomogeneous dynamical system**.

We first comment that nonhomogeneous dynamical systems **do not have fixed points**. To see this, assume that $A(k) = a$ is a constant solution to the nonhomogeneous dynamical system. Then, by substitution of $A(n+1) = a$ and $A(n) = a$, we get

$$a = ra + g(n),$$

that is, $g(n) = (1 - r)a$ for every value of n. But then the function g is constant and therefore does not depend explicitly on n. The dynamical system is thus affine.

We could consider a savings account in which we increase our deposit by 100 dollars each year, that is, at the beginning of year 1 we deposit 100 dollars, at the beginning of year 2 we deposit 200 dollars, at the beginning of year 3 we deposit 300 dollars, and so forth. This leads to the equations

$$A(1) = (1 + I)A(0) + 100, \quad A(2) = (1 + I)A(1) + 200, \quad \ldots.$$

These can be summarized by the dynamical system

$$A(n + 1) = (1 + I)A(n) + 100(n + 1), \quad \text{for } n = 0, 1, \ldots.$$

In this case,
$$g(n) = 100(n + 1) = 100n + 100.$$

We could also consider a savings account in which we increase our deposit by 10 per cent each year, that is, in year 1 we deposit 100, in year 2 we deposit $100 \times 1.1 = 110$, in year 3 we deposit $110 \times 1.1 = 121 = 100 \times 1.1^2$, and so forth. This leads to the equations

$$A(1) = (1 + I)A(0) + 100, \quad A(2) = (1 + I)A(1) + 100(1.1), \quad \ldots,$$

which can be summarized by the dynamical system

$$A(n + 1) = (1 + I)A(n) + 100(1.1)^n, \quad \text{for } n = 0, 1, \ldots.$$

In this case, $g(n) = 100(1.1)^n$.

We want to find the general and particular solutions to first order nonhomogeneous dynamical systems when the function $g(n)$ is

1. a polynomial in n, and

2. an exponential (a constant to the nth power).

We first deal with the case in which $g(n)$ is a polynomial.

Recall that the general solutions of the dynamical systems (with $r \neq 1$)

$$A(n+1) = rA(n) \quad \text{and} \quad A(n+1) = rA(n) + b$$

are

$$A(k) = cr^k \quad \text{and} \quad A(k) = cr^k + a,$$

respectively, where the constant a is determined by the dynamical system. We might then suspect that the general solution of the dynamical system

$$A(n+1) = rA(n) + b_1 n + b_0$$

is

$$A(k) = cr^k + a_1 k + a_0,$$

where a_1 and a_0 are two constants that are determined from the dynamical system. Let's test this hypothesis.

Example 2.35

Let's consider the dynamical system

$$A(n+1) = 3A(n) + 2n + 5,$$

in which $g(n) = 2n + 5$. We assume the general solution is of the form

$$A(k) = c\,3^k + a_1 k + a_0,$$

where a_1 and a_0 are determined from the dynamical system. In this case, we have

$$A(n+1) = c\,3^{n+1} + a_1(n+1) + a_0 \quad \text{and} \quad A(n) = c\,3^n + a_1 n + a_0.$$

Substitution into the dynamical system gives

$$c\,3^{n+1} + a_1(n+1) + a_0 = 3\left(c\,3^n + a_1 n + a_0\right) + 2n + 5.$$

Removing the parentheses on the right hand side gives

$$c\,3^{n+1} + a_1(n+1) + a_0 = c\,3^{n+1} + 3a_1 n + 3a_0 + 2n + 5.$$

Subtracting $c\,3^{n+1}$ from both sides gives

$$a_1 n + a_1 + a_0 = 3a_1 n + 3a_0 + 2n + 5.$$

Remember that a_1 and a_0 are constants which are to be determined, while n can be any integer.

There are several ways to solve for a_1 and a_0. One simple method is to collect **all** terms on the left, that is,

$$a_1 n + a_1 + a_0 - 3a_1 n - 3a_0 - 2n - 5 = 0.$$

Collect all terms involving an n, giving

$$(-2a_1 - 2)n + (a_1 - 2a_0 - 5) = 0$$

after simplification.

Since this equality must hold for **all** integer values n, it must hold when $n = 0$, that is, when

$$(a_1 - 2a_0 - 5) = 0.$$

But if this term equals zero, then we must have

$$(-2a_1 - 2)n = 0$$

for $n = 1$, 2, and so forth. For this to happen, we must have

$$(-2a_1 - 2) = 0.$$

But this means that $a_1 = -1$. Substituting -1 for a_1 into $a_1 - 2a_0 - 5 = 0$ gives

$$(-1 - 2a_0 - 5) = 0 \quad \text{or} \quad a_0 = -3.$$

Therefore, it follows that

$$A(k) = c\, 3^k - k - 3$$

satisfies the dynamical system and is thus a solution. This solution must be the general solution since, if we are given a_0, then solving

$$A(0) = c\, 3^0 - 0 - 3 = c - 3 = a_0$$

for c gives $c = a_0 + 3$, and we now have the particular solution. For example, given that $a_0 = 8$, we then have $c = 11$, and the particular solution to the dynamical system is

$$A(n) = 11\,(3)^n - n - 3.$$

All that was required to find the general solution was (1) to make a good guess at the solution, (2) substitute that guess into the equation, (3) solve two linear equations by setting the sum of the terms not involving an n equal to zero, and the sum of the terms involving n equal to zero.

Recall that, for first order affine dynamical systems, $r = 1$ is a special case. The solution of the first order affine dynamical system

$$A(n + 1) = A(n) + b \quad \text{is} \quad A(k) = c + ak.$$

In other words, **when** $r = 1$ and $g(n) = b$ is a zeroth order polynomial, the solution involves a first order polynomial $c + ak$. Thus, we might suspect that the solution to the first order nonhomogeneous dynamical system

$$A(n + 1) = A(n) + b_1 n + b_0,$$

is

$$A(k) = c + a_1 k^2 + a_0 k.$$

Example 2.36

Consider the dynamical system

$$A(n + 1) = A(n) + n + 1.$$

Since $r = 1$, we expect the general solution to be

$$A(k) = c + a_1 k^2 + a_0 k$$

for some value of a_0 and a_1. Since

$$A(n + 1) = c + a_1(n + 1)^2 + a_0(n + 1) = c + a_1 n^2 + 2a_1 n + a_1 + a_0 n + a_0,$$

substitution into the dynamical system gives

$$c + a_1 n^2 + 2a_1 n + a_1 + a_0 n + a_0 = c + a_1 n^2 + a_0 n + n + 1.$$

Cancellation gives

$$2a_1 n + a_1 + a_0 = n + 1, \quad \text{or} \quad (2a_1 - 1)n + (a_1 + a_0 - 1) = 0.$$

Setting the coefficient of n equal to zero and the constant term equal to zero gives the two equations $2a_1 - 1 = 0$ and $a_1 + a_0 - 1 = 0$. Solving these two equations gives $a_1 = 1/2$ and $a_0 = 1/2$. The general solution is therefore

$$A(k) = c + \frac{k^2}{2} + \frac{k}{2}.$$

Given that $a_0 = 0$ we find that $A(0) = c + (1/2)0^2 + (1/2)0 = 0$, and the particular solution is

$$A(k) = (0 + 1 + \ldots + k) = \frac{k^2}{2} + \frac{k}{2} = \frac{k(k+1)}{2}.$$

If we had tried to find a solution to the above dynamical system, of the form

$$A(k) = c + a_1 k + a_0,$$

then, after substitution into the dynamical system, canceling terms, and simplifying, we would have

$$a_1 = 2n + 3.$$

But a_1 is a constant and $2n + 3$ changes as n changes. Thus, we cannot pick an a_1 and a_0 to satisfy this equation.

This method can be extended in an obvious fashion to polynomials of higher degree.

Theorem 2.37
Nonhomogeneous dynamical systems in which $g(n)$ is a polynomial: *Consider the dynamical system*

$$A(n + 1) = rA(n) + g(n),$$

where
$$g(n) = b_m n^m + b_{m-1} n^{m-1} + \ldots + b_1 n + b_0.$$
Here, m is a fixed constant and $g(n)$ is an m-th order polynomial.

- *If $r \neq 1$, then the general solution is of the form*

$$A(k) = c r^k + a_m k^m + a_{m-1} k^{m-1} + \ldots + a_1 k + a_0.$$

- *If $r = 1$, then the general solution is of the form*

$$A(k) = c + a_m k^{m+1} + a_{m-1} k^m + \ldots + a_1 k^2 + a_0 k.$$

In both cases, the constant c depends on the initial value, and the constants $a_m, a_{m-1}, \ldots, a_1$, and a_0 can be found by substituting into the dynamical system and then solving $m+1$ equations for the $m+1$ unknowns by setting the coefficient of the n^m term, the coefficient of the n^{m-1} term, $\ldots$, the coefficient of the n term, and the constant terms equal to zero.

Let's now turn our attention to **mathematical applications** of non-homogeneous dynamical systems. The following 'applications' are important in calculus and other areas of mathematics.

Mathematicians are often interested in summing a certain number of terms, that is, $a_0 + a_1 + \ldots + a_n$. For example, what are the respective totals of the sums

$$0 + 1 + 2 + 3 + \ldots + 100 \quad \text{and} \quad 1 + 2^1 + 2^2 + \ldots + 2^{100}?$$

In general there is no quick way to add up n terms unless there is some relationship among the terms. By letting $g(x) = x$, we have

$$0 + 1 + 2 + 3 + \ldots + 100 = g(0) + g(1) + g(2) + \ldots + g(100).$$

By letting $g(x) = 2^x$, we have

$$1 + 2^1 + 2^2 + \ldots + 2^{100} = g(0) + g(1) + g(2) + \ldots + g(100).$$

Thus, in many cases, we want to compute the sum

$$g(0) + g(1) + g(2) + \ldots + g(n)$$

for an appropriate choice of $g(x)$. The trick is to define

$$A(n) = g(0) + g(1) + g(2) + \ldots + g(n).$$

The sequence of numbers, $A(n)$, defined in this manner (as the sum of the sequence of numbers $g(0)$ through $g(n)$) is called a **series** or **partial sum**. One method for studying series is to observe that $A(n)$ satisfies the dynamical system

$$A(n + 1) = A(n) + g(n + 1),$$

with $a_0 = g(0)$. So, to compute the sum of a finite number of terms, we only need to solve a nonhomogeneous dynamical system (with $r = 1$). (In many cases, the values $g(0)$, $g(1)$, $\ldots$ satisfy a dynamical system themselves. Thus the function $g(n)$ can often be found by solving this dynamical system. In the first case above, $g(n+1) = g(n)+1$ with $g(0) = 0$, and the solution is $g(k) = k$. In the second case above, $g(n+1) = 2g(n)$ with $g(0) = 2$, and the solution is $g(k) = 2^k$.)

Using the result of Example 2.36 we can compute sums of integers. For example, let's compute

$$0 + 1 + 2 + \ldots + 1000.$$

Let $A(n) = 0 + 1 + 2 + \ldots + n$. Then

$$A(n+1) = A(n) + (n+1)$$

with $a_0 = 0$. We found that the particular solution to this system is

$$A(k) = \frac{k^2}{2} + \frac{k}{2} = \frac{k(k+1)}{2}.$$

So

$$0 + 1 + 2 + \ldots + 1000 = A(1000) = \frac{1000 \times 1001}{2} = 500\,500.$$

Let's use the solution to find

$$200 + 201 + 202 + \ldots + 1000.$$

Note that this is just

$$A(1000) - A(199) = \frac{1000 \times 1001}{2} - \frac{199 \times 200}{2} = 480\,600.$$

This gives us the identity

$$0 + 1 + 2 + \ldots + k = \frac{k(k+1)}{2}.$$

We also note that we have developed a method for finding the sum of the mth powers of the first n integers, that is,

$$0^m + 1^m + 2^m + \ldots + n^m.$$

Example 2.38

Suppose we want to find the sum of the squares of the first n integers, that is,

$$0^2 + 1^2 + 2^2 + \ldots + n^2.$$

We only need to find the solution of the dynamical system

$$A(n+1) = A(n) + (n+1)^2 = A(n) + n^2 + 2n + 1,$$

with $a_0 = 0$. Note that the general solution is of the form

$$A(k) = c + a_2 k^3 + a_1 k^2 + a_0 k.$$

Substitution into the dynamical system gives

$$c + a_2(n+1)^3 + a_1(n+1)^2 + a_0(n+1) = c + a_2 n^3 + a_1 n^2 + a_0 n + n^2 + 2n + 1.$$

Multiplication, cancellation, and simplification gives

$$(3a_2 - 1)n^2 + (3a_2 + 2a_1 - 2)n + (a_2 + a_1 + a_0 - 1) = 0.$$

Solving the three equations

$$3a_2 - 1 = 0, \quad 3a_2 + 2a_1 - 2 = 0, \quad a_2 + a_1 + a_0 - 1 = 0$$

gives $a_2 = 1/3$, $a_1 = 1/2$, and $a_0 = 1/6$. Thus, the general solution is

$$A(k) = c + \tfrac{1}{3}k^3 + \tfrac{1}{2}k^2 + \tfrac{1}{6}k = c + \frac{k(2k+1)(k+1)}{6}.$$

Using the fact that $a_0 = 0$ gives $c = 0$ and we have the identity

$$0^2 + 1^2 + 2^2 + \ldots + k^2 = \frac{k(2k+1)(k+1)}{6}.$$

Let's now consider the case in which $g(n) = b\,s^n$, where s and b are fixed constants. Let's rewrite the affine dynamical system (with $r \neq 1$) as

$$A(n+1) = rA(n) + b\,1^n$$

and its general solution as

$$A(k) = c\,r^k + a\,1^k.$$

This should indicate that the general solution of the dynamical system

$$A(n+1) = rA(n) + b\,s^n$$

should be of the form

$$A(k) = c\,r^k + a\,s^k,$$

where the constant a depends on the system and the constant c depends on the initial value.

Example 2.39

Consider the dynamical system

$$A(n+1) = 3A(n) + 4^n.$$

In this case, $r = 3$, $s = 4$, and $b = 1$. From the previous discussion, we might guess that the general solution is of the form

$$A(k) = c\, 3^k + a\, 4^k,$$

where a is a constant which can be determined from the dynamical system, while c is determined from the initial value. Again we should remember that there is nothing wrong with making intelligent guesses as long as we verify that our guess is correct.

Since $A(n + 1) = c\, 3^{n+1} + a\, 4^{n+1}$, substitution into the dynamical system gives

$$c\, 3^{n+1} + a\, 4^{n+1} = 3(c\, 3^n + a\, 4^n) + 4^n = c3^{n+1} + 3a\, 4^n + 4^n.$$

After subtracting the term $c\, 3^{n+1}$ from both sides and then dividing by 4^n, we have

$$4a = 3a + 1, \quad \text{or} \quad a = 1.$$

Thus the general solution is

$$A(k) = c\, 3^k + 4^k.$$

Let's find the particular solution when $a_0 = 2$. Since $A(0) = c\, 3^0 + 4^0 = c + 1 = 2$, it follows that $c = 1$, and

$$A(k) = 3^k + 4^k.$$

For the dynamical system

$$A(n + 1) = r A(n) + b\, s^n \tag{12}$$

we expect the solution to be of the form

$$A(k) = c\, r^k + a\, s^k.$$

Substitution back into the dynamical system gives

$$c\, r^{n+1} + a\, s^{n+1} = r\, (c\, r^n + a\, s^n) + b\, s^k$$

or, after cancellation and division by s^n,

$$as = ra + b.$$

This gives that $a = b/(s - r)$. Thus, the general solution to the above dynamical system is, when $r \neq s$,

$$A(k) = c r^k + \left(\frac{b}{s - r}\right) s^k. \tag{13}$$

As an example of dynamical systems in which $r \neq s$ let's consider the sum of exponentials

$$1 + s^1 + s^2 + \ldots + s^n$$

where s is a fixed constant. Note that when $s = 1$, the sum is just $n + 1$, so we will assume that $s \neq 1$ in the following discussion. By letting

$$A(n) = 1 + s^1 + s^2 + \ldots + s^n,$$

we have

$$A(n + 1) = A(n) + s^{n+1} = A(n) + s\, s^n,$$

with $a_0 = 1$. Note that this is of the form of dynamical system (12) with $r = 1$ and $b = s$. Since $s \neq 1$, the general solution is, by equation (13),

$$A(k) = c + \left(\frac{s}{s - 1}\right) s^k.$$

Since $a_0 = 1 = c + s/(s - 1)$, we have that

$$c = 1 - \frac{s}{s - 1} = \frac{s - 1}{s - 1} - \frac{s}{s - 1} = \frac{-1}{s - 1},$$

so the particular solution is

$$A(k) = \frac{-1}{s - 1} + \frac{s^{k+1}}{s - 1} = \frac{s^{k+1} - 1}{s - 1}.$$

Definition 2.40

We call the infinite sum

$$g(0) + g(1) + g(2) + \ldots$$

*an **infinite series**. Suppose $A(k)$ is the solution to the dynamical system*

$$A(n + 1) = A(n) + g(n),$$

with $a_0 = g(0)$, that is,

$$A(n) = g(0) + g(1) + \ldots + g(n),$$

If

$$\lim_{k \to \infty} A(k) = a,$$

then we say that the infinite series **converges** *to a, and we write*

$$g(0) + g(1) + g(2) + \ldots = a.$$

From our discussion above, we have

$$A(k) = 1 + s^0 + \ldots + s^k = \frac{s^{k+1} - 1}{s - 1}.$$

We note that if $-1 < s < 1$, then s^{k+1} goes to zero as k goes to infinity so that

$$\lim_{k \to \infty} A(k) = \frac{-1}{s - 1} = \frac{1}{1 - s}.$$

Thus, if $|s| < 1$, then we have

$$1 + s + s^2 + \ldots = \frac{1}{1 - s}.$$

This infinite series is called a **geometric series**. In particular, we have, for $s = 1/2$,

$$1 + \frac{1}{2} + \left(\frac{1}{2}\right)^2 + \ldots = \frac{1}{1 - 1/2} = 2.$$

Finally, let's consider exponentials in which $r = s$, that is, the dynamical system

$$A(n + 1) = rA(n) + b\,r^n.$$

In particular, let's recall the case in which $r = 1$, that is, the affine dynamical system

$$A(n + 1) = A(n) + b\,(1)^n.$$

The general solution to this system is of the form

$$A(k) = (c + ka)1^k,$$

where a depends on the system. Thus, the solution when $r \neq 1$ should be of the form

$$A(k) = (c + ka)r^k.$$

**Example
2.41**

Find the general solution to the dynamical system

$$A(n+1) = 3A(n) + 6\,(3)^n.$$

In this case, $r = s = 3$ and $b = 6$. Applying the above principle, we try

$$A(k) = (c + ka)3^k$$

as the general solution. Substitution into the dynamical system gives

$$[c + (n+1)a]3^{n+1} = 3[(c + na)3^n] + 6\,(3)^n,$$

or, after simplification and division by 3^n,

$$3(n+1)a = 3na + 6.$$

Subtracting $3an$ from both sides gives

$$3a = 6, \quad \text{or} \quad a = 2.$$

Thus, the general solution is

$$A(k) = (c + 2k)3^k.$$

To find the particular solution when $a_0 = 5$, we set $A(0) = [c + 2(0)]3^0 = c = 5$. So the particular solution is

$$A(k) = (5 + 2k)3^k.$$

We now summarize these results.

**Theorem
2.42**

Nonhomogeneous dynamical system in which $g(n)$ is an exponential: *Consider the dynamical system*

$$A(n+1) = rA(n) + b\,s^n.$$

- *If $r \neq s$, then the general solution is of the form*

$$A(k) = c\,r^k + a\,s^k.$$

- *If $r = s$, then the general solution is of the form*

$$A(k) = (c + ak)r^k.$$

In both cases, the constant a is found by substituting into the dynamical system, while the constant c depends on the initial value.

Example 2.43

Most of the water flowing into Lake Ontario is from Lake Erie. Suppose that pollution of the lakes ceased. How long would it take for the pollution level in each lake to be reduced to 10 per cent of its present level?

First, to simplify matters, let's assume that 100 per cent of the water in Lake Ontario comes from Lake Erie. Let $A(n)$ and $B(n)$ be the total amount of pollution in Lake Erie and Lake Ontario, respectively, in year n. Since pollution has stopped, the concentration of pollution in the water coming into Lake Erie is $c = 0$. It has also been determined that, each year, the percentage of the water replaced in Lakes Erie and Ontario is approximately 38 and 13 per cent, respectively.

Assuming the concentration of the pollution in each lake is constant throughout that lake, we have that 38 per cent of the pollution in Lake Erie is removed each year. Thus, the dynamical system

$$A(n + 1) = 0.62A(n),$$

describes how the pollution is changing in Lake Erie from year to year.

Each year 13 per cent of the pollution in Lake Ontario is removed, but the pollution, $0.38A(n)$, that was removed from Lake Erie is added to Lake Ontario. This means that the pollution in Lake Ontario is described by the dynamical system

$$B(n + 1) = 0.87B(n) + 0.38A(n).$$

The particular solution for the first equation is

$$A(k) = (0.62)^k a_0.$$

The first question was, how long will it take for the amount of pollution $A(k)$ in Lake Erie to be equal to 10 per cent of its present value of a_0? That is, letting $A(k) = 0.1a_0$ in the formula for the solution, find k. Substitution gives

$$0.1a_0 = (0.62)^k a_0.$$

Dividing both sides by a_0 and taking logarithms gives

$$k \ln 0.62 = \ln 0.1, \quad \text{or} \quad k = 5$$

after rounding up to the next integer.

Substituting the solution for Lake Erie into the dynamical system for Lake Ontario gives

$$B(n + 1) = 0.87B(n) + 0.38(0.62)^k a_0.$$

Using equation (13) and $B(0) = b_0$, you should find that the particular solution is

$$B(k) = (b_0 + 1.52a_0)(0.87)^k - 1.52a_0(0.62)^k.$$

We cannot solve for k, the time it takes for $B(k)$ to decrease to $0.1b_0$, since there are three unknowns in this equation. To simplify matters, we observe that Lake Ontario is approximately three times the size of Lake Erie, so we assume it has three times the pollution (but the same concentration of pollution), that is, $b_0 = 3a_0$. Substitution into the above formula gives

$$B(k) = b_0[5.56(0.87)^k - 4.56(0.62)^k].$$

Substituting $0.1b_0$ for $B(k)$ and dividing by b_0 gives

$$0.1 = 5.56(0.87)^k - 4.56(0.62)^k.$$

While k cannot be determined explicitly from this equation, in Section 3.4 we will learn a technique called **Newton's method** which can be used to find the zeros of functions. This technique will then be used in Problem 3.4.7 to determine that $k = 28.85$, so it will take over 28 years for Lake Ontario to become as unpolluted as Lake Erie will become in 5 years.

Example 2.44

Geometric series can be used to rewrite numbers with an infinitely repeating decimal (including all zeros, such as $0.5 = 0.5\ldots$) as fractions. For example, the number $C = 1.11\ldots$ can be written as the geometric series

$$C = 1 + (0.1) + (0.1)^2 + \ldots.$$

Thus, it follows that $\lim_{k\to\infty} A(k) = C$, where $A(k)$ is the solution to the dynamical system

$$A(n + 1) = A(n) + (0.1)^{n+1}$$

with $A(0) = 1$. In this case, $s = 0.1$ so we can write

$$C = \frac{1}{1 - 0.1} = \frac{10}{9}.$$

We now have a method for rewriting any number with an infinitely repeating decimal as a fraction, thus showing that such numbers are rational numbers. Let's illustrate this method by way of another example. You should be able to use this method on any other repeating decimal.

Example 2.45

Write the number
$$2.361\,616\,1\ldots = 2.3\overline{61}$$
as a fraction. (The line over the 61 means that 61 keeps repeating.)

1. Rewrite the number as the sum of two numbers: the first part which does not repeat and the infinitely repeating decimal. Thus, we rewrite our number as
$$2.3\overline{61} = 2.3 + 0.0\overline{61}.$$

2. Factor a power of 10 out of the repeating part so that the first repetition occurs before the decimal place:
$$2.3\overline{61} = 2.3 + (10)^{-3}(61.\overline{61}).$$

3. Factor out the number that repeats:
$$2.3\overline{61} = 2.3 + (10)^{-3}(61)(1.\overline{01}).$$

4. Write the repeating part as a geometric series, and then replace the geometric series with its sum:
$$\begin{aligned} 2.3\overline{61} &= 2.3 + (10)^{-3}(61)(1 + 0.01 + (0.01)^2 + \ldots) \\ &= 2.3 + (10)^{-3}(61)\left(\frac{1}{1 - 0.01}\right) \\ &= 2.3 + (10)^{-3}(61)\left(\frac{100}{99}\right) \end{aligned}$$

5. Simplify:
$$2.3\overline{61} = \frac{23}{10} + \left(\frac{61}{1000}\right)\left(\frac{100}{99}\right) = \frac{1169}{495}.$$

From this discussion, it is clear that any number ending in a repeating sequence of digits can be rewritten as a fraction. It is also easy to show that any fraction can be rewritten as a number with an eventually repeating decimal expansion. These numbers are called **rational numbers**. All other numbers are called **irrational numbers**. The study of properties of rational and irrational numbers is an interesting area of mathematics, but is outside the scope of this text.

We now combine our rules for polynomials and for exponentials in an 'obvious' way.

Example 2.46

Find the general solution to the dynamical system

$$A(n+1) = 2A(n) - 3^n - 2n + 1.$$

In this case, you should be able to guess that the solution is of the form

$$A(k) = c\,2^k + a_2\,3^k + a_1 k + a_0.$$

Substitution into the dynamical system gives

$$c\,2^{n+1} + a_2 3^{n+1} + a_1(n+1) + a_0 = 2(c\,2^n + a_2 3^n + a_1 n + a_0) - 3^n - 2n + 1.$$

After simplifying, bringing all terms to the left, and grouping the 3^n terms, the n terms, and the constants, we have

$$3^n(a_2 + 1) + n(-a_1 + 2) + (a_1 - a_0 - 1) = 0.$$

Setting each of the terms in parentheses equal to zero and solving gives

$$a_2 = -1, \quad a_1 = 2, \quad a_0 = 1.$$

The general solution is then

$$A(k) = c2^k - 3^k + 2k + 1.$$

2.6.1 Problems

1. Find the general solution to each of the following dynamical systems.

    (a) $A(n+1) = 2A(n) - n$

    (b) $A(n+1) = 4A(n) + 6n + 5$

    (c) $A(n+1) = -A(n) + 4n^2 - 2$

    (d) $A(n+1) = 2A(n) + 3^n$

    (e) $A(n+1) = -3A(n) + 15\,(2)^n$

    (f) $A(n+1) = 2A(n) + 3^n - n$

    (g) $A(n+1) = A(n) + (-1)^n$

    (h) $A(n+1) = 3A(n) + 3^n$

    (i) $A(n+1) = 2A(n) - 2^n + 3^n$

    (j) $A(n+1) = A(n) + 6n + 1$

    (k) $A(n+1) = 3A(n) + 2\,(4)^n - 6$

2. Find the particular solution to each equation in Problem 1 above, given that $A(0) = 1$ in each case.

3. Find the general solution to the dynamical system

$$A(n+1) = 2A(n) + n\,3^n.$$

4. Find the general solution to the dynamical system

$$A(n+1) = 3A(n) + n\,3^n.$$

5. What should be the form of the general solution to the dynamical system

$$A(n+1) = rA(n) + ns^n?$$

There should be two cases, $r \neq s$ and $r = s$.

6. Consider the infinite series

$$0(0.2)^0 + 1(0.2)^1 + 2(0.2)^2 + \ldots .$$

Determine that this series converges and find to what value it converges. Do this by finding the general solution to the dynamical system

$$A(n+1) = A(n) + (n+1)(0.2)^{n+1}$$

and computing

$$\lim_{k \to \infty} A(k).$$

(Hint: Recall that $\lim_{k \to \infty} k\, s^k = 0$ when $|s| < 1$.)

7. Suppose you have a roll of paper, such as paper towels. Let the radius of the inner core (that the paper is wrapped about) be $r_0 = 1$ inch. Suppose that the paper is 0.002 inches thick, so when the paper is wrapped n times about the core, the radius of the entire roll is $r_1 = r_0 + 0.002n = 1 + 0.002n$ inches. Let $A(n)$ be the total length of paper when it is wrapped about the core n times.

   (a) Develop a dynamical system that gives the relationship between $A(n+1)$ and $A(n)$ by computing the length of paper when it is wrapped about the roll one more time.

   (b) Solve that dynamical system with $a_0 = 0$.

   (c) When the outer radius is $r_1 = 2$ inches, what is the total length of paper about the roll?

(d) What is the outer radius r_1 of the roll when the length of paper left is 500 inches?

8. Suppose your money is in the bank earning 8 per cent interest. Your initial deposit is 1000 dollars. Because you earn more money each year, your deposit each year will be 10 per cent more than the preceding year. That is, in year 1 your deposit will be $1000 + (0.1)1000 = (1.1)1000$ dollars. Likewise your deposit in year 2 will be $(1.1)1000 + (0.1)(1.1)1000 = (1.1)^2 1000$ dollars, and in year n it will be $1000(1.1)^n$ dollars. Thus the amount in your account will be given by the equation

$$A(n+1) = (1.08)A(n) + 1000(1.1)^{n+1}.$$

Find the amount in your account after 20 years, that is, find $A(20)$.

9. Repeat Problem 8 given that the bank pays 10 per cent interest each year.

10. Suppose your savings account has 1000 dollars. Suppose you deposit an additional 100 dollars at the beginning of year 1, an additional 200 at the beginning of year 2, an additional 300 at the beginning of year 3, etc. If your bank pays 8 per cent interest compounded annually, how much will be in your account after 20 years?

11. Suppose we have a savings account initially containing A dollars, which collects 10 per cent interest, compounded annually. We have determined that, to live comfortably, we presently need 40 000 dollars per year. We also assume that inflation is going to be 5 per cent per year, compounded annually, so next year, the first year we will withdraw money from our account, we will need to withdraw $(1.05)40\,000$ dollars from our account. The following year, we need to withdraw $(1.05)^2 40\,000$ from our account, etc.

    (a) Find the dynamical system that models this account.

    (b) Find the general solution to this dynamical system.

    (c) Find the particular solution, given that $a_0 = A$.

    (d) If you want this account to last for 20 years, that is, $A(20) = 0$, find A.

12. Using dynamical systems, find a formula for the sum

$$0(1) + 1(2) + 2(3) + \ldots + n(n+1),$$

and use that formula to compute

$$0(1) + 1(2) + 2(3) + \ldots + 100(101).$$

13. The following infinite series converge to what numbers?

   (a) $1 + (2/3) + (2/3)^2 + (2/3)^3 + \ldots$
   (b) $1 - (1/2) + (1/2)^2 - (1/2)^3 + \ldots$
   (c) $(1/4)^3 + (1/4)^4 + (1/4)^5 + \ldots$
   (d) $1 + (2/5)^2 + (2/5)^4 + (2/5)^6 + \ldots$

14. Express the following repeating decimals as fractions.

   (a) $0.55\overline{5}$
   (b) $0.131\,3\overline{13}$
   (c) $1.254\,\overline{54}$

Introduction to nonlinear dynamical systems

3.1 A model of population growth

Consider a population of rabbits. For simplicity, assume that on the average each rabbit gives birth to two new rabbits in one unit of time and that no rabbit dies. The easiest way to model this problem is to consider the **change** in the size of the population of rabbits in one time period. Let $A(0)$ be the number of rabbits at time $t = 0$ (the time when we start our observations). Then $A(1) - A(0)$ is the change in the population in the first unit of time. But the change equals the number of new rabbits, that is, the number that were born during that time interval. Thus $A(1) - A(0) = 2A(0)$. Likewise the change from period 1 to period 2, $A(2) - A(1)$, equals the number born to the population of size $A(1)$. Thus

$$A(2) - A(1) = 2A(1).$$

Continuing in this manner we see that the change in population in a time period is twice the population at the beginning of the time period, that is

$$A(n + 1) - A(n) = 2A(n), \quad \text{or} \quad A(n + 1) = 3A(n).$$

The solution is $A(k) = 3^k a_0$.

We now wish to make this model more realistic. Now assume that the number of births in time period n is proportional to the size of the population in that time period, that is, the number of births equals $bA(n)$, where b is the birth rate. Likewise, the number of deaths in time period n is proportional to $A(n)$, that is, the number of deaths equals $dA(n)$. The change in population in a time period is the number of births minus the number of deaths. Combining these assumptions gives

$$A(n + 1) - A(n) = bA(n) - dA(n), \quad \text{or} \quad A(n + 1) = (1 + r)A(n),$$

where $r = b - d$ is the (net) growth rate for the population. The solution, we know, is

$$A(k) = (1 + r)^k a_0.$$

Let r be a reasonable rate of growth, say $r = 0.2$, and let $a_0 = 100$. Then we obtain $A(10) = 619$, $A(20) = 3833$, $A(50) = 910\,041$, and $A(100) = 8\,281\,797\,451$. We see that while our model seems to make sense, the size of the population gets unrealistically large after a long period of time ($A(k)$ goes to infinity exponentially). This is Malthus's theory that populations grow exponentially and he thus predicted a world-wide catastrophe that hasn't happened yet.

Does this mean our model is wrong? Yes and no. It depends on what information we want from it. For small values of time this model gives 'good' estimates of population growth. For short periods of time, populations do appear to grow exponentially and growth rates are approximately constant. One of the things that is going wrong is that over long periods of time, the growth rate r is not constant, but changes as the size of the population changes. So we must replace the r in our dynamical system with $f(A(n))$, where f is a function of population size. In other words, our growth rate $f(A(n))$ changes as the size of the population changes.

The first assumption we make is that the environment of the population can only support a certain number, say L, of the species. Thus, if $A(n) > L$, there will not be enough food or space available and more animals will die (of starvation, etc.) than are born. So, it follows that the growth rate is negative, $f(A(n)) < 0$, when $A(n) > L$.

Our second assumption is that if the population is less than L, then there is extra food and space available, so the growth rate should be positive, that is, $f(A(n)) > 0$ when $A(n) < L$.

Our last assumption is that if the population is small relative to L, that is, there is plently of food and space for the existing population, then the growth rate should be close to the unrestricted growth rate r. But as the population increases, the growth rate should decrease and should, in fact, be zero when $A(n) = L$.

The simplest function that satisfies these conditions is the linear function

$$f(A(n)) = r\left(1 - \frac{A(n)}{L}\right).$$

Notice the following: (1) if $A(n)$ is small, $1 - A(n)/L$ is close to 1 and the growth rate, $f(A(n))$, is approximately r; (2) if $A(n) < L$, then $1 - A(n)/L > 0$ and the growth rate is positive; (3) if $A(n) = L$, the growth rate is zero; and (4) if $A(n) > L$, then $1 - A(n)/L < 0$ and the growth rate is negative. In fact, the larger $A(n)$, the more negative the growth rate.

The number r is called the **unrestricted growth rate** and the number L is called the **carrying capacity** of the environment. The dynamical system that models population growth is then

$$A(n + 1) - A(n) = r\left(1 - \frac{A(n)}{L}\right)A(n),$$

or, after simplification,

$$A(n + 1) = (1 + r)A(n) - bA^2(n), \tag{1}$$

where $b = r/L$. This is called the **logistic equation**. Mathematicians often call the term $-bA^2(n)$ a **damping term** because it dampens the growth of the population, that is, keeps it from going to infinity.

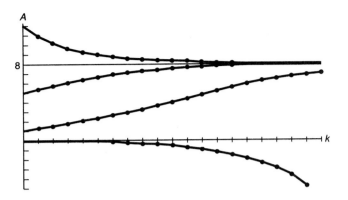

Fig. 13. Points $(k, A(k))$ for the dynamical system $A(n+1) = 1.2A(n) - 0.025A^2(n)$.

**Example
3.1**

Suppose $r = 0.2$, $L = 8$ (where one unit represents 1000 of the species), and therefore $b = 0.2/8 = 0.025$. The logistic equation becomes

$$A(n+1) = 1.2A(n) - 0.025A^2(n). \tag{2}$$

If $a_0 = 3$, then

$$A(1) = (1.2)3 - (0.025)9 = 3.375, \quad A(2) = 3.765,$$

and so forth. Figure 13 gives graphs of solutions $(n, A(n))$ for several different initial values (the one with $a_0 = -0.1$ being a little unrealistic but mathematically interesting). The horizontal line, $L = 8$, is the limit to population size or the stable equilibrium value. Remember that only the points $(0, A(0))$, $(1, A(1))$, etc. are important, but these points have been connected with lines so that a pattern is easier to distinguish.

Let's recall the definition of equilibrium value or fixed point.

**Definition
3.2**

Consider a first order dynamical system

$$A(n+1) = f(A(n)).$$

A number a is called an **equilibrium value** *or a* **fixed point** *for this dynamical system if a satisfies the equation*

$$a = f(a).$$

In this case,

$$A(k) = a$$

is a particular solution to the dynamical system.

Let's solve for the equilibrium values of the logistic equation (2) of Example 3.1, by substituting $a = A(n+1) = A(n)$. This gives

$$a = 1.2a - 0.025a^2.$$

Collecting terms on the left and factoring out an a gives

$$a(-0.2 + 0.025a) = 0.$$

The solutions are given by $a = 0$ and $-0.2 + 0.025a = 0$, that is,

$$a = 0 \quad \text{and} \quad a = 8.$$

This makes sense since a population of size 0 would remain there. Also, as discussed previously, if $a_0 = 8$, the carrying capacity, then the growth rate is zero and again the population remains constant.

Let's find the equilibrium value for the general logistic equation (1). Substituting a for $A(n+1)$ and $A(n)$ we have

$$a = (1+r)a - \left(\frac{r}{L}\right)a^2,$$

or, after subtracting a from both sides then factoring out an a and an r,

$$0 = r\left(1 - \frac{a}{L}\right)a.$$

Dividing by r, which we know is not zero, we have the equilibrium values of

$$a = L \quad \text{and} \quad a = 0$$

as expected.

Let's recall the definitions of stable and unstable equilibrium values.

Definition 3.3

Suppose a first order dynamical system has an equilibrium value a. This equilibrium value is said to be **stable** *or* **attracting** *if there is a number ϵ such that, when*

$$|a_0 - a| < \epsilon, \quad \text{then} \quad \lim_{k \to \infty} A(k) = a.$$

An equilibrium value is **unstable** *or* **repelling** *if there is a number ϵ such that, when*

$$0 < |a_0 - a| < \epsilon, \quad \text{then} \quad |A(k) - a| > \epsilon$$

for **some** *(but not necessarily all) values of k.*

Suppose that a_0 is 'close' to a. Intuitively, a fixed point is attracting if $A(k)$ goes towards a and is repelling if $A(k)$ goes away from a. There are fixed points that are neither stable nor unstable. For example, a could be semistable, that is, a attracts solutions that start on the right but repels solutions that start on the left (or vice versa).

Referring to Figure 13, it appears that the fixed point $a = 8$ is attracting. In particular, it appears that if $1 < a_0 < 12$, then

$$\lim_{k \to \infty} A(k) = 8.$$

In fact, if you construct a cobweb graph for this function, you will see that if a_0 is between 0 and 48 (the roots of $1.2x - 0.025x^2$), then $A(k)$ will converge to 8. In this case, any $\epsilon \leq 8$ will suffice when using the definition. Note that since the interval $(0, 48)$ is not symmetric about $a = 8$, no value of ϵ gives the entire interval of convergence.

Also note that the fixed point $a = 0$ appears to be repelling.

Example 3.4

Let $r = 1.4$ and $L = 10$ in the logistic equation (1). Then

$$A(n + 1) = 2.4A(n) - 0.14A^2(n).$$

The equilibrium values are $a = 0$ and $a = 10$. A cobweb graph is given in Figure 14 where $a_0 = 1$. Notice that in the linear model, if $r = 1.4$, $A(k)$ would increase rapidly toward positive infinity, but here (with a_0 relatively close to equilibrium) $A(k)$ oscillates to the equilibrium value $a = 10$, so this equilibrium value appears to be stable. The cobweb graph also indicates that $a = 0$ is unstable.

By observing the graph of $f(x) = 2.4x - 0.14x^2$, it appears that if a_0 is on an interval in which $f(a_0) > 0$, then $A(k)$ goes to 10. Since the roots of $2.4x - 0.14x^2$ are $x = 0$ and $x = 17\frac{1}{7}$, it follows that if $0 < a_0 < 17.14$, then $A(k) \to 10$. This interval is what we mean by the phrase 'a_0 is close to a'.

There are several questions to be asked. What is the **general solution** to the logistic equation? For what values of r and L is the equilibrium value $a = L$ stable? For what values of r and L is the equilibrium value $a = 0$ stable? When an equilibrium value is stable, for what a_0 values does the solution $A(k)$ go to that equilibrium value?

To give a negative answer to the first question, it is **usually** impossible to find a solution to a nonlinear dynamical system. (In Section 2.5 we saw an exception to this rule.) We can compute $A(0)$, $A(1)$, ..., $A(k)$ for large values of k using a computer, so solutions exist. But we cannot

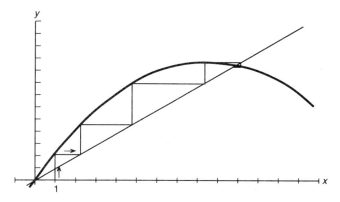

Fig. 14. Cobweb for the dynamical system $A(n+1) = 2.4A(n) - 0.14A^2(n)$, with $a_0 = 1$.

find a 'simple' algebraic expression for $A(k)$ in terms of k. This is very unsettling, for no matter how many values of $A(k)$ we compute, there is always the nagging feeling that something strange might happen on the next value we compute.

This reminds me of the story of two people having a discussion about prime numbers. The first said that all odd integers were prime. "1's prime, 3's prime, 5's prime, 7's prime, so all odd integers are prime" he argued. "No", said the second, "you're wrong. 1, 3, 5, and 7 are prime. 9 is not prime, so we'll throw it out for experimental error. 11's prime and 13's prime. Now we can conclude all odd integers are prime."

There are two morals to this story. First, no matter how many values of $A(k)$ we compute and no matter how convincing the pattern, we can still make no **certain** conclusion about the next value. Second, many people will find a pattern, but when one value disagrees with the pattern, they ignore the value instead of looking for a better pattern. But we digress.

Since we cannot write a solution to our equation, we must develop some other techniques to determine if the fixed points are attracting. Remember, knowing a fixed point is attracting tells us a lot about the long term behavior of the solution to a dynamical system and thus about the real world it models.

In Section 1.5, we observed that if we drew a cobweb using the tangent line to the curve $y = f(x)$ at the point $(a, f(a)) = (a, a)$, it would behave similarly to the cobweb drawn using the actual curve $y = f(x)$, at least if a_0 was close to a. This led to Theorem 1.18 which we restate as follows.

**Theorem
3.5**

Suppose a is a fixed point for the dynamical system

$$A(n+1) = f(A(n)).$$

Then a is attracting if

$$|f'(a)| < 1,$$

and is repelling if

$$|f'(a)| > 1.$$

If $|f'(a)| = 1$, our work is inconclusive.

In Figure 1.6, we saw an indication why this theorem should be true. When the graph is magnified near an equilibrium point, it appears to be straight, that is, the tangent line is a good approximation and we can use its cobweb to decide the stability of a. The proof of Theorem 3.5 depends on the mean value theorem. Let's recall this important theorem from calculus.

**Theorem
3.6**

Mean value theorem: *Suppose that the function f is continuous and differentiable on the interval (c, d) and continuous at the end points. Then there is some point x_0 in that interval such that*

$$f'(x_0) = \frac{f(d) - f(c)}{d - c}.$$

Proof of Theorem 3.5: We are given that $a = f(a)$ and that $|f'(a)| < 1$. Therefore there is an interval $I = (a - \epsilon, a + \epsilon)$ about the number a and a number $1 > b > |f'(a)|$ such that $|f'(x)| < b < 1$ for every x in that interval.

Let $A(0) = a_0$ be in interval I. We will show that $|A(1) - a|$ is smaller than $|A(0) - a|$, that is, we are getting closer to equilibrium. Using the dynamical system, we get

$$|A(1) - a| = |f(A(0)) - a|.$$

Using the substitution $a = f(a)$ (which is true since a is an equilibrium value), we get

$$|A(1) - a| = |f(A(0)) - f(a)|.$$

Using the mean value theorem with $c = a$ and $d = A(0)$ (or vice versa if $A(0) < a$), we find that there is a number x_0 between $A(0)$ and a such that

$$|A(1) - a| = |f(A(0)) - f(a)| = |f'(x_0)||A(0) - a|.$$

Since x_0 is between $A(0)$ and a, then $x_0 \in I$ also. Thus we know that $|f'(x_0)| < b$. Therefore

$$|A(1) - a| = |f'(x_0)||A(0) - a| < b|A(0) - a|.$$

Similarly, we get

$$|A(2) - a| < b|A(1) - a| < b^2|A(0) - a|.$$

(Since $A(1)$ is closer to a than $A(0)$, then $A(1)$ must also be in interval I.) Using induction,

$$|A(k) - a| < b|A(k - 1) - a| < b^k|A(0) - a|.$$

Thus, since $b < 1$, we have

$$\lim_{k \to \infty} |A(k) - a| = 0 \quad \text{or} \quad \lim_{k \to \infty} A(k) = a,$$

and so a is attracting.

Suppose that $a = f(a)$ and that $|f'(a)| > 1$. Then there is an interval $I = (a - \epsilon, a + \epsilon)$ about the number a and a number $1 < b < |f'(a)|$ such that $|f'(x)| > b$ for every x in I. Let $A(0) = a_0 \in I$. We want to show that there is some number k such that $A(k)$ is **not** in interval I.

We first show that $|A(1) - a|$ is larger than $|A(0) - a|$, that is, we are getting farther from equilibrium. Using the dynamical system and the mean value theorem, we again find that

$$|A(1) - a| = |f(A(0)) - f(a)| = |f'(x_0)||A(0) - a|.$$

But we know that $|f'(x_0)| > b$, and therefore

$$|A(1) - a| = |f'(x_0)||A(0) - a| > b|A(0) - a|.$$

If $A(1)$ is no longer in interval I, then we are finished. If $A(1)$ is in interval I, then we repeat the process, giving

$$|A(2) - a| > b|A(1) - a| > b^2|A(0) - a|.$$

Again, by induction, either some value $A(k)$ is not in I or

$$|A(k) - a| > b|A(k - 1) - a| > b^k|A(0) - a|.$$

Since I is a finite interval, but b^k goes to infinity as k goes to infinity, at some point $A(k)$ must be out of the interval. Therefore, a is repelling and the theorem is proved.

We must point out that $A(k)$ does not necessarily go to infinity in the unstable case. Once $A(k)$ leaves interval I, the behavior of the solution can change. It could be that $A(k)$ goes to some other equilibrium value. There are even cases in which $A(k)$ eventually comes close to the original equilibrium value a (only to go away once again).

Example 3.7

Recall that $a = 0$ and $a = 10$ are equilibrium values for the dynamical system

$$A(n+1) = 2.4A(n) - 0.14A^2(n).$$

Since the derivative of $f(x) = 2.4x - 0.14x^2$ is

$$f'(x) = 2.4 - 0.28x,$$

it follows that $|f'(0)| = 2.4 > 1$ so $a = 0$ is repelling, and that $|f'(10)| = |2.4 - 2.8| = 0.4 < 1$ so $a = 10$ is attracting.

3.1.1 Problems

1. For each of the following dynamical systems find the fixed points and use Theorem 3.5 to determine which are attracting and which are repelling. For those that are attracting, use cobwebs to determine an interval (c, d) for which, if a_0 is in that interval, then $A(k)$ goes to a.

   (a) $A(n+1) = 1.7A(n) - 0.14A^2(n)$

   (b) $A(n+1) = 0.8A(n) + 0.1A^2(n)$

   (c) $A(n+1) = 3.4A(n) - 2.4A^2(n)$

   (d) $A(n+1) = 0.2A(n) - 0.2A^3(n)$

2. Suppose that $r = 0.3$ and $L = 3$ in the logistic equation (1). In addition, assume that there is a constant immigration of 0.4 units of the species into the region each time period. Develop a dynamical system to model the size of the population, find the equilibrium values, and determine which equilibrium values are stable and the interval of stability.

3. The dynamical system

$$A(n+1) = 3A(n) - A^2(n) + 3$$

has the two equilibrium values $a = -1$ and $a = 3$.

   (a) Show, using Theorem 3.5, that $a = -1$ is unstable.

(b) Show that $a = 3$ is unstable.

4. The dynamical system

$$A(n+1) = 1.4A(n) - 0.2A^2(n) + 3$$

has the two equilibrium values $a = -3$ and $a = 5$. Use Theorem 3.5 to find their stability.

5. The dynamical system

$$A(n+1) = A^3(n) - A^2(n) + 1$$

has the two equilibrium values $a = -1$ and $a = 1$.

(a) Show that $a = -1$ is unstable.

(b) Show that no conclusion can be made for the fixed point $a = 1$ using Theorem 3.5.

(c) Carefully draw a cobweb using the curve

$$f(x) = x^3 - x^2 + 1$$

and show that $a = 1$ is semistable.

3.2 Harvesting strategies

Consider a population of some species of animal that is harvested or hunted, say deer. Remember that the growth rate for our species is given as $r[1 - A(n)]$, where r is the unrestricted growth rate, and the size of the units are chosen so that one unit equals the carrying capacity of the environment. For ease of explanation, let's pretend that one unit equals 10 000 deer. Let's also assume that $r = 0.8$. Since the change in population, $A(n+1) - A(n)$, equals the growth rate times the size of the population, our dynamical system becomes

$$A(n+1) - A(n) = 0.8(1 - A(n))A(n),$$

or, after simplification,

$$A(n+1) = 1.8A(n) - 0.8A^2(n).$$

In this section, we will use the theory of nonlinear dynamics to study two different harvesting (or hunting) strategies for this population.

3.2.1 Fixed harvest

Suppose that in our forest we allow hunters to kill b units of deer per season, where b may be a fraction. Then the dynamical system that models growth becomes

$$A(n + 1) = 1.8A(n) - 0.8A^2(n) - b,$$

since $A(n+1)$ is reduced by the b deer that were killed. (We are assuming that all the deer are killed at the end of the time period, for otherwise, the killing of the deer would affect the number of births and deaths and, consequently, the growth rate. But for simplicity, we will ignore this problem.)

Example 3.8

Let $b = 0.072$ (720 deer are killed each year if one unit equals $10\,000$ deer). Then our dynamical system becomes

$$A(n + 1) = 1.8A(n) - 0.8A^2(n) - 0.072.$$

The fixed points are the solutions to the equation

$$a = 1.8a - 0.8a^2 - 0.072,$$

that is, the fixed points are $a = 0.9$ and $a = 0.1$.

To check the stability of the fixed points, we note that

$$f(x) = 1.8x - 0.8x^2 - 0.072 \quad \text{and} \quad f'(x) = 1.8 - 1.6x.$$

The equilibrium value $a = 0.9$ is stable since $f'(0.9) = 0.36$, and $a = 0.1$ is unstable since $f'(0.1) = 1.64$.

In Figure 15, cobwebs are drawn for this dynamical system using several different values of a_0. Note that for the a_0 values close to 0.9, the $A(k)$ values go to 0.9, while if a_0 is close to 0.1, the $A(k)$ values go away from 0.1 (towards extinction if $a_0 < 0.1$ and towards 0.9 if $a_0 > 0.1$). What we have shown is that when we kill 720 deer each year, $a = 0.9$ is a stable equilibrium value, that is, the population of deer will stabilize at 9000. The increased growth rate at this level (there is more food available since there are less deer) makes up for the deer being killed. Being stable says that even if a minor catastrophe happened and the population of deer dropped to some lower level, say 2000 (or $a_0 = 0.2$), eventually the population would grow back to 9000.

The equilibrium $a = 0.1$ being unstable means that if the population drops **below** 1000, then we will be killing off more deer than are born and the population will eventually die out unless we cut back in our hunting. This is seen in Figure 15.

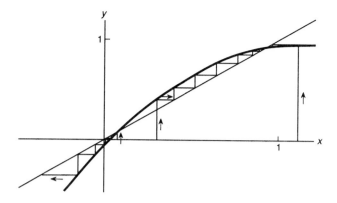

Fig. 15. Cobweb for the logistic equation with fixed hunting at 720 deer per year.

Example 3.9

We now let $b = 0.24$, that is, the hunters kill 2400 deer each year. Thus the growth equation is

$$A(n+1) = 1.8A(n) - 0.8A^2(n) - 0.24.$$

The fixed points are the solutions to $a = 1.8a - 0.8a^2 - 0.24$, and after solving using the quadratic formula, we obtain

$$a = 0.5 \pm \sqrt{-0.05}.$$

These roots are complex, and thus there are no **real** fixed points. The numbers $A(k)$ go to negative infinity for all initial values as can be seen in the cobweb of Figure 16. This implies that we are killing too many deer. Either the deer will be exterminated or we will have to reduce the amount of hunting.

Let's see how we can prove that $A(k)$ goes to negative infinity in the previous example. To do this, we need to determine the **change** in population in each time period. The change is given by the equation

$$A(n+1) - A(n) = 0.8A(n) - 0.8A^2(n) - 0.24.$$

The change is determined by the function

$$g(x) = 0.8x - 0.8x^2 - 0.24,$$

that is, for each $A(n)$ value, the number $g(A(n))$ is the amount of increase or decrease in the size of the population in that time period.

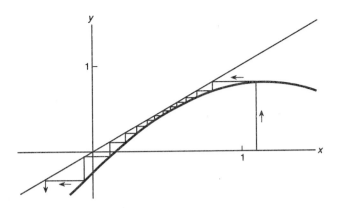

Fig. 16. Cobweb for the logistic equation with fixed hunting at 2400 deer per year.

The function $g(x)$ is a parabola with maximum value at the point where

$$g'(x) = 0.8 - 1.6x = 0,$$

that is, at $x = 0.5$ and $g(0.5) = -0.04$. This says that

$$g(x) \leq -0.04$$

for every value of x.

Thus, $g(A(n)) \leq -0.04$ for every $A(n)$ and the population decreases by **at least** 0.04 units each time period. After n time periods, it must decrease by at least $0.04n$ (actually by a lot more). So if $A(n)$ is decreasing by at least 0.04 in each time period, it must be going to negative infinity since $-0.04n$ goes to negative infinity.

Theorem 3.10

Suppose a dynamical system has no equilibrium values and that it can be rewritten as

$$A(n+1) - A(n) = g(A(n)),$$

*where $g(x) = f(x) - x$. If the **absolute maximum** value of $g(x)$ is negative, then $A(k)$ goes to negative infinity. If the **absolute minimum** value of $g(x)$ is positive, then $A(k)$ goes to positive infinity.*

Proof: The proof is identical to the proof in the example above. Suppose the absolute maximum of $g(x)$ is $-c$, where c is positive. Then

$$A(1) < A(0) - c, \quad A(2) < A(1) - c < A(0) - 2c,$$

and so forth. By induction, we get

$$A(k) < A(0) - kc \quad \text{and} \quad \lim_{k \to \infty} A(k) = -\infty,$$

which completes the proof.

What we have seen is that, for two different hunting schemes, that is, for $b = 0.072$ and $b = 0.24$, we had a different number of fixed points: 2 and 0, respectively.

We would like to predict what happens for **any** fixed harvesting plan, that is, for any value of b. The equation to be considered is the dynamical system

$$A(n + 1) = 1.8A(n) - 0.8A^2(n) - b.$$

We now assume that b is some fixed constant. The fixed points are the solutions to the equation

$$a = 1.8a - 0.8a^2 - b,$$

where b is a constant and a is the as yet unknown fixed point. After simplifying then dividing by 0.8, the equation becomes

$$a^2 - a + 1.25b = 0.$$

Using the quadratic formula, the solutions are

$$a = \frac{1 \pm \sqrt{1 - 5b}}{2}.$$

We have three cases. The first case is when $1 - 5b < 0$, that is, $b > 0.2$. When $b > 0.2$, there are **no equilibrium values**. We now use Theorem 3.10 to show that $A(k)$ goes to negative infinity for any a_0 value. The dynamical system is rewritten as

$$A(n + 1) - A(n) = 0.8A(n) - 0.8A^2(n) - b,$$

so that

$$g(x) = 0.8x - 0.8x^2 - b.$$

The critical point for this function is when

$$g'(x) = 0.8 - 1.6x = 0, \quad \text{that is, when} \quad x = 0.5.$$

Since $g''(x) = -1.6$, this is a **maximum** value. Since it's a parabola, we know that the absolute maximum value of $g(x)$ is

$$g(0.5) = 0.8(0.5) - 0.8(0.5)^2 - b = 0.2 - b.$$

Since $b > 0.2$, it follows that the maximum value of $g(x)$ is $0.2 - b < 0$. Therefore, Theorem 3.10 implies that $A(k)$ goes to negative infinity whenever $b > 0.2$.

The second case is when $1 - 5b > 0$, that is, when $b < 0.2$. In this case, we have the two equilibrium values

$$a = \frac{1 \pm \sqrt{1 - 5b}}{2}.$$

Let's examine the stability of these using derivatives. We previously computed $f'(x) = 1.8 - 1.6x$, so

$$f'(0.5(1 - \sqrt{1 - 5b})) = 1 + 0.8\sqrt{1 - 5b} > 1$$

for all $b < 0.2$. Therefore, $a = 0.5(1 - \sqrt{1 - 5b})$ is unstable for $b < 0.2$.

We also have

$$f'(0.5(1 + \sqrt{1 - 5b})) = 1 - 0.8\sqrt{1 - 5b}.$$

The question is, for what b values does the inequality $-1 < 1 - 0.8\sqrt{1 - 5b} < 1$ hold? It is clear that the inequality on the right is always true. To solve

$$-1 < 1 - 0.8\sqrt{1 - 5b},$$

subtract 1 from both sides, multiply both sides by $-5/4$ (making sure you reverse the inequality sign), and square both sides, giving

$$\tfrac{25}{4} > 1 - 5b, \quad \text{or} \quad b > -1.05.$$

In conclusion, if $-1.05 < b < 0.2$, then the fixed point $a = 0.5(1 + \sqrt{1 - 5b})$ is attracting. Thus, for hunting strategies in which less than 2000 deer are removed each year, the population will stabilize. Any $b < 0.2$ is a **sustainable harvesting strategy**.

Note that $b < 0$ means we are adding more of the species to the environment instead of taking some of the species out of the environment. This is equivalent to stocking lakes or immigration.

The last case is when $b = 0.2$. In this case the dynamical system which models population growth becomes

$$A(n + 1) = 1.8A(n) - 0.8A^2(n) - 0.2.$$

The equilibrium values satisfy

$$a = 1.8a - 0.8a^2 - 0.2, \quad \text{or} \quad a^2 - a + 0.25 = 0.$$

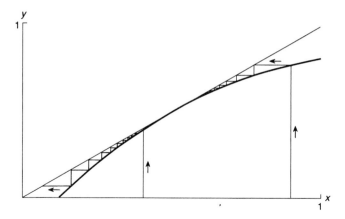

Fig. 17. Cobweb for the logistic equation with fixed hunting at 2000 deer per year.

This factors into $(a - 0.5)^2 = 0$, and there is only one (multiple) root,

$$a = 0.5.$$

In this case,

$$f(x) = 1.8x - 0.8x^2 - 0.2 \quad \text{and} \quad f'(x) = 1.8 - 1.6x.$$

Since $f'(0.5) = 1$, our methods are inconclusive. In Figure 17, it can be seen that $a = 0.5$ is semistable in the sense that if $a_0 > 0.5$ then $A(k)$ goes to 0.5, but if $a_0 < 0.5$ then $A(k)$ goes to negative infinity. (Later, we will develop a simple calculus technique that will determine stability in the case where $f'(a) = 1$.)

This implies that when we kill 2000 deer a year, the population of deer will drop to 5000. But this population is very fragile and if a minor catastrophe struck, dropping the population below 5000 (say 4999), then the population would die out or we would have to adjust our hunting habits until the population recovered.

What we have shown is that the **maximum sustainable harvest** is $b = 0.2$. For a harvest above that, the population dies out. This is a very tenuous position, because at $b = 0.2$, the equilibrium value $a = 0.5$ is unstable from below. To be safe, we might restrict b to some number slightly below 0.2. Even this would be risky, since the stable and unstable equilibrium values will be close together and a small catastrophe could cause the population to drop below the unstable equilibrium.

3.2.2   Proportional harvest

Because of the unsatisfactory solution to our fixed harvesting problem, we might try an alternative strategy, that is, to hunt or harvest, not a fixed number of the population, but **a fixed proportion of the population**. Let b represent the proportion of the population that will be removed. Then the total number removed, or harvested, will be $bA(n)$ and the dynamical system becomes

$$A(n+1) = 1.8A(n) - 0.8A^2(n) - bA(n),$$

or, after simplification,

$$A(n+1) = (1.8 - b)A(n) - 0.8A^2(n).$$

The equilibrium values, that is, the solutions to

$$a = (1.8 - b)a - 0.8a^2,$$

are $a = 0$ and $a = 1 - 1.25b$. We use the fact that

$$f(x) = (1.8 - b)x - 0.8x^2 \quad \text{and} \quad f'(x) = 1.8 - b - 1.6x$$

to determine the stability of these two equilibrium values.

For $a = 0$ we have $f'(0) = 1.8 - b$. Thus, $a = 0$ is stable when $-1 < 1.8 - b < 1$, that is, $2.8 > b > 0.8$. To reiterate, $a = 0$ **is stable if** $0.8 < b < 2.8$ **and is unstable if** $b < 0.8$ **or** $b > 2.8$. (If $b = 0.8$, $f'(0) = 1$, and we need to draw a cobweb or use the techniques we develop later. If you draw the cobweb, you will see that $a = 0$ is semistable when $b = 0.8$.)

To analyze the equilibrium value $a = 1 - 1.25b$, we compute

$$f'(1 - 1.25b) = 1.8 - b - 1.6(1 - 1.25b) = 0.2 + b.$$

Solving $-1 < 0.2 + b < 1$, we find that $a = 1 - 1.25b$ **is stable if** $-1.2 < b < 0.8$ **and is unstable if** $b < -1.2$ **or** $b > 0.8$. (When $b = 0.8$, then we have $a = 1 - 1.25(0.8) = 0$, which is semistable as discussed above.)

Note that there are two equilibrium values when $b \neq 0.8$ and there is one semistable equilibrium value when $b = 0.8$.

We are interested in harvesting strategies that have a positive stable equilibrium value for the species. We have found that b values in the interval $0 < b < 0.8$ give us a stable equilibrium values of $a = 1 - 1.25b$. Our harvest H depends on our strategy b. In particular, the **harvest** (the amount of the species killed) is $bA(k)$, that is,

$$H = bA(k).$$

Since $a = 1 - 1.25b$ is a stable equilibrium value, $A(k)$ goes to a. Therefore, we can substitute $a = 1 - 1.25b$ for $A(k)$ in the formula for our harvest, giving us

$$H = ba = b(1 - 1.25b) = b - 1.25b^2,$$

as the long range yearly harvest.

What value of b gives us our maximum harvest? The maximum value of H occurs where $dH/db = 0$, that is, when

$$H' = 1 - 2.5b = 0,$$

or when $b = 0.4$. (How do you know $b = 0.4$ is an absolute maximum for $H = b - 1.25b^2$?) If $b = 0.4$, then the harvest is $H = 0.2$. The maximum harvest occurs when we harvest $b = 0.4$ or 40 per cent of the species each time period, and that maximum harvest is $H = 0.2$ or 2000 deer. Notice that this harvest is stable since $b = 0.4 < 0.8$, so that $a = 1 - 1.25 \times 0.4 = 0.5$ is stable.

3.2.3 Comparison of harvesting strategies

We have two harvesting strategies. The first is to harvest a fixed amount of the species in each time period. The second is to harvest a fixed proportion of the species in each time period. Notice that the maximum sustainable harvest is the same for both policies. But this harvest is stable using the second strategy while it is unstable using the first strategy.

What is happening in the second strategy is that, when b is slightly larger than 0.4 or when the population drops because of outside influences, the actual harvest $H = bA$ also drops, which allows the population to recover.

It should be clear that the fixed proportion strategy is the superior harvesting strategy, but will be harder to implement. Normally, we can't count the number of the species in order to compute our kill $bA(n)$. There are methods for estimating the number $A(n)$.

An alternative might be to use a constant **effort** in our harvesting. For example, if we hunt for three days each week, it might be argued that our kill will be proportional to $A(n)$.

Another observation is that **the maximum harvest occurs when we harvest 40 per cent of the species**. In real life, people might try increasing their hunting efforts in order to increase their catch, say in the fishing industry. But we have shown that, over the long term, they will reduce the population, and their catch will drop. We are faced with the dilemma that **if we increase our effort in harvesting, we will decrease our harvest**.

3.2.4 Problems

1. Consider the equation

$$A(n+1) = 5A(n) - A^2(n) - b.$$

(a) Find the fixed points for this equation in terms of b. Notice that (1) if $b < 4$ there are two fixed points, (2) if $b = 4$ there is one fixed point, and (3) if $b > 4$ there are no fixed points.

(b) Determine for what values of b each of the two equilibrium values are attracting and repelling (given that $b < 4$). Skip cases in which $f'(a) = \pm 1$.

(c) Use Theorem 3.10 to determine whether $A(k)$ goes to positive infinity or negative infinity when $b > 4$.

(d) Sketch a cobweb when $b = 4$ to determine the stability of the one equilibrium value, $a = 2$.

2. Consider the equation

$$A(n+1) = -bA(n) + A^3(n).$$

(a) Find the fixed points for this equation. Note that, for $b \leq -1$, there is one fixed point, but there are three fixed points when $b > -1$.

(b) Under what conditions on b are each of the three fixed points attracting or repelling? Note that for two of these fixed points, the conditions must be restricted to $b > -1$. Also, you will have to draw a cobweb for the case in which $b = -1$.

3. Consider the dynamical system

$$A(n+1) - A(n) = 0.5(1 - 0.5A(n))A(n) - bA(n),$$

which corresponds to a fixed proportion harvesting policy for a population in which the unrestricted growth rate is $r = 0.5$ and the carrying capacity is $L = 2$.

(a) Find the nonzero fixed point for this equation, and determine for what values of b it is stable.

(b) Find the maximum sustainable harvest for this equation and note that it is stable.

3.3 More on genetics

In this section, we will use the theory of nonlinear dynamical systems to continue our study on the effects of selection and mutation in genetics. The computations will be somewhat messy, but if you stick with the algebra you should find the results interesting.

We will continue to study one particular gene, say gene $\mathcal{A}$, which has two forms or alleles, A and a. In our introduction to genetics, we discussed the case in which allele a was fatal. Now let's assume that those homozygotes with the trait caused by allele a are at a selective disadvantage, but do not necessarily die. In particular, assume that all individuals with at least one A-allele reach adulthood, but that only a certain fraction, say $1 - s$, of the a-homozygotes reach adulthood. The number $1 - s$ is called the **relative fitness** of the a-homozygotes.

Also assume that the alleles mutate from A- to a-alleles and that μ is the mutation rate (the fraction of A-alleles that mutate).

We will now develop a dynamical system for the fraction of A-alleles in generation $n + 1$ in terms of the fraction of A-alleles in generation n. Let $p(n)$ be the fraction of A-alleles among the adults of generation n (and $q(n) = 1 - p(n)$ is the fraction of a-alleles) just after mutation. As before, the fraction of A-homozygotes, heterozygotes, and a-homozygotes born into generation $n + 1$ are

$$u = p^2(n), \quad v = 2p(n)q(n), \quad w = q^2(n),$$

respectively.

If there are T individuals born to that generation, then there are Tu, Tv, and Tw of each type among the children. Since only $1 - s$ of the a-homozygotes reach adulthood, there are Tu, Tv, and $Tw(1-s)$ individuals among the adults of generation $n+1$, for a total of $T - Tsw$ adults. Since each A-homozygote has two A-alleles and each heterozygote has one A-allele, the total number of A-alleles (before mutation) in generation $n+1$ is $2Tu + Tv$. Since the total number of genes is twice the total number of adults, $2T - 2Tsw$, it follows that the fraction of A-alleles in generation $n + 1$ before mutation is

$$\frac{2Tu + Tv}{2T - 2Tsw} = \frac{2u + v}{2(1 - sw)} = \frac{2p^2(n) + 2p(n)q(n)}{2(1 - sq^2(n))}.$$

Since, as a fraction, μ of these alleles mutate to a-alleles, the fraction of the A-alleles that remains is $1 - \mu$. Thus,

$$p(n + 1) = (1 - \mu)\frac{2p(n)[p(n) + q(n)]}{2[1 - sq^2(n)]}.$$

Canceling the 2's and remembering that $p(n) + q(n) = 1$, we have

$$p(n + 1) = (1 - \mu)\frac{p(n)}{1 - sq^2(n)} = (1 - \mu)\frac{p(n)}{1 - s + 2sp(n) - sp^2(n)}.$$

To find the fixed points of this equation, we need to solve

$$p = (1 - \mu)\frac{p}{1 - s + 2sp - sp^2}.$$

After cross multiplying, collecting terms, and factoring out a p, we get

$$p(-sp^2 + 2sp + \mu - s) = 0.$$

Clearly, one root is $p = 0$. Using the quadratic formula, the other two roots are

$$p = 1 \pm \sqrt{\frac{\mu}{s}}.$$

Since we must have $0 \leq p \leq 1$, the only admissible fixed point is

$$p = 1 - \sqrt{\frac{\mu}{s}}.$$

To find when this fixed point is attracting, we must find the derivative of

$$f(x) = (1 - \mu)\frac{x}{1 - s + 2sx - sx^2}.$$

Using the quotient rule and simplifying, we get

$$f'(x) = (1 - \mu)\frac{1 - s + sx^2}{(1 - s + 2sx - sx^2)^2}.$$

Substituting the fixed point $1 - \sqrt{\mu/s}$ for x and simplifying gives

$$f'\left(1 - \sqrt{\frac{\mu}{s}}\right) = \frac{1 + \mu - 2\sqrt{\mu s}}{1 - \mu}.$$

Solving the inequality

$$\frac{1 + \mu - 2\sqrt{\mu s}}{1 - \mu} < 1$$

gives

$$\mu < s.$$

Thus, this fixed point is stable for any fitness less than 1 as long as the mutation rate is smaller than s.

Since $f'(0) = (1 - \mu)/(1 - s)$, it is seen that $p = 0$ is stable if $\mu > s$, in which case the A-alleles die out. This makes sense, since if $\mu > s$ then the fixed points $p = 1 \pm \sqrt{\mu/s}$ are not between 0 and 1, so they could not represent the long term behavior.

To reiterate, if the fitness of the a-homozygotes is $1 - s$, where $s > 0$ and the mutation rate from A- to a-alleles is $\mu < s$, then the fraction of A-alleles will stabilize at

$$p = 1 - \sqrt{\frac{\mu}{s}}$$

and the fraction of a-alleles will stabilize at

$$q = 1 - p = \sqrt{\frac{\mu}{s}}.$$

Thus, the fraction of a-homozygotes born in each generation will be

$$w = q^2 = \frac{\mu}{s}.$$

In the case of albinism, it has been determined that the fitness (before modern medical advances) was 0.9, so $s = 0.1$. The relative frequency of albinism in the population is $w = 1/20\,000$. From this, we get

$$w = \frac{1}{20\,000} = \frac{\mu}{s} = \frac{\mu}{0.1}.$$

Solving for μ, gives us an estimate for the mutation rate from normal alleles to albinism:

$$\mu = 5 \times 10^{-6}.$$

Note that $\mu < s$ in this case.

Let's now discuss another problem. Sometimes heterozygotes have a higher fitness than either homozygote. In this case, the alleles A and a are said to be additive. In the case of the allele a that causes sickle cell anemia, a heterozygote with this allele will not have sickle cell anemia, but will have partial immunity to malaria. The A-homozygote will not have sickle cell anemia or immunity to malaria.

Thus, we are going to consider the case in which the A-homozygotes have fitness $1 - t$ and the a-homozygotes have fitness $1 - s$, both relative to the heterozygotes with fitness 1. We will not consider mutation in this case.

Let $p(n)$ be the fraction of A-alleles in generation n. As before, the total number of A-homozygotes, heterozygotes, and a-homozygotes born to generation $n + 1$ and then surviving to adulthood are

$$(1 - t)Tp^2(n), \quad 2Tp(n)q(n), \quad (1 - s)Tq^2(n),$$

respectively. The total number of adults (by subtracting those that do not survive) is $T - Ttp^2(n) - Tsq^2(n)$. The fraction of A-alleles among the adults of generation $n + 1$ is then (after canceling the T's)

$$p(n+1) = \frac{2(1-t)p^2(n) + 2p(n)q(n)}{2(1 - tp^2(n) - sq^2(n))}.$$

Canceling the 2's, and recalling that $p(n) + q(n) = 1$, we have

$$p(n+1) = \frac{p(n)(1 - tp(n))}{1 - tp^2(n) - sq^2(n)}.$$

Substituting for $q(n)$, we get

$$p(n+1) = \frac{p(n)(1 - tp(n))}{1 - s + 2sp(n) - (s+t)p^2(n)}.$$

To find the fixed points, we need to solve

$$p = \frac{p(1 - tp)}{1 - s + 2sp - (s+t)p^2}$$

for p. Cross multiplying and collecting terms on the left gives

$$-(s+t)p^3 + (2s+t)p^2 - sp = 0.$$

Factoring this equation gives

$$p(p-1)(-(s+t)p + s) = 0,$$

so the fixed points are

$$p = 0, \quad p = 1, \quad p = \frac{s}{s+t}.$$

To test the stability of these fixed points, we need to differentiate

$$f(x) = \frac{x(1 - tx)}{1 - s + 2sx - (s+t)x^2}.$$

Using the quotient rule, we get

$$f'(x)$$

$$= \frac{(1 - 2tx)[1 - s + 2sx - (s+t)x^2] - (x - tx^2)[2s - 2(s+t)x]}{[1 - s + 2sx - (s+t)x^2]^2}$$

$$= \frac{1 - 2tx}{1 - s + 2sx - (s+t)x^2} - \frac{(x - tx^2)[2s - 2(s+t)x]}{[1 - s + 2sx - (s+t)x^2]^2}.$$

Therefore,

$$f'(0) = \frac{1}{1-s} - 0.$$

Since $1 - s < 1$, $f'(0) > 1$, so $p = 0$ is unstable. Likewise, you will find that $f'(1) = 1/(1-t)$, so $p = 1$ is unstable.

Substitution of $x = s/(s+t)$ gives

$$f'\left(\frac{s}{s+t}\right) = \frac{1 - 2ts/(s+t)}{1 - s + s^2/(s+t)} - 0.$$

Simplification gives

$$f'\left(\frac{s}{s+t}\right) = \frac{s + t - 2st}{s + t - st} = 1 - \frac{st}{s + t - st}.$$

Since $s \leq 1$ and $t \leq 1$, it's easy to see that $1 - st/(s + t - st) < 1$, and so the equilibrium value $p = s/(s+t)$ is stable.

This says that, when the fitness of the A-homozygotes is $1 - t$ and the fitness of the a-homozygotes is $1 - s$, the fraction of A-alleles will stabilize at $p = s/(s+t)$, and the fraction of a-alleles will stabilize at $q = 1 - p = t/(s+t)$. It has been determined that, before modern medical advances, the fitness of A-homozygotes in Africa (where malaria is a problem) was $1 - t = 0.85$, while the fitness of a-homozygotes was $1 - s = 0$ (Cavalli-Sforza and Bodmer 1971). Thus, $t = 0.15$, $s = 1$, and the fraction of a-alleles (which causes sickle cell anemia) is $q = 0.15/1.15 = 0.13$.

From the fraction of affected individuals, $w = q^2$, it has been estimated that the allele frequencey of sickle cell anemia is $0.10 < q < 0.15$, which is consistent with our results.

This case of heterozygote advantage may help explain the diversity of genes, that is, individuals with a mix of alleles may have a selective advantage over homozygotes, so that neither the A- nor the a-alleles will die out.

3.3.1 Problems

1. Develop a dynamical system for the fraction of A-alleles in the case where A-homozygotes have a fitness of 0.8, a-homozygotes have a fitness of 0.7, and 2 per cent of the A-alleles mutate to a-alleles each generation. Find the fixed points for this equation (using the quadratic formula) and determine their stability.

2. Develop a dynamical system for the fraction of a-alleles in the case where A-homozygotes and heterozygotes both have a fitness of 0.2, relative to the a-homozygotes. (These are approximately the fitnesses for the dominant genetic disease, chondrodystrophy.) Also assume that 1 per cent of the a-alleles mutate to A-alleles in each generation. Find the fixed points for this equation (using the quadratic formula) and determine their stability. (In reality, the fixed points are known since $w = q^2$ can be estimated. This is then used to determine the mutation rate.)

3.4 Newton's method

In studying nonlinear dynamical systems, the first thing we usually want to do is to find the equilibrium values, that is, the solutions to the equation $x = f(x)$. By rewriting this as

$$g(x) = f(x) - x,$$

our problem becomes, how do we find the zeros of the function $g(x)$, that is, values for which $g(x) = 0$? For the rest of this section, we will study a method for finding the zeros of a function, which we will henceforth call $f(x)$.

In several of the examples we have studied, $f(x)$ was a second order polynomial, so we could use the quadratic formula to find the zeros. In practice, $f(x)$ might be a higher order polynomial which cannot be easily factored. In Example 2.22, when finding the effective interest rate I, we needed to find a root of a kth order polynomial, where k was the number of payments. In Example 2.43, we needed to find a zero of a function that was the difference of two exponentials to find the time it takes for Lake Ontario to become relatively unpolluted. In the preceding section, we needed to find the roots of a cubic. For the given example this was easy, but for more general problems relating to fitness and mutation, the cubic cannot be easily factored. Thus, it is important to develop methods for approximating the roots of a function that we cannot factor. One such method is called **Newton's method**.

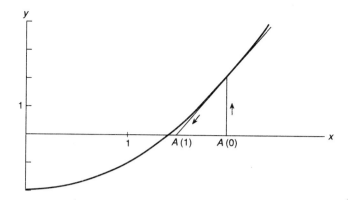

Fig. 18. A root of $f(x) = x^2 - 2$ is approximated by the x intercept of the tangent line to $f(x)$ at the point $(2, 2)$.

Suppose we wish to find a root of a polynomial $f(x)$, that is, find a number a such that $f(a) = 0$. (Another way to phrase this problem is that we wish to find an x intercept of the function $y = f(x)$.) The idea behind Newton's method is to guess at a root, say $A(0) = a_0$. Next, plot the point $(a_0, f(a_0))$ on the graph of the polynomial. Then draw the tangent line to the curve $f(x)$ at that point. Finally, use the x intercept of the tangent line as $A(1)$, the next approximation of the x intercept of the polynomial. This is shown graphically in Figure 18.

Example 3.11

Approximate $\sqrt{2}$ as a decimal. To do this, we note that $\sqrt{2}$ is a root of the polynomial

$$f(x) = x^2 - 2.$$

Let's 'guess' at a solution, say $a_0 = 2$. Since $f(2) = 4 - 2 = 2 \neq 0$, our guess is wrong. We now construct the tangent line to the curve $f(x) = x^2 - 2$ at the point $(a_0, f(a_0)) = (2, 2)$. Since

$$f'(x) = 2x,$$

the slope of the tangent line at $(2, 2)$ is $f'(2) = 4$. So the equation of the tangent line is

$$y - 2 = 4(x - 2), \quad \text{or} \quad y = 4x - 6$$

after simplification.

The x intercept of the tangent line is the point where $y = 0$, so $4x - 6 = 0$ or $x = 3/2$. We now let this be our next guess, that is, $A(1) = 3/2 = 1.5$. See Figure 18.

Now repeat this process. We get the point $(1.5, f(1.5)) = (1.5, 0.25)$. The slope of the tangent line is $f'(1.5) = 2(1.5) = 3$. The equation of the tangent line is

$$y - 0.25 = 3(x - 1.5) \quad \text{or} \quad y = 3x - 4.25.$$

The x intercept is at $0 = 3x - 4.25$, or $x = 17/12$. This is our next guess, that is,
$$A(2) = \tfrac{17}{12} = 1.4167.$$

Notice that $\sqrt{2} = 1.4142$, so $A(2)$ is accurate to within 0.003.

Let's repeat the process one more time. Check the following computations. First, we get the point $(17/12, 1/144)$. Then we get $f'(17/12) = 17/3$. The tangent line is

$$y - \tfrac{1}{144} = \tfrac{17}{3}\left(x - \tfrac{17}{12}\right), \quad \text{or} \quad y = \tfrac{17}{3}x - \tfrac{1155}{144}.$$

The x intercept is $x = 1155/816 = 1.415\,44 = A(3)$. Note that $f(A(3)) = 0.003$, almost zero.

How do we know the accuracy of our estimate? Suppose we want our estimate to be correct to 2 decimal places. We observe that $f(A(1)) = (1.5)^2 - 2 = 0.25 > 0$. We then compute $f(A(1) \pm 0.01)$, that is, $f(1.49) = 0.22$ and $f(1.51) = 0.28$. Since all these values are positive, we do not believe there is a root between them, so $x = 1.5$ is not within 0.01 of a root.

Now try $A(2)$. We see that $f(A(2)) = (1.4167)^2 - 2 = 0.007 > 0$. We then compute $f(1.4067) = -0.02 < 0$. Since we get a positive and a negative value, there must be a root between 1.4067 and 1.4167. Therefore, our $x = 1.4167$ is accurate to within 0.01.

For the rest of this section, we will ignore the discussion of accuracy. By repeating the process given above, it is usually clear that the answer is accurate to many decimal places.

Suppose we are given a function $f(x)$ and we want to find one of its roots, that is, find a such that $f(a) = 0$. First we make a guess, a_0. Then we plot the point $(a_0, f(a_0))$. Next we find the slope of the tangent line, $f'(a_0)$. The equation of the tangent line is

$$y - f(a_0) = f'(a_0)(x - a_0).$$

Finally, we find the x intercept, that is, we substitute $y = 0$ into the equation for the tangent line and solve for x. This gives

$$-f(a_0) = f'(a_0)(x - a_0).$$

Dividing by $f'(a_0)$ and then adding a_0 to both sides gives

$$x = a_0 - \frac{f(a_0)}{f'(a_0)}.$$

We use this value as our next guess, that is,

$$A(1) = A(0) - \frac{f(A(0))}{f'(A(0))}.$$

Repeating this process for $A(1)$, $A(2)$, and so forth gives the nonlinear dynamical system

$$A(n+1) = A(n) - \frac{f(A(n))}{f'(A(n))}.$$

Notice that the equilibrium value for this equation occurs when

$$a = a - \frac{f(a)}{f'(a)},$$

or, after subtracting a from both sides and multiplying by $f'(a)$,

$$0 = f(a).$$

Thus, the equilibrium values are the roots of $f(x)$ (at least when $f'(a)$ exists and $f'(a) \neq 0$).

From our study of stability, we know an equilibrium value a for the nonlinear dynamical system

$$A(n+1) = g(A(n))$$

is stable if

$$-1 < g'(a) < 1.$$

In the dynamical system we developed above, we have

$$g(x) = x - \frac{f(x)}{f'(x)},$$

and the equilibrium value is a, where $f(a) = 0$. By the quotient rule, we have

$$g'(x) = 1 - \frac{f'(x)f'(x) - f(x)f''(x)}{(f'(x))^2},$$

or, after dividing out the fraction and canceling the 1's,

$$g'(x) = \frac{f(x)f''(x)}{(f'(x))^2}.$$

Since $f(a) = 0$, it follows that

$$g'(a) = \frac{f(a)f''(a)}{(f'(a))^2} = 0$$

(if $f'(a) \neq 0$), and so

$$-1 < g'(a) = 0 < 1.$$

Thus, a is a stable equilibrium value. This gives the following.

Theorem 3.12

Newton's method: *Suppose we have a function $f(x)$ and a number a such that $f(x)$ is continuous and differentiable in a neighborhood of a, $f(a) = 0$, and $f'(a) \neq 0$. Then the number a is a stable equilibrium value for the dynamical system*

$$A(n + 1) = A(n) - \frac{f(A(n))}{f'(A(n))}.$$

This means that if we pick an a_0 value close enough to the root a, then

$$\lim_{k \to \infty} A(k) = a.$$

Because $g'(a) = 0$, it follows that $A(k)$ converges to a very rapidly (on the order of 0^k), if a_0 is close to a. This is called **quadratic convergence** and is much faster than linear convergence (r^k for $0 < |r| < 1$). More on this at the end of this section.

Example 3.13

Let's estimate the cube root of 5. We know that $5^{\frac{1}{3}}$ is a root of the polynomial

$$f(x) = x^3 - 5.$$

Since $f'(x) = 3x^2$, Newton's method gives us the dynamical system

$$A(n + 1) = A(n) - \frac{A^3(n) - 5}{3A^2(n)},$$

or, after simplification,

$$A(n + 1) = \tfrac{2}{3}A(n) + \tfrac{5}{3}A^{-2}(n).$$

Pick any reasonable starting value, say $a_0 = 3$. We then get

$$A(1) = 2.185\,185, \quad A(2) = 1.805\,828, \quad \ldots, \quad A(5) = 1.709\,976.$$

The number $A(5)$ is actually the correct answer to 6 decimal places.

Example 3.14

Find a root of the polynomial

$$f(x) = -x^3 + 2x^2 + 5x + 6.$$

Let's try guessing a root. We compute

$$f(0) = 6, \quad f(1) = 12, \quad f(2) = 16, \quad f(3) = 12, \quad f(4) = -6.$$

Since $f(x)$ is positive at $x = 3$ and negative at $x = 4$, we know that $f(x) = 0$ for some value of x between 3 and 4. Thus, we might try $a_0 = 3$ or $a_0 = 4$. Let's use the latter.

The dynamical system given by Newton's method is

$$A(n+1) = A(n) - \frac{-A^3(n) + 2A^2(n) + 5A(n) + 6}{-3A^2(n) + 4A(n) + 5}.$$

In this case, simple computations give

$$A(0) = 4, \quad A(1) = 3.777\,778, \quad A(2) = 3.756\,510, \quad A(3) = 3.756\,321.$$

The number $A(3)$ is off by less than 10^{-6}.

Dividing our original polynomial by the factor $(x - 3.756\,321)$, we get a second order polynomial (plus a very small remainder which we ignore). We can then use the quadratic formula to factor this second order polynomial to find the other roots of the original polynomial. In this case, the other roots are complex.

Once we estimate one root of our mth order polynomial, say a, we can then divide the polynomial by the factor $(x - a)$ to get a polynomial of order $m - 1$. To find another root of our polynomial, we apply Newton's method to this $(m - 1)$th order polynomial. By repeating this process, we can (theoretically) estimate all the roots of our polynomial. This can be a long and algebraically messy problem.

Alternatively, we can use a graphing program on a computer or graphic calculator to estimate each of the roots. Then we can use Newton's method on each of these estimates to get an accurate estimate.

You might be asking yourself what happens if a_0 is **not close** to a root of the polynomial $f(x)$. In this case, $A(k)$ may not go to a root of the polynomial.

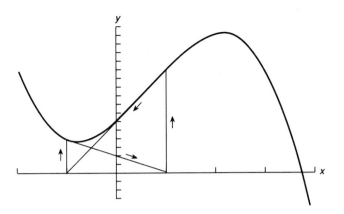

Fig. 19. A 2-cycle results when using Newton's method on the function $f(x) = -x^3 + 2x^2 + 5x + 6$ with $a_0 = 1$. The four corners are $(-1, 4)$, $(-1, 0)$, $(1, 12)$, and $(1, 0)$.

Example 3.15

Let's again use Newton's method to find a root of the polynomial

$$f(x) = -x^3 + 2x^2 + 5x + 6.$$

Recall that the dynamical system given by Newton's method is

$$A(n + 1) = A(n) - \frac{-A^3(n) + 2A^2(n) + 5A(n) + 6}{-3A^2(n) + 4A(n) + 5}.$$

This time, let's use $a_0 = 1$. Now we get

$$A(1) = -1, \quad A(2) = 1, \quad A(3) = -1, \quad A(4) = 1,$$

and so forth. It is clear that $A(k)$ forms a 2-cycle, and therefore does not go to a root of this polynomial. See Figure 19.

There are methods for determining when Newton's method will work, that is, for determining if a given a_0 is close enough to a root so that $A(k)$ will converge to a root. These conditions are somewhat technical and are derived using analysis similar to that which we have just done, although a little more complicated.

If a_0 is not close to a root, almost anything can happen. The numbers $A(k)$ can form a cycle, they can go to infinity, or they can wander randomly never converging. Therefore, it is important to pick a_0 carefully. One approach that often works is to plot a graph of the function $f(x)$ on a computer, estimate the point where it crosses the x axis, and use that estimate as a_0 (there are graphing calculators that can do this).

Let's now discuss what happens when a is a root of $f(x)$, but $f'(a) = 0$ (and thus a is a double root of $f(x)$). Since we have a zero in the denominator of

$$g(a) = a - \frac{f(a)}{f'(a)},$$

technically a is not an equilibrium value for the dynamical system. Suppose that $f''(a) \neq 0$. Then by L'Hôpital's rule, we have

$$\lim_{x \to a} \frac{f(x)}{f'(x)} = \lim_{x \to a} \frac{f'(x)}{f''(x)} = 0.$$

Thus, $g(a) = a$ in the sense that

$$\lim_{x \to a} g(x) = \lim_{x \to a} x - \frac{f(x)}{f'(x)} = a.$$

Thus, a is considered an equilibrium value in this case.

Is a a stable equilibrium value in this case? We have

$$
\begin{aligned}
g'(a) &= \lim_{x \to a} \frac{g(x) - g(a)}{x - a} = \lim_{x \to a} \frac{x - f(x)/f'(x) - a}{x - a} \\
&= \lim_{x \to a} \left(1 - \frac{f(x)}{(x - a)f'(x)} \right).
\end{aligned}
$$

Using L'Hôpital's rule twice, we get

$$
\begin{aligned}
\lim_{x \to a} \frac{f(x)}{(x - a)f'(x)} &= \lim_{x \to a} \frac{f'(x)}{f'(x) + (x - a)f''(x)} \\
&= \lim_{x \to a} \frac{f''(x)}{2f''(x) + (x - a)f'''(x)} = \tfrac{1}{2}. \quad (3)
\end{aligned}
$$

Thus,

$$g'(a) = 1 - \tfrac{1}{2} = \tfrac{1}{2} < 1,$$

so a is a stable equilibrium value.

Since $g'(a) = 1/2$, it follows that $A(k)$ converges to a at the rate of $(1/2)^k$, which is slower than the rate of convergence when $f'(a) \neq 0$. Convergence at the rate r^n, where $0 < |r| < 1$, is called **linear convergence**.

Since a is also a root of $f'(x)$, we could use Newton's method on this function, that is, use the dynamical system

$$A(n + 1) = A(n) - \frac{f'(A(n))}{f''(A(n))}.$$

The convergence is much faster (quadratic) using this method.

3.4.1 Problems

1. Suppose we want to find $a^{\frac{1}{m}}$, that is, we want to find the mth root of the positive number a. This is the positive root of the polynomial

$$f(x) = x^m - a.$$

Develop a dynamical system for finding the mth root of a number a.

2. Estimate the following numbers using the dynamical system developed in Problem 1. Use $A(4)$ as your estimate. Using a calculator, compute the exact number and compare your answers. To save calculations, try to use an appropriately good a_0 value.

   (a) $3^{\frac{1}{2}}$

   (b) $15^{\frac{1}{4}}$

   (c) $2^{\frac{1}{5}}$

   (d) $29^{\frac{1}{3}}$

3. Find a root of the following polynomials. Evaluate the polynomial at several values of x (as in Example 3.14) to get an idea of an appropriate a_0 value. Use $A(4)$ as your estimate.

   (a) $f(x) = x^4 + x - 1$
   (b) $f(x) = x^3 + 2x^2 - 5$

4. Notice that, for the polynomial

$$f(x) = x^5 - 7x^2 + 4,$$

$f(-1) = -4$, $f(0) = 4$, $f(1) = -2$, and $f(2) = 8$. Therefore this polynomial must have one root between -1 and 0, a second root between 0 and 1, and a third root between 1 and 2.

   (a) Use $a_0 = -1$ to estimate one root, use $a_0 = 1$ to estimate a second root, and use $a_0 = 2$ to estimate a third root. You can use $A(4)$ as your estimate in each case.

   (b) Try to esimate a root using $a_0 = 0$. Note that you get division by 0, since $f'(0) = 0$. This is because the tangent line at the point $(0, f(0))$ is horizontal, and does not have an x intercept.

   (c) Draw a graph of $f(x)$. From this graph, you should see that $f(x)$ can only have the three roots you have found.

5. We know that $x = 2$ is a double root of the function
$$f(x) = x^3 - 4x^2 + 4x.$$

(a) Use Newton's method to find this root using $a_0 = 4$. For what value of k is $A(k)$ accurate to within 3 decimal places?

(b) Use Newton's method on $f'(x)$ to find this root. Again use $a_0 = 4$. For what value of k is $A(k)$ accurate to within 3 decimal places?

6. A variation on Newton's method is the dynamical system
$$A(n+1) = A(n) - c\left(\frac{f(A(n))}{f'(A(n))}\right).$$

For appropriate choices of c, this also converges to the root a.

(a) Assuming that $f'(a) \neq 0$, for what values of c does this dynamical system converge? That is, for what values of c is the root a a stable equilibrium value?

(b) Suppose $f'(a) = 0$ but $f''(a) \neq 0$. Then for what values of c is the root a a stable equilibrium value?

(c) Using $c = 2$, compute the root $a = 2$ in Problem 5 for $a_0 = 4$. For what value of k is $A(k)$ accurate to within 3 decimal places?

7. Use Newton's method to find a zero of the function
$$f(x) = 5.56(0.87)^x - 4.56(0.62)^x - 0.1,$$

which was discussed in Example 2.43. Recall that if $f(x) = a^x$, then $f'(x) = (\ln a)a^x$.

8. Use Newton's method to find a zero of the function
$$f(x) = \left(1 + \frac{x}{12}\right)^{360}(100\,000x - 9848.64) + 9838.64.$$

The root of this function near $a_0 = 0.09$ is the effective interest rate from Example 2.22.

9. Suppose that $f(a) = 0$, $f'(a) = 0$, and $f''(a) = 0$. By applying L'Hôpital's rule again to equation (3), show that a is still a stable equilibrium by showing that $|g'(a)| < 1$. Recall that $A(k)$ converges to a on the order of $(g'(a))^k$. Thus, you can see that, in this case, the rate of convergence is even slower.

Complex behavior for nonlinear dynamical systems

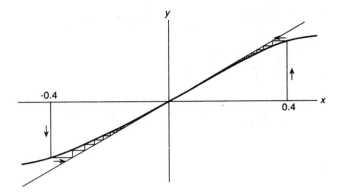

Fig. 20. Cobweb for the dynamical system $A(n + 1) = A(n) - A^3(n)$ showing the fixed point $a = 0$ is attracting.

4.1 Stability when the first derivative is inconclusive

When studying the stability of the size of a population under different harvesting schemes in Section 3.2, we studied the dynamical systems

$$A(n + 1) = 1.8A(n) - 0.8A^2(n) - 0.2 \tag{1}$$

and

$$A(n + 1) = A(n) - 0.8A^2(n). \tag{2}$$

The equilibrium value was $a = 0.5$ for the first system and $a = 0$ for the second. In both cases, $f'(a) = 1$ and we had to draw a cobweb to determine the stability: The systems were semistable in both cases. Let's consider two more systems

$$A(n + 1) = A(n) - A^3(n) \tag{3}$$

and

$$A(n + 1) = A(n) + A^3(n). \tag{4}$$

Each equation has $a = 0$ as its only equilibrium value and in both cases $f'(0) = 1$. In Figure 20 is a cobweb for the first of these equations. Note that the cobweb indicates that $a = 0$ is stable. You should draw the cobweb for the second system. If you do, you will see that $a = 0$ is unstable.

From the above, we see that almost any type of stability can occur when $f'(a) = 1$. The stability for these equations was easily determined using cobwebs. It would be nice if we had a simple calculus technique for studying this situation. In this section we will first develop techniques for

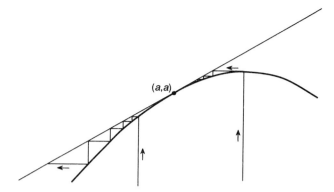

Fig. 21. This cobweb at the equilibrium point (a, a) in which $f'(a) = 1$ and $f''(a) < 0$ shows that a is semistable from above.

studying the stability of fixed points for which $f'(a) = 1$. We will then use the results to study fixed points a at which $f'(a) = -1$.

4.1.1 When the derivative equals one

Let's review. A number a being a fixed point means that the curve $y = f(x)$ intersects the line $y = x$ at the point (a, a). Since $f'(a) = 1$ the line $y = x$ **is the tangent line** to $y = f(x)$ at the point (a, a). We also know that, at the point (a, a), we must have

$$f''(a) > 0, \quad f''(a) < 0, \quad \text{or} \quad f''(a) = 0.$$

Recalling our graphing techniques, we know that the curve $y = f(x)$ is (1) concave up at (a, a) if $f''(a) > 0$, and (2) concave down at (a, a) if $f''(a) < 0$. In Figure 21 is a curve that is tangent to $y = x$ at (a, a) and is concave down, that is, $f'(a) = 1$ and $f''(a) < 0$. Notice, from the cobweb in that figure, that the point (a, a) is semistable in the sense that, for $a_0 > a$, $A(k)$ goes towards a, but for $a_0 < a$, $A(k)$ goes away from a. We call this **semistable from above**. In Figure 22 is a curve that is tangent to $y = x$ at (a, a) and is concave up, that is, $f'(a) = 1$ and $f''(a) > 0$. Notice from the cobweb in that figure, that the point (a, a) is semistable in the sense that, for $a_0 < a$, $A(k)$ goes towards a, but for $a_0 > a$, $A(k)$ goes away from a. We call this **semistable from below**. We have shown the following.

Theorem 4.1

Suppose a is an equilibrium value for the dynamical system

$$A(n + 1) = f(A(n)).$$

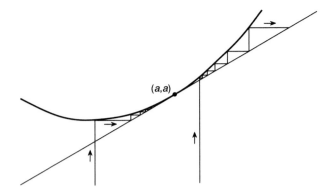

Fig. 22. This cobweb at the equilibrium point (a, a) in which $f'(a) = 1$ and $f''(a) > 0$ shows that a is semistable from below.

If $f'(a) = 1$ and $f''(a) \neq 0$, then a is semistable. In particular, if $f''(a) < 0$ then a is semistable from above, while if $f''(a) > 0$ then a is semistable from below.

In the case of the dynamical systems (1) and (2) we have $f''(x) = -1.6 < 0$, so the equilibrium values, $a = 0.5$ for the first and $a = 0$ for the second, are semistable from above. For the dynamical systems (3) and (4) we have $f''(x) = -6x$, so $f''(0) = 0$ and Theorem 4.1 does not apply.

Let's suppose we have an equilibrium value a such that $f'(a) = 1$, $f''(a) = 0$, and $f'''(a) \neq 0$. Then, again, $y = x$ is tangent to the curve $y = f(x)$ at (a, a), but we also have that the point (a, a) is a point of inflection for $y = f(x)$. This can be seen in Figure 20.

Being a point of inflection means that the concavity of the curve changes at that point, that is, either (1) the curve is concave up to the left of $x = a$ and is concave down to the right, or (2) the curve is concave down to the left of $x = a$ and is concave up to the right. Thus the curve must have the shape of either Figure 23 or Figure 24. Notice in Figure 23 that, by drawing cobwebs, a is seen to be a stable equilibrium value. In Figure 24, the cobweb indicates that a is unstable. Let's see if we can derive calculus techniques that differentiate between these two figures.

In Figure 23, we see that $y = f(x)$ is concave up to the left of a so that $f''(x) > 0$ for $x < a$. Also $y = f(x)$ is concave down to the right of a so that $f''(x) < 0$ for $x > a$. Since the function $f''(x)$ is positive to the left of a, zero at $x = a$, and negative to the right of a, it is decreasing at a. Thus $f''(x)$ is decreasing at $x = a$. If a function is decreasing at a

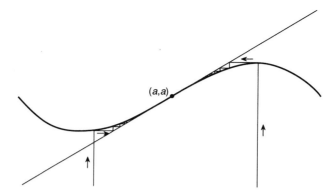

Fig. 23. This cobweb shows that when the curve changes from concave up to concave down at the equilibrium point (a, a), that is, when $f'(a) = 1$, $f''(a) = 0$, and $f'''(a) < 0$, then a is attracting.

point, its derivative must be negative (or zero) at that point, that is,

$$f'''(a) < 0$$

(since we assumed it wasn't zero).

In Figure 24, we see that $y = f(x)$ is concave down to the left of a so that $f''(x) < 0$ for $x < a$. Also $y = f(x)$ is concave up to the right of a so that $f''(x) > 0$ for $x > a$. Since the function $f''(x)$ is negative to the left of a, zero at $x = a$, and positive to the right of a, it is increasing at a. Thus the derivative of $f''(x)$ must be positive at a, that is, $f'''(a) > 0$ (since we assumed it wasn't zero).

Theorem 4.2

Suppose that a is a fixed point for the dynamical system

$$A(n + 1) = f(A(n)),$$

and that $f'(a) = 1$ and $f''(a) = 0$. Then,

- *if $f'''(a) < 0$ the fixed point a is stable, and*
- *if $f'''(a) > 0$ the fixed point a is unstable.*

For the dynamical system (3) we have $f(x) = x - x^3$, $f'(x) = 1 - 3x^2$, $f''(x) = -6x$, and $f'''(x) = -6$. Since $f'(0) = 1$ and $f''(0) = 0$, Theorem 4.2 applies. Since $f'''(0) = -6$, this theorem tells us that $a = 0$ is stable, which agrees with our previous findings. Similarly, you should find that $a = 0$ is unstable for dynamical system (4).

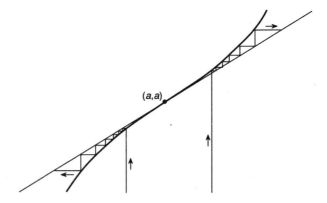

Fig. 24. This cobweb shows that when $f'(a) = 1$, $f''(a) = 0$, and $f'''(a) > 0$, then the fixed point a is repelling.

Example 4.3

Consider the dynamical system

$$A(n + 1) = A^4(n) - 2A^3(n) + 3A(n) - 1.$$

In an attempt to solve the equation

$$a = a^4 - 2a^3 + 3a - 1, \quad \text{or} \quad a^4 - 2a^3 + 2a - 1 = 0,$$

we try guessing. Letting $a = 1$, we find that this works. (We could have used Newton's method.) Long division gives

$$(a - 1)(a^3 - a^2 - a + 1) = 0.$$

It is easy to see that $a = 1$ is a root of the right-most term also, so we continue factoring, to get

$$(a - 1)^2(a^2 - 1) = (a - 1)^3(a + 1) = 0.$$

Thus this equation has $a = 1$ and $a = -1$ as its fixed points.

From the dynamical system, we use the function

$$f(x) = x^4 - 2x^3 + 3x - 1$$

to determine stability. First,

$$f'(x) = 4x^3 - 6x^2 + 3.$$

To determine the stability of $a = -1$, we compute $f'(-1) = -7$, so $a = -1$ is repelling.

Since $f'(1) = 1$, we compute

$$f''(x) = 12x^2 - 12x.$$

Since $f''(1) = 0$, we compute

$$f'''(x) = 24x - 12.$$

Since $f'''(1) = 12 > 0$, by Theorem 4.2, $a = 1$ is unstable.

We could continue this analysis with examples where $f'(a) = 1$, $f''(a) = 0$, $f'''(a) = 0$, and $f^{(4)}(a) \neq 0$, and so forth, but this is going too far.

4.1.2 When the derivative equals minus one

We will now discuss fixed points in which $f'(a) = -1$. Fixed points with $f'(a) < 0$ (or affine dynamical systems, $A(n + 1) = rA(n) + b$, with negative r) imply that when a_0 is close to a (but not equal to a), $A(k)$ oscillates about a. So we have $A(k) > a$ for k even and $A(k) < a$ for k odd, or vice versa. The trick is to study $A(0)$, $A(2)$, $A(4)$, ...

Example 4.4

The dynamical system

$$A(n + 1) = -A(n) + 2A^2(n) \tag{5}$$

has the two fixed points $a = 0$ and $a = 1$. Since $f'(1) = 3$, then $a = 1$ is unstable. It is more difficult to compute the stability of $a = 0$, since $f'(0) = -1$. Observe that, in Figure 25, $A(k)$ appears to be going to $a = 0$, although very slowly. Thus, $a = 0$ appears to be stable.

One method for computing the stability of $a = 0$ is to compute $A(n+2)$ in terms of $A(n)$. By substitution of $-A(n) + 2A^2(n)$ for $A(n + 1)$ into

$$A(n + 2) = -A(n + 1) + 2A^2(n + 1),$$

we get

$$A(n + 2) = -(A(n) + 2A^2(n)) + 2(-A(n) + 2A^2(n))^2.$$

Simplification gives

$$A(n + 2) = A(n) - 8A^3(n) + 8A^4(n).$$

Note that $a = 1$ is an equilibrium value for this equation also.

Figure 26 displays the cobwebs to this dynamical system (using the curve $y = x - 8x^3 + 8x^4$) for two initial values. The first initial value is the same a_0 value used above. The second initial value is the $A(1)$ value from

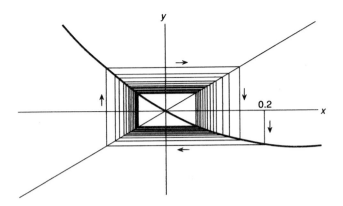

Fig. 25. A cobweb for the dynamical system $A(n + 1) = f(A(n))$ where $f(x) = -x + 2x^2$ near the fixed point $a = 0$. It appears that $A(k)$ is oscillating towards zero, so that $a = 0$ is attracting.

above. Note that one cobweb in Figure 26 consists of the $A(k)$ values for even k in Figure 25, that is, $A(0)$, $A(2)$, $A(4)$, and so forth. The other cobweb in Figure 26 consists of the $A(k)$ values for odd k in Figure 25, that is, $A(1)$, $A(3)$, $A(5)$, and so forth.

To use our calculus techniques to show that $a = 0$ is stable in Figure 26, note that, for

$$A(n + 2) = A(n) - 8A^3(n) + 8A^4(n),$$

we have

$$
\begin{aligned}
f(x) &= x - 8x^3 + 8x^4, & f'(x) &= 1 - 24x^2 + 32x^3, \\
f''(x) &= -48x + 96x^2, & f'''(x) &= -48 + 192x.
\end{aligned}
$$

Notice that $f'(0) = 1$, $f''(0) = 0$, and $f'''(0) = -48 < 0$. By Theorem 4.2, $a = 0$ is a stable equilibrium for the $A(n + 2)$ dynamical system. Thus, there is an interval about zero such that if a_0 is in that interval, then $A(k)$ goes to zero for even k.

Since a_0 is close to zero, then $A(1)$ will be in that interval (we might have to take a_0 in a slightly smaller interval to make sure $A(1)$ is in the original interval). By the $A(n + 2)$ equation, $A(k)$ goes to zero for k odd. Thus $a = 0$ is an attracting fixed point for the dynamical system (5).

We now demonstrate an easier way of finding the stability of an equilibrium value a in which $f'(a) = -1$. Notice in Example 4.4 that we had $A(n + 1) = f(A(n))$, and $A(n + 2) = f(A(n + 1))$ with $f(x) = -x + 2x^2$.

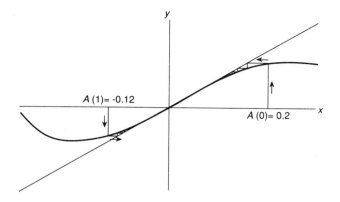

Fig. 26. Cobwebs for the dynamical system $A(n + 2) = f(f(A(n)))$ where $f(x) = -x + 2x^2$. Notice that $A(k)$ goes to zero from the right for even k and to the left for odd k. Thus, $a = 0$ is attracting.

We made the substitution of $f(A(n))$ for $A(n + 1)$ giving

$$A(n + 2) = f(f(A(n))).$$

Let $g(x) = f(f(x))$. Then this equation becomes

$$A(n + 2) = g(A(n)).$$

Theorem 4.5

If a is an equilibrium value for

$$A(n + 1) = f(A(n)),$$

where f is a continuous function, then a is an equilibrium value for the dynamical system

$$A(n + 2) = g(A(n)),$$

where $g(x) = f(f(x))$. Also, if a is stable for one dynamical system, then it is stable for the other.

Proof: If a is an equilibrium value for $A(n + 1) = f(A(n))$, then $a = f(a)$. Note that since $a = f(a)$, then by substitution we have

$$g(a) = f(f(a)) = f(a) = a,$$

so that a is an equilibrium value for

$$A(n + 2) = g(A(n)).$$

Now assume that a is an equilibrium value for both equations and that a is stable for

$$A(n+2) = g(A(n)).$$

This means that there is an interval I about a such that if a_0 is in that interval, then $A(2)$, $A(4)$, $\ldots$, go to a, that is,

$$\lim_{k \to \infty} A(2k) = a.$$

Since f is continuous, if a_0 is close enough to a (possibly making us choose a new interval I'), then $A(1) = f(A(0))$ is in interval I also. Using $A(1)$ as the initial value for the equation $A(n+2) = g(A(n))$, we find that $A(1)$, $A(3)$, $\ldots$, converge to a also, that is,

$$\lim_{k \to \infty} A(2k+1) = a.$$

Putting these results together, we get

$$\lim_{k \to \infty} A(k) = a,$$

so that a is a stable equilibrium value for the equation $A(n+1) = f(A(n))$.

If a is stable for the equation $A(n+1) = f(A(n))$, then there is an interval I about a such that if a_0 is in that interval, then $A(k)$ goes to a. But then $A(k)$ goes to a for even and for odd k, so a is stable for $A(n+2) = g(A(n))$, which completes the proof.

To review, suppose we that have a dynamical system

$$A(n+1) = f(A(n))$$

with equilibrium value a and that $f'(a) = -1$. To determine the stability of a, we construct the dynamical system

$$A(n+2) = g(A(n)) = f(f(A(n))),$$

which also has a as an equilibrium value. If we can determine the stability of a for the latter equation, then we know the stability of a is the same for the former equation.

To determine the stability of a for the equation $A(n+2) = g(A(n))$, we need to compute $g'(x)$. We will see that $g'(a) = 1$ and $g''(a) = 0$, so we must apply Theorem 4.2, which means we must compute $g'''(a)$ and see if it is positive or negative.

Remember that a is an equilibrium value ($a = f(a)$) and that $f'(a) = -1$. This means that whenever we see $f(a)$ we can replace it with a, and whenever we see $f'(a)$ we can replace it with -1, throughout this discussion.

Notice that, by the chain rule, $g'(x) = f'(f(x))f'(x)$. Thus,

$$g'(a) = f'(f(a))f'(a).$$

We then have by substitution

$$g'(a) = f'(f(a))f'(a) = f'(a)f'(a) = (-1)(-1) = 1.$$

Thus, either Theorem 4.1 or Theorem 4.2 may help.

By the product rule and chain rule,

$$g''(x) = \frac{d}{dx}[f'(f(x))f'(x)] = f''(f(x))f'(x)f'(x) + f'(f(x))f''(x)$$
$$= f''(f(x))[f'(x)]^2 + f'(f(x))f''(x).$$

Again, since $a = f(a)$ and $f'(a) = -1$, we have

$$g''(a) = f''(f(a))[f'(a)]^2 + f'(f(a))f''(a)$$
$$= f''(a)(-1)^2 + f'(a)f''(a) = f''(a) - f''(a) = 0.$$

Since $g'(a) = 1$ and $g''(a) = 0$, we need to use Theorem 4.2. To do this we need to compute $g'''(x)$ **very carefully**. We do this in parts by computing the derivative of each of the parts of $g''(x)$ above, then putting them together using the product rule.

$$\frac{d}{dx}f''(f(x)) = f'''(f(x))f'(x), \quad \frac{d}{dx}[f'(x)]^2 = 2f'(x)f''(x),$$

and

$$\frac{d}{dx}[f'(f(x))f''(x)] = f''(f(x))f'(x)f''(x) + f'(f(x))f'''(x).$$

Putting this all together with the product rule gives

$$g'''(a) = f'''(f(a))[f'(a)]^3 + 2f''(f(a))f''(a)f'(a)$$
$$+ f''(f(a))f''(a)f'(a) + f'(f(a))f'''(a).$$

Since $f(a) = a$ and $f'(a) = -1$, we have

$$g'''(a) = f'''(a)(-1)^3 + 3f''(a)f''(a)f'(a) + f'(a)f'''(a)$$
$$= -f'''(a) - 3[f''(a)]^2 - f'''(a) = -2f'''(a) - 3[f''(a)]^2$$

By Theorem 4.2, a is a stable equilibrium for $A(n+2) = g(A(n))$ if $g'''(a) < 0$, and a is unstable if $g'''(a) > 0$. Since

$$g'''(a) = -2f'''(a) - 3[f''(a)]^2,$$

we have the following theorem.

Theorem 4.6

Suppose that a is a fixed point for the dynamical system

$$A(n+1) = f(A(n))$$

and that $f'(a) = -1$. Compute the number

$$g'''(a) = -2f'''(a) - 3[f''(a)]^2.$$

- *If $g'''(a) < 0$ then a is an attracting fixed point, and*
- *if $g'''(a) > 0$ then a is a repelling fixed point.*

Remark: Observe that if $f(x)$ is quadratic, that is, $f(x) = ax^2 + bx + c$, then $f'''(x) = 0$ and so

$$g'''(a) = -3[f''(a)]^2 < 0.$$

Thus, if $f(x)$ is a second order polynomial and $f'(a) = -1$, then a is an attracting fixed point.

Again consider the dynamical system

$$A(n+1) = -A(n) + 2A^2(n)$$

of Example 4.4. We recall that the fixed points are $a = 0$ and $a = 1$. We note that $f'(0) = -1$, so by the above remark we know that $a = 0$ is stable.

Example 4.7

Find the stability of the fixed point $a = 0$ for the dynamical system

$$A(n+1) = -A(n) - A^3(n).$$

For this equation, $f(x) = -x - x^3$, $f'(x) = -1 - 3x^2$, $f''(x) = -6x$, and $f'''(x) = -6$. Since $f'(0) = -1$, we compute

$$g'''(0) = -2(-6) - 3(0)^2 = 12 > 0,$$

and so $a = 0$ is a repelling fixed point.

Most of the previous material studied has been somewhat intuitive. It seems clear that the slope of the tangent line to a curve at the equilibrium point should determine the stability of that point. By graphing and using our knowledge of concavity, we developed stability results when $f'(a) = 1$. When $f'(a) = -1$, we determined, using calculus and algebra, that a is stable when the strange number $-2f'''(a) - 3(f''(a))^2$ is negative. This result could not be developed on an intuitive basis and shows that **careful mathematical analysis** is often necessary to develop important techniques for use in the study of mathematical models of the real world. These techniques can then lead to new knowledge of the real world that would be difficult to derive on an intuitive level.

4.1.3 Problems

1. Consider the dynamical system

$$A(n+1) = A^2(n) + 5A(n) + 4.$$

   (a) Find all equilibrium values for this dynamical system.

   (b) Determine the stability of the equilibrium values using calculus techniques.

   (c) Verify your results by sketching a cobweb for this dynamical system close to the fixed points.

2. Consider the dynamical system

$$A(n+1) = -2A^2(n) + 13A(n) - 18.$$

   (a) Find all equilibrium values for this dynamical system.

   (b) Determine the stability of the equilibrium values using calculus techniques.

   (c) Verify your results by sketching a cobweb for this dynamical system close to the fixed points.

3. Consider the dynamical system

$$A(n+1) = -0.5A^3(n) + 0.5A^2(n) + A(n).$$

   (a) Find all equilibrium values for this dynamical system.

   (b) Determine the stability of the equilibrium values using calculus techniques.

   (c) Verify your results by sketching a cobweb for this dynamical system close to the fixed points.

4. Find all the equilibrium values for the following dynamical systems and determine their stability.

(a) $A(n+1) = -0.5A^3(n) + 0.5A^2(n) + A(n)$

(b) $A(n+1) = A^3(n) - 12A^2(n) + 49A(n) - 64$

(c) $A(n+1) = A^4(n) - A^3(n) + A(n)$

(d) $A(n+1) = 0.5A^2(n) + 2A(n) - 1.5$

(e) $A(n+1) = (1/101)[-200A^3(n) + 20A^2(n) - 99A(n) + 20]$. (Hint: $a = 0.1$)

(f) $A(n+1) = -0.01A^3(n) + 2A(n)$

(g) $A(n+1) = -2A^3(n) + 4A^2(n) - A(n)$

5. Suppose that $f(a) = b$ and $f(b) = a$. Find $g'(a)$ in terms of $f'(a)$ and $f'(b)$, where $g(x) = f(f(x))$.

6. Every equilibrium value for the dynamical system

$$A(n+1) = f(A(n))$$

is also an equilibrium value for

$$A(n+2) = f(f(A(n))).$$

Show that the converse is not true by finding an equilibrium value for the latter dynamical system that is not an equilibrium value for the former when

$$f(x) = 4x(1-x).$$

4.2 Cycles and stability

In Section 3.1, we developed the logistic equation

$$A(n+1) = (1+r)A(n) - bA^2(n)$$

as a model for population growth, where r is the unrestricted growth rate, and $b = r/L$ where L is the carrying capacity of the environment. We can choose the size of our units, that is, we can define $a = 1$ to mean one hundred or one thousand. For simplicity, we will define one unit to be L of the species. Thus the logistic equation becomes

$$A(n+1) = (1+r)A(n) - rA^2(n). \tag{6}$$

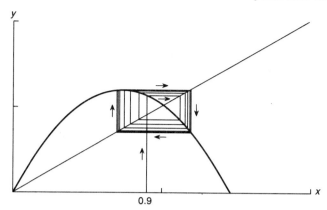

Fig. 27. The cobweb for $A(n+1) = f(A(n))$ where $f(x) = 3.2x - 2.2x^2$ with $a_0 = 0.9$ appears to go to a stable 2-cycle.

It is easy to see that $a = 0$ and $a = 1$ are the equilibrium values. Notice that $f(x) = (1 + r)x - rx^2$, $f'(x) = 1 + r - 2rx$, $f''(x) = -2r$, and $f'''(x) = 0$.

Since $f'(0) = 1 + r$, it follows that $a = 0$ is unstable if $r > 0$. We also have $f'(1) = 1 - r$, so that $a = 1$ is stable if $-1 < 1 - r < 1$, that is, if $0 < r < 2$. Similarly, $a = 1$ is unstable if $r > 2$ or if $r < 0$. If $r = 2$, then $f'(1) = -1$, and by Theorem 4.6, since $g'''(1) = -2f'''(1) - 3[f''(1)]^2 = -2(0) - 3(-4)^2 = -48 < 0$, then $a = 1$ is stable.

To reiterate, we now know that if the unrestricted growth rate satisfies $0 < r \le 2$, then the size of the population stabilizes at $a = 1$ (for reasonable a_0 values).

There is still a question as to the behavior of $A(k)$ for species, such as insects, with large unrestricted growth rates, that is, for species in which $r > 2$. The only thing we know in these cases is that the equilibrium value $a = 1$ is unstable, so the size of the population **will not go to** $a = 1$. In Figures 27 and 28 are cobwebs for $A(k)$ when $r = 2.2$, that is, for the dynamical system

$$A(n + 1) = 3.2A(n) - 2.2A^2(n).$$

The initial value a_0 was chosen close to the equilibrium value $a = 1$ in Figure 27, and close to the equilibrium value $a = 0$ in Figure 28. It is seen in these figures that $a = 1$ and $a = 0$ are both unstable and that $A(k)$ **appears to go to a stable 2-cycle.**

Remark: The vertex of the parabola in Figures 27 and 28 is at $x = 0.73$. It is only a coincidence that the vertex and one of the points of the 2-cycle are close together.

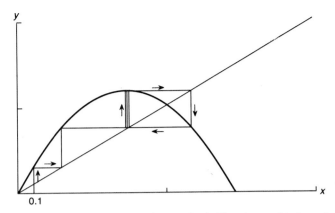

Fig. 28. The cobweb for $A(n+1) = f(A(n))$ where $f(x) = 3.2x - 2.2x^2$ with $a_0 = 0.1$ appears to go to a stable 2-cycle.

Definition 4.8

*Two numbers a_1 and a_2 form a **2-cycle** for a first order dynamical system if, when $A(n) = a_1$, then $A(n+1) = a_2$ and $A(n+2) = a_1$. A 2-cycle is **stable** or **attracting** if there are intervals (c_1, d_1) and (c_2, d_2) about a_1 and a_2, respectively, such that*

- *if $A(0)$ is in (c_1, d_1), then*

$$\lim_{k \to \infty} A(2k) = a_1 \quad and \quad \lim_{k \to \infty} A(2k+1) = a_2;$$

- *if $A(0)$ is in (c_2, d_2), then*

$$\lim_{k \to \infty} A(2k) = a_2 \quad and \quad \lim_{k \to \infty} A(2k+1) = a_1.$$

Intuitively, this means that if $A(0)$ is close to a_1, then $A(k)$ goes to a_1 for k even and to a_2 for k odd, and similarly if $A(0)$ is close to a_2.

**Example
4.9**

Let $r = 2.2$. Then $a_1 = 1.163\ldots$ and $a_2 = 0.746\ldots$ form a 2-cycle for the dynamical system

$$A(n + 1) = 3.2A(n) - 2.2A^2(n).$$

To see this, note that if $a_0 = 1.163$, then

$$A(1) = 3.2(1.163) - 2.2(1.163)^2 = 0.746.$$

Likewise,

$$A(2) = 3.2(0.746) - 2.2(0.746)^2 = 1.163.$$

Continuing, it is easy to see that $A(4) = A(6) = \ldots = 1.163$ and $A(3) = A(5) = \ldots = 0.746$. All computations have been rounded off to 3 decimal places. A more accurate representation of the 2-cycle is $a_1 = 1.162\,844\,35\ldots$ and $a_2 = 0.746\,246\,559\ldots$. It appears in Figures 27 and 28, that this is a stable 2-cycle.

How do we **show** algebraically that a 2-cycle is stable? We use a method similar to that for determining the stability of an equilibrium value which has $f'(a) = -1$, that is, we compute $A(n + 2)$ in terms of $A(n)$. In Figure 29, we plot the cobweb for the dynamical system

$$A(n + 2) = f(f(A(n))) = g(A(n)),$$

where $f(x) = 3.2x - 2.2x^2$, that is,

$$A(n + 2) = 3.2[3.2A(n) - 2.2A^2(n)] - 2.2[3.2A(n) - 2.2A^2(n)]^2.$$

The two points where $y = f(f(x))$ intersects $y = x$, with slope less than 1, are the points $a_1 = 1.163$ and $a_2 = 0.746$ from the previous example. Also note that the other two points of intersection are the original unstable equilibrium values 0 and 1.

To show algebraically that a_1 and a_2 form a stable 2-cycle, we need to compute the derivative of $f(f(x))$ at the points (a_1, a_1) and (a_2, a_2). If this derivative is between -1 and 1 in both cases, then $A(k)$ goes to a_1 for even k, and to a_2 for odd k.

**Example
4.10**

We now want to determine if the 2-cycle, $a_1 = 1.163$ and $a_2 = 0.746$, for the dynamical system of Example 4.9,

$$A(n + 1) = 3.2A(n) - 2.2A^2(n),$$

is stable. To do this, we compute

$$g'(x) = \frac{d}{dx} f(f(x)) = f'(f(x))f'(x),$$

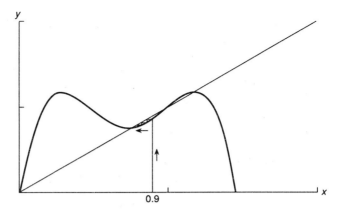

Fig. 29. The cobweb for $A(n+2) = f(f(A(n)))$ where $f(x) = 3.2x - 2.2x^2$ with $a_0 = 0.9$ goes to one of the two points of the stable 2-cycle.

where $f(x) = 3.2x - 2.2x^2$. Do not multiply the function out before computing the derivative as this will lead to more work.

Now substitute $a_1 = 1.163$ in for x, giving

$$g'(a_1) = f'(f(a_1))f'(a_1).$$

Since $A(n+1) = f(A(n))$, and a_1 and a_2 form a 2-cycle, it follows that $a_2 = f(a_1)$. Substituting a_2 for $f(a_1)$ gives

$$g'(a_1) = f'(a_2)f'(a_1).$$

Thus, the derivative of $f(f(x))$ at the point (a_1, a_1) is

$$f'(a_2)f'(a_1) = [3.2 - 4.4(0.746)][3.2 - 4.4(1.163)] = 0.16.$$

Thus, after a bit of algebra, we find that $f'(a_2)f'(a_1) = 0.16 < 1$. It now follows that a_1 is a stable equilibrium value for the equation

$$A(n + 2) = f(f(A(n))),$$

so it will be part of a stable 2-cycle for

$$A(n + 1) = f(A(n)).$$

Substituting $a_2 = 0.746$ into $g'(x) = f'(f(x))f'(x)$ gives

$$f'(f(a_2))f'(a_2) = f'(a_1)f'(a_2),$$

using the fact that $a_1 = f(a_2)$, which we have already computed as $0.16 <$ 1, so a_2 is the other half of the stable 2-cycle.

Let's review. We have to accomplish two goals. First, we must find algebraically two numbers, a_1 and a_2, that form a 2-cycle. Second, we must use calculus to determine the stability of the 2-cycle we have found. Note that although the algebra involved can be long and messy, the **idea** behind this method is quite simple. Don't let the algebra cause you to miss the point.

First, we wish to find a 2-cycle for the dynamical system

$$A(n+1) = f(A(n)),$$

that is, we are looking for two numbers a_1 and a_2 such that

$$a_2 = f(a_1) \quad \text{and} \quad a_1 = f(a_2),$$

or equivalently by substituting $f(a_1)$ for a_2 in the second of these equations, we require numbers a that satisfy

$$a = f(f(a)).$$

Theorem 4.11

The number a satisfies the equation

$$a = f(f(a))$$

if a is either a fixed point or is part of a 2-cycle for the dynamical system

$$A(n+1) = f(A(n)).$$

Finding a 2-cycle can be algebraically tedious, but it is not complicated. Just be careful with your computations.

Let's find a 2-cycle for the dynamical system

$$A(n+1) = 3.2A(n) - 2.2A^2(n)$$

of Example 4.9. Since $f(x) = 3.2x - 2.2x^2$, it follows that

$$f(f(x)) = 3.2(3.2x - 2.2x^2) - 2.2(3.2x - 2.2x^2)^2.$$

Carefully multiplying this out and collecting terms, gives

$$f(f(x)) = 10.24x - 29.568x^2 + 30.976x^3 - 10.648x^4.$$

We want to find a values such that $f(f(a)) = a$, or

$$f(f(a)) - a = 9.24a - 29.568a^2 + 30.976a^3 - 10.648a^4 = 0.$$

We know that $a = 0$ and $a = 1$ are equilibrium values for the original dynamical system. By Theorem 4.11, we know that $a = 0$ and $a = 1$ must be solutions to our equation $f(f(a)) - a = 0$, so we can factor out an a (this is easy), and we can also factor out the term $a - 1$. Dividing the fourth order polynomial by a and then by $a - 1$ gives

$$f(f(a)) - a = a(a - 1)(-10.648a^2 + 20.328a - 9.24) = 0.$$

Using the quadratic formula, the roots of $-10.648a^2 + 20.328a - 9.24 = 0$ are

$$a = \frac{-20.328 \pm \sqrt{(20.328)^2 - 4(10.648)(9.24)}}{-21.296}$$

$$= \frac{20.328 \pm \sqrt{19.677\,504}}{21.296} = \frac{21(0.968) \pm \sqrt{21(0.968)^2}}{22(0.968)}.$$

Factoring 0.968 out of the numerator and denominator gives us the two roots, that is, the 2-cycle

$$a_1 = \frac{21 + \sqrt{21}}{22} = 1.163 \quad \text{and} \quad a_2 = \frac{21 - \sqrt{21}}{22} = 0.746,$$

which is the 2-cycle we worked with originally.

Finding a 2-cycle is usually the hardest part of a problem. Remember that the idea is easy, but the computations are often messy.

Once we have found a 2-cycle, how can we determine its stability? Notice the similarity to Section 4.1. A 2-cycle a_1 and a_2 for the dynamical system

$$A(n + 1) = f(A(n))$$

is stable when the equilibrium values a_1 and a_2 for the dynamical system

$$A(n + 2) = g(A(n)),$$

are stable, where $g(x) = f(f(x))$. But a_1 and a_2 are stable only when $|g'(a_1)| < 1$ and $|g'(a_2)| < 1$, respectively.

By the chain rule,

$$g'(x) = \frac{d}{dx}f(f(x)) = f'(f(x))f'(x).$$

Since $f(a_1) = a_2$ and $f(a_2) = a_1$, it follows that

$$g'(a_1) = f'(f(a_1))f'(a_1) = f'(a_2)f'(a_1).$$

Similarly, we have
$$g'(a_2) = f'(a_1)f'(a_2).$$
So $|g'(a_1)| < 1$ and $|g'(a_2)| < 1$ only when

$$|f'(a_1)f'(a_2)| < 1.$$

Theorem 4.12

Suppose the dynamical system

$$A(n+1) = f(A(n))$$

has a 2-cycle consisting of the numbers a_1 and a_2. This 2-cycle

- *is stable if $|f'(a_1)f'(a_2)| < 1$, and*
- *is unstable if $|f'(a_1)f'(a_2)| > 1$.*

For the dynamical system of Example 4.9, we computed that

$$|f'(a_1)f'(a_2)| = 0.16,$$

so the 2-cycle, $a_1 = (21 + \sqrt{21})/22$ and $a_2 = (21 - \sqrt{21})/22$, is **stable**.

Let's use Theorems 4.11 and 4.12 to find for what r values the logistic equation (6),
$$A(n+1) = (1+r)A(n) - rA^2(n),$$
has a stable 2-cycle, and what that 2-cycle is.

We first need to find the 2-cycle, that is, we need to find numbers a that satisfy

$$a = f(f(a)), \quad \text{where} \quad f(a) = (1+r)a - ra^2.$$

Substitution gives

$$\begin{aligned}
a &= (1+r)((1+r)a - ra^2) - r((1+r)a - ra^2)^2 \\
&= (1+r)^2 a - (1+r)ra^2 - r(1+r)a^2 + 2r^2(1+r)a^3 - r^3a^4,
\end{aligned}$$

or, collecting terms on the left and factoring out ra,

$$[r^2a^3 - 2r(1+r)a^2 + (1+r)(2+r)a - (2+r)]ra = 0.$$

We know that $a = 0$ and $a = 1$ are roots, since they are fixed points of the original dynamical system. The a term is already factored out. Factoring out an $a - 1$ term (by long division) gives

$$ra(a - 1)(r^2 a^2 - r(2 + r)a + (2 + r)) = 0.$$

Using the quadratic formula, we get

$$a = \frac{2 + r \pm \sqrt{r^2 - 4}}{2r}.$$

These two numbers form our 2-cycle. Notice that, when $0 < r < 2$, we don't have a 2-cycle, but then we have an attracting fixed point $a = 1$. Also note that, when $r = 2.2$, we get the points

$$a_1 = \frac{21 + \sqrt{21}}{22} \quad \text{and} \quad a_2 = \frac{21 - \sqrt{21}}{22},$$

discussed above.

How do we determine if this 2-cycle is stable? Using Theorem 4.12, with $f(x) = (1 + r)x - rx^2$, we get

$$f'(x) = (1 + r) - 2rx,$$

so

$$f'(a_1)f'(a_2) = \left[1 + r - 2r\left(\frac{2 + r + \sqrt{r^2 - 4}}{2r}\right)\right]\left[1 + r - 2r\left(\frac{2 + r - \sqrt{r^2 - }}{2r}\right)\right.$$

Canceling the $2r$'s in both factors gives

$$\begin{aligned} f'(a_1)f'(a_2) &= \left[1 + r - (2 + r + \sqrt{r^2 - 4})\right]\left[1 + r - (2 + r - \sqrt{r^2 - 4})\right] \\ &= (-1 - \sqrt{r^2 - 4})(-1 + \sqrt{r^2 - 4}) \\ &= 1 - r^2 + 4 = 5 - r^2. \end{aligned}$$

If

$$-1 < f'(a_1)f'(a_2) = 5 - r^2 < 1,$$

then the 2-cycle is stable. (Notice that $5 - (2.2)^2 = 0.16$, which we derived in Example 4.9.) Subtracting 5 from all sides and dividing by -1 gives

$$6 > r^2 > 4.$$

Assuming that r is a positive growth rate, we take positive square roots of all sides, so that

$$a_1 = \frac{2 + r + \sqrt{r^2 - 4}}{2r} \quad \text{and} \quad a_2 = \frac{2 + r - \sqrt{r^2 - 4}}{2r}$$

form a stable 2-cycle if

$$2 < r < \sqrt{6} = 2.4495\ldots.$$

We have shown that for populations with large growth rates (greater than 2), but not too large (less than 2.4495), the size of the population will form a stable oscillation. Some people think that this helps explain the oscillations in the size of certain species of insects.

The question you might now ask is, what happens when $r > \sqrt{6}$? We know that the equilibrium values are unstable and that the 2-cycle is unstable. What happens is that, for r slightly larger than $\sqrt{6}$, $A(k)$ goes to a **stable 4-cycle**. In fact, dynamical systems may have 3-cycles, 4-cycles, and so forth.

A 3-cycle consists of 3 numbers a_1, a_2, and a_3 such that $a_2 = f(a_1)$, $a_3 = f(a_2)$, and $a_1 = f(a_3)$. Notice that $a_1 = f(f(f(a_1)))$. To find the numbers of a 3-cycle, we must factor the polynomial,

$$f(f(f(a))) - a = 0.$$

If $f(x) = (1+r)x - rx^2$, then $f(f(f(x)))$ is an eighth order polynomial. To find a 4-cycle, we would have to factor a sixteenth order polynomial. You can imagine that it is usually difficult or impossible to compute these cycles exactly. They could be approximated, with some difficulty, using Newton's method.

When a 3-cycle or 4-cycle is stable or attracting, it can often be easily approximated by computing $A(k)$ for large values of k.

Example 4.13

Consider the dynamical system

$$A(n+1) = 3.5A(n) - 3.5A^2(n).$$

In Figure 30, we see the stable 4-cycle consisting of four numbers which are approximately

$$0.874\,997, \qquad 0.382\,820, \qquad 0.826\,941, \qquad 0.500\,884.$$

These four numbers were obtained by computing $A(1)$, $A(2)$, $\ldots$, $A(50)$ on a computer, then drawing the cobweb starting with $A(51)$. Almost any a_0 you pick (between 0 and 1) will work.

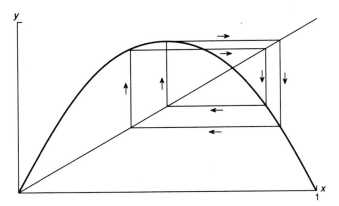

Fig. 30. This cobweb for the dynamical system $A(n + 1) = 3.5A(n) - 3.5A^2(n)$ displays a stable 4-cycle.

Example 4.14

In Figure 31, we see the stable 3-cycle for the dynamical system

$$A(n + 1) = 3.84A(n) - 3.84A^2(n)$$

The three numbers are approximately

$$0.1494, \qquad 0.4880, \qquad 0.9594.$$

Again, these numbers were obtained by computing $A(1)$, $A(2)$, $\ldots$, on a computer. Eventually, the same three numbers keep repeating, so we hypothesize that they form a stable 3-cycle.

Using the same technique as above, we could prove the following theorem.

Theorem 4.15

Suppose that the dynamical system

$$A(n + 1) = f(A(n))$$

has a k-cycle, consisting of the k values, $a_1, \ldots, a_k$. This k-cycle is stable if

$$|f'(a_1)f'(a_2)\ldots f'(a_k)| < 1,$$

and is unstable if

$$|f'(a_1)f'(a_2)\ldots f'(a_k)| > 1.$$

The difficulty with this theorem is that we usually can't find the k-cycle.

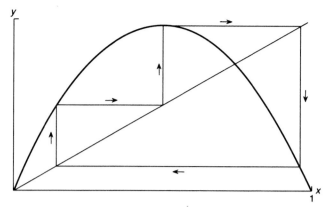

Fig. 31. This cobweb for the dynamical system $A(n+1) = 3.84A(n) - 3.84A^2(n)$ displays a stable 3-cycle.

For the dynamical system

$$A(n+1) = 3.5A(n)(1 - A(n))$$

of Example 4.13, we have $f'(x) = 3.5 - 7x$. Therefore, with a little work, we see that

$$f'(0.874\,997)f'(0.382\,820)f'(0.826\,941)f'(0.500\,884) = -0.0305.$$

Since $|-0.0305| < 1$, this 4-cycle is stable.
For the dynamical system

$$A(n+1) = 3.84A(n)(1 - A(n))$$

of Example 4.14 we have that $f'(x) = 3.84 - 7.68x$, and so

$$f'(0.1494)f'(0.4880)f'(0.9594) = -0.8755.$$

Since $|-0.8755| < 1$, this is a stable 3-cycle.

4.2.1 Problems

1. Consider the dynamical system

$$A(n+1) = 3.1A(n) - 3.1A^2(n).$$

(a) Show that $a_1 = 0.764\,566\,52$ and $a_2 = 0.558\,014\,125$ form a 2-cycle by showing that, if $A(0) = a_1$, then $A(1) = a_2$, and $A(2) = a_1$.

(b) Show that this 2-cycle is stable by showing that

$$|f'(a_1)f'(a_2)| < 1.$$

2. Consider the dynamical system

$$A(n + 1) = 3.2A(n) - 3.2A^2(n).$$

The numbers $a = 0$ and $a = 0.6875$ are equilibrium values for this dynamical system.

(a) Find the equation, $f(f(a)) - a = 0$, factor out the terms a and $a - 0.6875$, then use the quadratic formula to find the 2-cycle for this equation.

(b) Show that this 2-cycle is stable.

3. Consider the dynamical system

$$A(n + 1) = 3.3A(n) - 3.3A^2(n).$$

(a) Find a 2-cycle for this dynamical system.

(b) Show that this 2-cycle is stable by showing that

$$|f'(a_1)f'(a_2)| < 1.$$

4. Consider the dynamical system

$$A(n + 1) = 3.6A(n) - 3.6A^2(n).$$

(a) Find a 2-cycle for this system.

(b) Show that this 2-cycle is unstable by showing that

$$|f'(a_1)f'(a_2)| > 1.$$

5. Consider the dynamical system

$$A(n + 1) = 3.5A(n) - 2.5A^2(n).$$

(a) Show that $a_1 = 0.701\,237\,896$ is one point in a 4-cycle by finding $a_2 = f(a_1)$, $a_3 = f(a_2)$, and $a_4 = f(a_3)$, and showing that $a_1 = f(a_4)$.

(b) Show that this 4-cycle is stable by showing that

$$|f'(a_1)f'(a_2)f'(a_3)f'(a_4)| < 1.$$

6. Consider the dynamical system

$$A(n+1) = 3.2A(n) - 1.6A^2(n).$$

   (a) Approximate the numbers a_1 and a_2 that form a 2-cycle for this dynamical system, by letting $a_0 = 1$ and computing $A(1)$, $A(2)$, and so forth, until you repeat the same two numbers. Round off each $A(k)$ value to 3 decimal places.

   (b) Show that this is a stable 2-cycle by computing $f'(a_1)f'(a_2)$.

7. Suppose a_1 and a_2 form a 2-cycle for the dynamical system

$$A(n+1) = f(A(n)),$$

   where $f(x)$ is quadratic (and so $f''(x) = c$ for all x and $f'''(x) = 0$). Suppose that

$$f'(a_1)f'(a_2) = -1,$$

   that is, we cannot tell if the equilibrium values a_1 and a_2 are stable for the dynamical system

$$A(n+2) = f(f(A(n))).$$

   Use Theorem 4.6 on the dynamical system $A(n+2) = f(f(A(n)))$ to show that these equilibrium values are stable so that the 2-cycle is stable. (Be careful taking derivatives and remember that you can use the substitutions $a_2 = f(a_1)$, $f''(a_1) = f''(a_2) = c$, $f'''(a_1) = f'''(a_2) = 0$, and $f'(a_1)f'(a_2) = -1$.)

4.3 Bifurcation theory

We often think that the world is continuous in the sense that a small change in input causes a small change in the output. But this is not always the case, as exemplified by the phrase 'the straw that broke the camel's back'. Bifurcation theory is the study of that breaking point, that is, it is the study of the point at which the qualitative behavior of a system changes.

While you may not be familiar with the term 'bifurcation', you are certainly familiar with the concept. Consider a vertical metal rod. Suppose you start putting weights on the top of the rod. At first nothing happens, but after you put enough weight on the bar, the bar bends to one side or the other. There is some weight w such that if the total weight is less than w the rod has **one** equilibrium value (it is straight), but if the weight exceeds w then the rod has three equilibrium values (bent to the left and bent to the right which are stable equilibriums, and straight which is an unstable equilibrium). The weight w is a bifurcation value in that as the weight on the rod goes from less than w to greater than w, one equilibrium point divides (or bifurcates) into three equilibrium values.

The melting point of ice is a bifurcation value in that the qualitative behavior of 'water' when the temperature is above freezing is different from the behavior when the temperature is below freezing. Another example is the velocity v of a rocket. If its velocity is below a fixed velocity v_e (for escape velocity), it will fall back to earth; if its velocity exceeds v_e, it will break free of earth's gravitational force and go into outer space.

The key to bifurcation theory is that we have one unknown input (or parameter) in our dynamical system (the weight on the rod, the temperature of the water, or velocity of the rocket). For some values of the parameter we have one number m_1 of equilibrium values, but for another value of the parameter we have a different number of equilibrium values, say m_2, that is, the qualitative behavior of the system we are studying changes as the parameter changes.

We have actually been studying bifurcation in the previous sections. In Section 3.2 we studied the dynamical system

$$A(n + 1) = 1.8A(n) - 0.8A^2(n) - b, \qquad (7)$$

as a model of harvesting a fixed amount b of a population. The constant b is our parameter. We showed that (1) if $b > 0.2$ there are no equilibrium values and $A(k)$ goes to negative infinity, (2) if $b = 0.2$ then there is one equilibrium value, $a = 0.5$, which is semistable from above, and (3) if $-1.05 < b < 0.2$, there are two equilibrium values, $a_1 = 0.5(1 + \sqrt{1 - 5b})$ which is stable and $a_2 = 0.5(1 - \sqrt{1 - 5b})$ which is unstable. The value of the parameter $b = 0.2$ is called the **bifurcation value**.

Another purpose of this section is to learn how to display graphically the information we have already derived. In other words, we will learn how to draw one graph that displays **all the information** given in the preceding discussion.

Suppose we have a dynamical system with a stable equilibrium value a. This means that if a_0 is close enough to a then $A(k)$ goes to a. If we plotted the points $(k, A(k))$, we might get a figure such as Figure 32 (a).

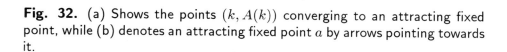
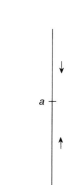

(a)   (b)

Fig. 32. (a) Shows the points $(k, A(k))$ converging to an attracting fixed point, while (b) denotes an attracting fixed point a by arrows pointing towards it.

If we looked at Figure 32 (a) with our eyes at the right end of the k axis, we would see a figure such as Figure 32 (b). Notice that these two figures give the same information. In particular, the arrows pointing towards the number a indicate that the $A(k)$ values are going towards a. Thus, we graphically display a stable equilibrium value as a point on a line with arrows pointing towards it. (The arrows pointing towards a imply that **attracting fixed point** may be a better terminology.)

   Remark: If $A(k)$ oscillates towards a, we will still draw arrows towards a. The information that the arrows are meant to convey is that

$$\lim_{k \to \infty} A(k) = a.$$

   Suppose we have a dynamical system with an unstable equilibrium value a. This means that if a_0 is close to a then $A(k)$ goes away from a. If we plotted the points $(k, A(k))$, we might get a figure such as Figure 33 (a). Again, if we look at this figure from the end of the k axis, we would see a figure such as Figure 33 (b). Notice that these two figures give the same information. In particular, the arrows pointing away from the number a indicate that the $A(k)$ values are going away from a. Thus, we graphically display a repelling fixed point as a point on a line with arrows pointing away from it. (We will also use this method to display an unstable equilibrium in which $A(k)$ oscillates away from a.)

   These ideas can be combined. In Figure 34 (a) is a representation of the behavior of dynamical system (7) with $b = 0.72$, in which the fixed point $a = 0.9$ is attracting and $a = 0.1$ is repelling.

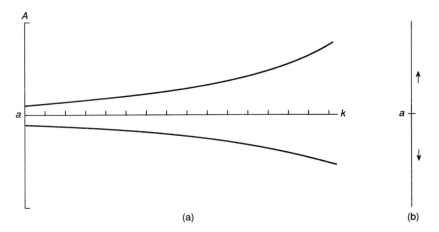

Fig. 33. (a) Shows the points $(k, A(k))$ diverging from a repelling fixed point, while (b) denotes a repelling fixed point a by arrows pointing away from it.

Suppose a is semistable from above for a dynamical system. This means that if a_0 is close enough to but above a then $A(k)$ goes towards a, but if a_0 is close to but below a then $A(k)$ goes away from a. Similar to Figures 32 (b) and 33 (b), we could represent semistable from above by a figure such as Figure 34 (b). In particular, the arrows pointing towards a from above indicate that if a_0 is above a then the $A(k)$ values go towards a, while the arrows pointing away from a from below indicate that if a_0 is below a then the $A(k)$ values are going away from a. The number a can be thought of as a barrier on the line. Thus, we graphically display an equilibrium value which is semistable from above as a point on a line with arrows pointing towards it from above and away from it from below.

If a dynamical system has no equilibrium value, then we know that the $A(k)$ values increase to positive infinity or decrease to negative infinity no matter what the a_0 value. If $A(k)$ is going to negative infinity, we could represent the solution as in Figure 34 (c). Notice that Figure 34 (c) is different from Figure 34 (b), in that one has a barrier a, but the other has no barrier.

For each value of the parameter b, we have learned how to display the information about the solution $A(k)$ on a line instead of in a plane. By 'putting all the lines together', we can display the behavior of $A(k)$ for all (relevant) values of b on a plane, called the ba plane.

Again, consider the dynamical system (7),

$$A(n+1) = 1.8A(n) - 0.8A^2(n) - b.$$

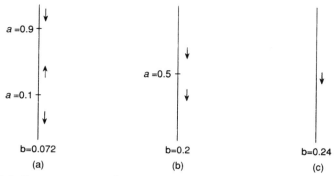

Fig. 34. (a) Denotes a repelling and an attracting fixed point, (b) denotes a fixed point that is semistable from above, and (c) denotes solutions going to negative infinity.

We know from Section 3.2 that if $b = 0.072$ then there are two equilibrium values, $a = 0.9$ which is stable, and $a = 0.1$ which is unstable. For this value of b, we get Figure 34 (a). If $b = 0.2$, there is one equilibrium value, $a = 0.5$, which is semistable from above, and the behavior of $A(k)$ is given in Figure 34 (b). If $b = 0.24$, there are no equilibrium values, and $A(k)$ decreases to negative infinity. This behavior is given in Figure 34 (c).

Let's put it all together. Let's consider a plane with the vertical axis being the a axis, and the horizontal axis being the b axis. We know from Section 3.2, that for each value of b, the equilibrium values are of the form

$$a = \tfrac{1}{2}(1 \pm \sqrt{1 - 5b}).$$

We would like to plot these points on our ba axis. Multiplying by 2, subtracting 1 from both sides, and then squaring both sides gives

$$(2a - 1)^2 = (1 - 5b).$$

The graph of this equation is the parabola in Figure 35. Notice that the vertex $(b, a) = (0.2, 0.5)$ of this parabola corresponds to, the bifurcation value $b = 0.2$ and the corresponding equilibrium value $a = 0.5$.

We now fix a value of b and draw a vertical line at this value of b. The points of intersection (if any) between this vertical line and the parabola are the equilibrium values for that value of b. We then draw arrows to correspond to the stability of the equilibrium values for that value of b. Notice that we have drawn vertical lines at $b = 0.072$, $b = 0.24$, and $b = 0.2$. Notice that these lines are identical to the lines in Figure 34.

In Figure 36, we draw arrows going up inside the parabola, and arrows going down outside the parabola. Notice that if you pick a b value and

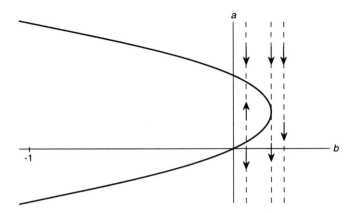

Fig. 35. Bifurcation diagram for the fixed points a on the parabola $(2a - 1)^2 = (1 - 5b)$ with vertex $(0.2, 0.5)$. Vertical lines correspond to $b = 0.72$, 0.2, and 0.24.

draw a vertical line, this line will intersect the parabola at the equilibrium values corresponding to that value of b. (If $b > 0.2$, there are no points of intersection because there are no equilibrium values.) If you draw arrows on that line in the direction indicated by the arrows on the graph (up if inside the parabola and down if outside the parabola), you will have the stability of the equilibrium values.

Notice that Figure 36 displays **all the information** we derived about this dynamical system in Section 3.2, that is, it shows that (1) if $b > 0.2$, then $A(k)$ goes to negative infinity, (2) if $b = 0.2$, then there is one equilibrium value, $a = 0.5$, which is semistable from above, and (3) if $-1.05 < b < 0.2$, then there are two equilibrium values, $a = 0.5(1 + \sqrt{1 - 5b})$ which is stable and $a = 0.5(1 - \sqrt{1 - 5b})$ which is unstable.

Definition 4.16

Bifurcation diagrams: *For a dynamical system involving a parameter b, find all fixed points a as functions of b. Plot these functions on the ba axis. Find ranges of b for which each of these fixed points is attracting and draw vertical arrows towards them. In those same ranges, draw arrows away from repelling fixed points, and appropriate arrows for semistable fixed points. Also draw arrows either up or down for values of b for which there are no fixed points.*

Consider a dynamical system involving a parameter b. Let N_b be the number of equilibrium values for the dynamical system when the parameter equals b. Note that N_b is a function of b. For example, for the

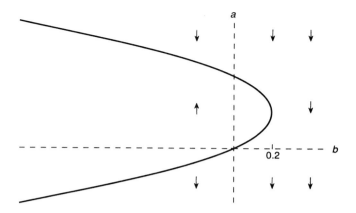

Fig. 36. Bifurcation diagram for the dynamical system $A(n+1) = 1.8A(n) - 0.8A^2(n) - b$.

dynamical system (7),

$$N_b = \begin{cases} 2, & \text{for } b < 2 \\ 1, & \text{for } b = 2 \\ 0, & \text{for } b > 2. \end{cases}$$

Definition 4.17

*If N_b is not constant for b in any interval $(b_0 - \epsilon, b_0 + \epsilon)$, then the number b_0 is called a **bifurcation value** and the dynamical system is said to undergo a **bifurcation** as b passes through b_0.*

Note that dynamical system (7) has $b_0 = 2$ as its only bifurcation value.

Example 4.18

Consider the dynamical system

$$A(n + 1) = (1.8 - b)A(n) - 0.8A^2(n)$$

which was derived in Section 3.2 as a model of harvesting a fixed proportion b of a species. Recall that the fixed point $a = 0$ is attracting for $0.8 < b < 2.8$, is semistable from above for $b = 0.8$, and is repelling for $b < 0.8$. Also recall that the fixed point $a = 1 - 1.25b$ is attracting for $-1.2 < b < 0.8$ and is repelling for $b > 0.8$. Notice that, when $b = 0.8$, $a = 1 - 1.25b = 0$, which is semistable from above.

In Figure 37 is a graph of the lines $a = 0$ and $a = 1 - 1.25b$ which intersect at $b = 0.8$. For $-1.2 < b < 0.8$, we draw arrows (vertically) **towards** the attracting fixed point, given by the line $a = 1 - 1.25b$, and **away** from the repelling fixed point, given by the line $a = 0$. For $0.8 <$

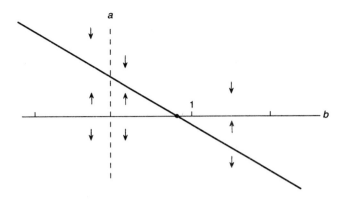

Fig. 37. Bifurcation diagram for the dynamical system $A(n+1) = (1.8 - b)A(n) - 0.8A^2(n)$. Fixed points given by lines $a = 0$ and $a = 1 - 1.25b$.

$b < 2.8$, we draw arrows **towards** the line $a = 0$, and **away** from the line $a = 1 - 1.25b$. At $b = 0.8$, we draw arrows towards $a = 0$ from above, and away from $a = 0$ from below. This figure gives all the information we had derived concerning this model. From Figure 37, we can see that

$$N_b = \begin{cases} 2, & \text{for } b < 0.8 \\ 1, & \text{for } b = 0.8 \\ 2, & \text{for } b > 0.8. \end{cases}$$

Thus, $b_0 = 0.8$ is a bifurcation value.

Notice that the equilibrium lines $a = 0$ and $a = 1 - 1.25b$ divide the plane into four regions, and that the direction of the arrows is the same throughout each of these regions, but the direction changes as you cross a line from one region to the next.

Example 4.19

Consider the dynamical system

$$A(n+1) = (1+b)A(n) - A^3(n),$$

where b is some fixed constant. The fixed points are solutions to

$$a = (1+b)a - a^3, \quad \text{or} \quad 0 = a(b - a^2).$$

Factoring gives
$$0 = a(\sqrt{b} - a)(\sqrt{b} + a).$$

Notice that, for all b values, $a = 0$ is a fixed point, while $a = \pm\sqrt{b}$ are fixed points only when $b > 0$. (When $b=0$, then $a = \pm\sqrt{b} = 0$ which has already been included.) Thus, if $b \leq 0$ we have one fixed point, while if $b > 0$ we have three fixed points.

Since $f(x) = (1 + b)x - x^3$ it follows that

$$f'(x) = (1 + b) - 3x^2, \quad f''(x) = -6x, \quad f'''(x) = -6.$$

From this we see that $a = 0$ is attracting when $-1 < f'(0) = 1 + b < 1$, that is, when $-2 < b < 0$. Likewise, $a = 0$ is repelling when $b < -2$ and when $b > 0$.

Remember to check the end points, that is, the values $b = 0$ and $b = -2$. If $b = 0$, then $f'(0) = 1$, $f''(0) = 0$, and $f'''(0) = -6$, so by Theorem 4.2, $a = 0$ is stable. Also, by Theorem 4.6, if $b = -2$ then $f'(0) = -1$, and

$$g'''(0) = -2f'''(0) - 2(f''(0))^2 = 12 - 2(0)^2 > 0,$$

and so $a = 0$ is unstable. To summarize, if $-2 < b \leq 0$ then $a = 0$ is stable, and if $b \leq -2$ or if $b > 0$ then $a = 0$ is unstable.

To find the stability of $a = \pm\sqrt{b}$, we compute $f'(\pm\sqrt{b}) = 1 + b - 3b = 1 - 2b$. It follows that both fixed points $a = \pm\sqrt{b}$ are attracting when $-1 < 1 - 2b < 1$, that is, when $0 < b < 1$. We have already studied the case in which $b = 0$. When $b = 1$, we have $f'(\pm 1) = -1$ and

$$g'''(\pm 1) = -2f'''(\pm 1) - 3(f''(\pm 1))^2 = 12 - 108 = -96 < 0,$$

so that $a = \pm\sqrt{b}$ are attracting when $b = 1$.

To review, if $0 < b \leq 1$ then $a = \pm\sqrt{b}$ are attracting. The bifurcation diagram for this dynamical system is given in Figure 38, where $-2 < b < 1$. We see that

$$N_b = \begin{cases} 1, & \text{for } b \leq 0 \\ 3, & \text{for } b > 0. \end{cases}$$

Thus, $b_0 = 0$ is a bifurcation value.

Notice also in Figure 38, that the parabola $a^2 = b$ and the line $a = 0$ divide the plane into four regions. The direction of the arrows is the same throughout each of these four regions. Pick a value for b between -2 and 1, and draw a vertical line at that point. The points where this line intersects the parabola and the b axis are the equilibrium values, one if $b \leq 0$ and three if $b > 0$. The behavior of the solutions is given by the direction of the appropriate arrows. Notice that this figure summarizes all of our work, that is, it shows that (1) if $-2 < b \leq 0$ then $a = 0$ is stable and (2) if $0 < b \leq 1$ then $a = \pm\sqrt{b}$ are stable.

Suppose we have a vertical rod on which we put a weight b ($b > 0$ means positive weight on top and $b < 0$ means we pull up on the rod).

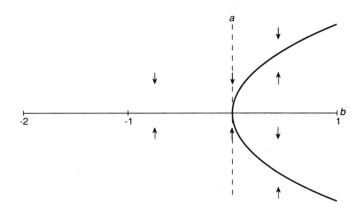

Fig. 38. Bifurcation diagram for the dynamical system $A(n+1) = (1+b)A(n) - A^3(n)$. Fixed points given by lines $a = 0$ and parabola $b = a^2$.

The above example in some sense models the behavior of this beam, that is, if $b < 0$ the midpoint of the beam is 0 units from straight up or down. If we apply weight $0 < b \leq 1$, the midpoint of the beam bends $\sqrt{b}$ units to the right ($a = \sqrt{b}$) or to the left ($a = -\sqrt{b}$). Note that the larger the weight b, the more the beam bends a.

Suppose we draw curves representing the fixed points of a dynamical system. How do the number of fixed points change? Geometrically, there are two ways for the number of fixed points to change: (1) a curve might double back on itself, as in Figure 36; and (2) two curves intersect, as in Figure 37. Note that in Figure 38 we have a combination of (1) and (2), that is, two curves intersect at the point where one double backs. Because of this, there are only three types of bifurcations when we have one parameter, b.

Definition 4.20

Types of bifurcations: *Suppose at the bifurcation value b_0 the fixed points form a U-shaped curve, opened to the left or to the right, such as the vertex of the parabola in Figure 36. Then this bifurcation value is called* a **saddle node bifurcation**.

Suppose at the bifurcation value b_0 the fixed points are on two intersecting curves (neither of which double backs at b_0), such as in Figure 37. This bifurcation value is called a **transcritical bifurcation**.

Suppose at the bifurcation value b_0 the fixed points are given by a U-shaped curve, opened to the left or right, with another curve crossing the **vertex** *of the U, such as in Figure 38. Then this bifurcation value is called* a **pitchfork bifurcation**.

In Figure 39 we have a bifurcation diagram with the bifurcation points

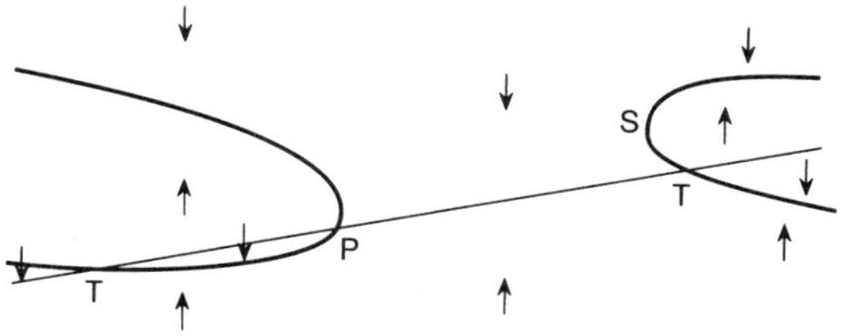

Fig. 39. Bifurcation diagram with saddle node bifurcations marked with s, pitchfork bifurcations marked with p, and transcritical bifurcations marked with t.

marked by the letters S, T, and P. The bifurcation point marked by an S is a saddle node bifurcation, those marked by a T are transcritical bifurcations, and the one marked by a P is a pitchfork bifurcation.

Example 4.21

In the previous section we considered the logistic equation

$$A(n + 1) = (1 + b)A(n) - bA^2(n)$$

as a model of population growth. We then considered the dynamical system

$$A(n + 2) = g(A(n)) = f(f(A(n))),$$

where $f(x) = (1 + b)x - bx^2$. (We used the letter r instead of b in that section.) We found, for the system involving $g(A(n))$, that (1) the fixed point $a = 1$ is attracting if $0 < b \leq 2$, and (2) the fixed points $a = 0.5b^{-1}(2 + b \pm \sqrt{b^2 - 4})$ are attracting if $2 < b < \sqrt{6}$. This is displayed in Figure 40. The graph of

$$a = \frac{2 + b \pm \sqrt{b^2 - 4}}{2b}$$

was computer generated, but you could plot the graph it using calculus techniques.

We note that, for the latter dynamical system, $b_0 = 2$ is a pitchfork bifurcation. In this case, $b_0 = 2$ is sometimes called a **period doubling bifurcation** for the original dynamical system.

Example 4.22

Consider

$$A(n + 1) = bA(n) - bA^2(n), \quad \text{where} \quad b > 0.$$

This dynamical system is also called the **discrete logistic equation** and it is often the system used to model population growth. (Since the fixed points are $a = 0$, and $a = (b - 1)/b$, it follows that the carrying capacity of the environment is $(b - 1)/b$.) The graphs $a = 0$ and $a = (b - 1)/b$

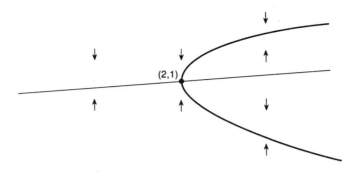

Fig. 40. Bifurcation diagram for the dynamical system $A(n + 1) = f(f(A(n)))$ where $f(x) = (1+b)x - bx^2$. Horizontal axis is $1.5 \leq b \leq 2.45$ and vertical axis is $0.5 \leq a \leq 1.3$.

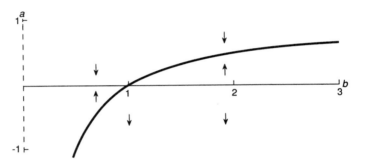

Fig. 41. Bifurcation diagram for dynamical system $A(n + 1) = f(A(n))$ where $f(x) = bx - bx^2$. Fixed points are given by the line $a = 0$ and the curve $a = 1 - 1/b$.

are given in Figure 41. Note that we have a transcritical bifurcation at $b_0 = 1$.

Using the fact that $f(x) = bx - bx^2$, $f'(x) = b - 2bx$, and $f''(x) = -2b$, you should be able to deduce that: (1) $a = 0$ is attracting when $0 < b < 1$ (since we are assuming b is positive), is semistable from above when $b = 1$, and is repelling when $b > 1$; and (2) $a = (b - 1)/b$ is attracting when $1 < b \leq 3$ and is repelling when $b < 1$ or $b > 3$. The composite behavior of this example is given in Figure 41. Again pick any b value of interest and draw a vertical line. The points of intersection with the b axis and the curve $a = (b-1)/b$ are the fixed points and the arrows tell you the behavior of the solutions. You should be able to plot the curve $a = (b - 1)/b$ using calculus techniques. Note that it has a vertical asymptote at $b = 0$ (which is why we assumed that $b > 0$) and a horizontal asymptote at $a = 1$.

Example 4.23

Space, the final frontier: In the popular *Star Trek* series, the Federation's Prime Directive was that the *Enterprise* crew could not interfere in any world that had not had previous contact with other worlds. The fear was that any contact from another world could alter the course of history on a developing planet. But we will see that the Federation could have used a good mathematician.

Suppose that Earth is actually being watched by intelligent creatures from another planet. These aliens wish to study us without having us know they are there or at least they want most of us not to believe they exist. They might reason as follows. Let $A(n)$ be the fraction of people on earth that believes in flying saucers at time n (and consequently $1 - A(n)$ is the fraction that doesn't). They assume that, in each time period, the believers convince a certain proportion of the nonbelievers that flying saucers do exist, that proportion depending on the interaction of believers and nonbelievers, that is, on the product $A(n)[1 - A(n)]$ (and vice versa). (When a population is broken into two parts, $A(n)$ and $1 - A(n)$, their product, $A(n)[1 - A(n)]$, is called the contact ratio and is used extensively in the study of epidemics.) So, in the absence of flying saucers, $A(n)$ would satisfy the dynamical system

$$A(n + 1) = A(n) + kA(n)[1 - A(n)].$$

If $k > 0$, then there is a tendency to believe, while if $k < 0$, there is a tendency not to believe in flying saucers. Let's assume the aliens have determined through their studies that $k = -0.01$.

Let's also assume that flying saucers do land in certain areas and b per cent (as a fraction) of the people see them each time period. Thus we have (up to) $100b$ per cent of new believers and the above dynamical system becomes

$$A(n + 1) = 0.99A(n) + 0.01A^2(n) + b.$$

Our aliens must ask themselves how large b can be without having everyone believe in flying saucers. In other words they are willing to have some people believe since, if most people do not believe, Earth's behavior will not change.

Solving $a = 0.99a + 0.01a^2 + b$ for a in terms of b gives

$$a = 0.5 \pm \sqrt{0.25 - 100b}.$$

Since we are interested in real equilibrium values, it is necessary that $0.25 - 100b \geq 0$, which means that

$$b \leq 0.0025.$$

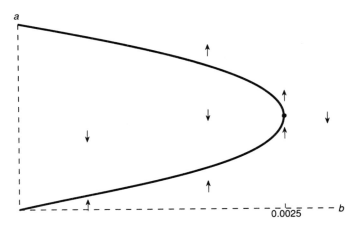

Fig. 42. Bifurcation diagram for the dynamical system $A(n + 1) = 0.99A(n) - 0.01A^2(n) + b$. The fixed points are given by the parabola $(a - 0.5)^2 = (0.25 - 100b)$.

For $b < 0.0025$, there are two fixed points, $a = 0.5 \pm \sqrt{0.25 - 100b}$. Using calculus techniques, and being careful solving inequalities, you should be able to show that $a = 0.5 + \sqrt{0.25 - 100b}$ is repelling for $b < 0.0025$, while $a = 0.5 - \sqrt{0.25 - 100b}$ is attracting for $-99.9975 \leq b < 0.0025$. If $b = 0.0025$ then $a = 0.5$ is the only fixed point and it is semistable from below. If $b > 0.0025$ there are no fixed points and $A(k)$ increases to infinity.

The previous information for $b > 0$ is summarized in Figure 42. Note that $b = 0.0025$ is a saddle node bifurcation. Thus if our aliens restrict their activity to a point where less than 0.25 per cent, that is, $b < 0.0025$, of the people observe them in one time period, then most people will not believe in flying saucers.

Suppose they feel that it would be harmful for the development of a civilization if more than 10 per cent believed in flying saucers. Then they wish the stable equilibrium to be

$$a = 0.5 - \sqrt{0.25 - 100b} \leq 0.10.$$

Simplification gives

$$0.4 \leq \sqrt{0.25 - 100b}, \quad 0.16 \leq 0.25 - 100b, \quad \text{or} \quad b \leq 0.0009.$$

The moral is that if aliens are watching us, then they are smart enough to control their behavior and go (relatively) unseen. Thus, most of us may never be certain they are there. Can you envision an alien anthropologist having to apply for permission to investigate the primitive societies on Earth?

This section gives a graphical analysis of whole classes of dynamical systems that we were studying for individual b values earlier in this text.

4.3.1 Problems

1. Consider the equation

$$A(n+1) = 5A(n) - A^2(n) - b.$$

(a) Find the fixed points.

(b) There are no fixed points for b greater than what number? For b greater than this value, do the $A(k)$ values go to positive or negative infinity?

(c) For what values of b are the two fixed points attracting? Semistable?

(d) Plot the graph of the parabola given by the two fixed points on the ba axis.

(e) Draw arrows in the appropriate directions to complete the bifurcation diagram. This diagram should be drawn for $3 < b < 5$. Note that you have a **saddle node bifurcation**.

2. Consider the dynamical system

$$A(n+1) = -bA(n) + A^3(n).$$

(a) Find the three equilibrium values.

(b) Plot the graph of the equilibrium values, letting the b axis go from -3 to 1.

(c) For what values of b is the constant fixed point attracting, semistable, and repelling?

(d) Show that the fixed points on the parabola are repelling for all values of b for which they exist.

(e) Draw arrows in the appropriate directions on the graph. You should have a **pitchfork bifurcation**.

3. Consider the dynamical system

$$A(n+1) - A(n) = 0.5[1 - 0.5A(n)]A(n) - bA(n),$$

which corresponds to a fixed proportion harvesting policy for a population in which the unrestricted growth rate is $r = 0.5$ and the carrying capacity is $L = 2$.

(a) Find the fixed points for this equation, and determine for what values of b they are attracting.

(b) Plot the graph of the fixed points on the ba axis, with $-1.5 < b < 2.5$, and draw arrows in the appropriate directions. This is a **transcritical bifurcation**.

4. Consider the dynamical system

$$A(n + 1) = A^2(n) + (b + 1)A(n) - 2b^2.$$

(a) Find the fixed points for this equation, and determine for what values of b they are attracting.

(b) Plot the graph of the fixed points on the ba axis, with $-2/3 < b < 2/3$, and draw arrows in the appropriate directions. This is a **transcritical bifurcation**.

5. Consider the dynamical system

$$A(n + 1) = A^2(n) - b^2 A(n) + b^2.$$

(a) Find the fixed points for this equation, and determine for what values of b they are attracting.

(b) Plot the graph of the fixed points on the ba axis, with $-\sqrt{3} < b < \sqrt{3}$. Notice that the two curves intersect **twice**. When you draw arrows in the appropriate directions, you will find that each point of intersection is a **transcritical bifurcation**.

6. Consider the dynamical system

$$A(n + 1) = A^3(n) - A^2(n) + (1 - b)A(n) + b.$$

(a) Show that the fixed points are $a = 1$ and $a = \pm\sqrt{b}$.

(b) Find values of b for which $a = 1$ is attracting.

(c) Show that $a = -\sqrt{b}$ is repelling for $b > 0$. (Hint: You will find that $f'(-\sqrt{b}) = 1 + $ (positive term).)

(d) Show that $f'(\sqrt{b}) = 2b - 2\sqrt{b} + 1$. Solve the inequality $-1 < f'(\sqrt{b}) < 1$ to find the interval of stability.

(e) Plot the graph of the fixed points for $-2 < b < 1$, and draw arrows in appropriate directions. When $b = 0$ you should see a **saddle mode bifurcation** at the vertex of the parabola, and when $b = 1$ you should see a **transcritical bifurcation** where the parabola and line intersect.

4.4 Chaos

In this section we will investigate what happens when all of the fixed points and cycles are repelling. We will consider the logistic equation

$$A(n+1) = rA(n)[1 - A(n)] \qquad (8)$$

(which has been studied extensively by mathematicians and biologists). Note that this equation is related to the equation for population growth, but this form is slightly simpler. We will only consider values of r greater than zero.

We saw in the previous section that this equation has two fixed points, $a = 0$ which is attracting if $0 < r < 1$, and $a = (r-1)/r$ which is attracting if $1 < r \leq 3$. When $r > 3$, both fixed points are repelling, so $A(k)$ does not go to a fixed point. How does $A(k)$ behave?

In a similar situation, we found in Section 4.2 that, for the dynamical system

$$A(n+1) = (1+r)A(n) - rA^2(n),$$

if $2 < r < \sqrt{6}$ then the fixed points are repelling and $A(k)$ goes to an attracting 2-cycle. A similar computation shows that, for the dynamical system (8), $A(k)$ goes to the attracting 2-cycle

$$a = \sqrt{r+1}\left(\frac{\sqrt{r+1} \pm \sqrt{r-3}}{2r}\right) \qquad (9)$$

for $3 < r < 1 + \sqrt{6} = 3.45$, to 2 decimal places.

This 2-cycle corresponds to two attracting fixed points for the dynamical system

$$A(n+2) = f(f(A(n))), \quad \text{where} \quad f(x) = rx(1-x),$$

which is seen to be a pitchfork bifurcation in Figure 43, or a period doubling bifurcation for the original system.

If $r > 3.45$ then the fixed points are repelling and the 2-cycle is repelling. What happens to $A(k)$ in this case? In Section 4.2, we considered the dynamical system (8) with $r = 3.5$. We saw in this case that $A(k)$ went to an attracting 4-cycle. To show this algebraically, we could compute the dynamical system

$$A(n+4) = f(f(f(f(A(n))))),$$

where $f(x) = 3.5x(1-x)$, and find its fixed points. We would find four repelling fixed points (the two repelling fixed points for equation (8)

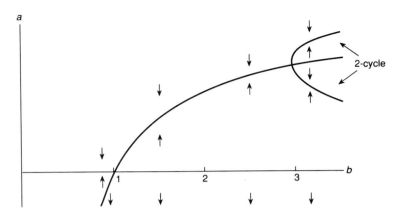

Fig. 43. Pitchfork bifurcation for the dynamical system $A(n + 2) = f(f(A(n)))$ where $f(x) = bx - bx^2$. The horizontal axis is $0 \le b \le 3.45$.

and the repelling 2-cycle of equation (9)). We would also find four attracting fixed points, corresponding to an attracting 4-cycle for equation (8). In Figure 44 is a graph of the function $y = f(f(f(f(x))))$, where $f(x) = 3.5x - 3.5x^2$. The eight points of intersection with the line $y = x$ correspond to the eight fixed points. Labeling the eight points of intersection from left to right as 1 through 8 (with $a = 0$ being point 1), we have the following: points 1 and 5 are the repelling fixed points; points 3 and 7 form the repelling 2-cycle; and points 2, 4, 6, and 8 form the attracting 4-cycle. Newton's method could be used on the function $y = f(f(f(f(x))))$ to find the eight fixed points.

If we continued our study, we could find a number c (approximately 3.54), such that if $3.45 < r < c$, then equation (8) has an attracting 4-cycle. This can be given in terms of two period doubling bifurcations at $r = 3.45$. See Figure 45, which is a continuation of the bifurcation diagram of Figure 43. It should now be clear why these are called period doubling bifurcations.

This all seems rather complicated, so why bother you may ask. If you remember, equation (8) models the growth of populations. This previous argument may explain the cyclic fluctuations in certain species of insects or other species with large growth rates. Similar behavior has been seen in areas such as mechanics, astronomy, meteorology, and chemistry.

Now back to the dynamical system (8),

$$A(n + 1) = rA(n)[1 - A(n)].$$

We now know that this dynamical system has one attracting fixed point

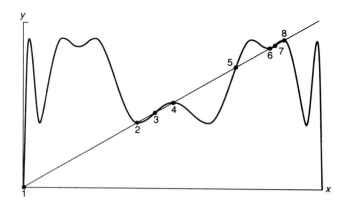

Fig. 44. The graph of $y = f(f(f(f(x))))$ where $f(x) = 3.5x - 3.5\,x^2$. The four attracting fixed points (slopes less than 1) form a 4-cycle for the dynamical system $A(n+1) = f(A(n))$.

for $1 < r < 3$, an attracting 2-cycle for $3 < r < 3.45$, and an attracting 4-cycle for $3.45 < r < 3.54$.

If we continued, then we would find a number C such that, for $3.54 < r < C$, the dynamical system (8) has an **attracting 8-cycle**. In fact there is a sequence of numbers $c_1 < c_2 < \ldots$ such that when $c_n < r < c_{n+1}$ the dynamical system has an attracting 2^n-cycle. We already know that $c_1 = 3$, $c_2 = 3.45$, and $c_3 = 3.54$.

But there is more. If $c_{10} < r < c_{11}$, we know that eventually $A(k)$ will settle into an attracting $2^{10} = 1024$-cycle, that is, every 1024 time periods, we will get the same $A(k)$ value back. If we had been computing $A(0)$, $A(1)$, $\ldots$ for that r value, it is unlikely we would ever have noticed the pattern of repetition. We would probably have only looked at one or two hundred values and then concluded, erroneously, that there was no pattern.

As strange as this seems, it gets even more bizarre. The values c_n are **all** smaller than the number 3.57. It is very much like the numbers $0.3 < 0.33 < 0.333 < \ldots < 1/3$. Thus the closer r is to 3.57, the larger the attracting cycle of equation (8). This can be seen in the bifurcation diagram of Figure 46. Notice that a vertical line intersects the curves at eight points, corresponding to the attracting 8-cycle. The repelling points are not sketched.

Figure 47 is a magnification of the bottom righthand corner of Figure 46. The two lines coming in from the left of the figure correspond to two of the eight points of an attracting 8-cycle. They divide into four points of an attracting 16-cycle, which divide into eight points of an at-

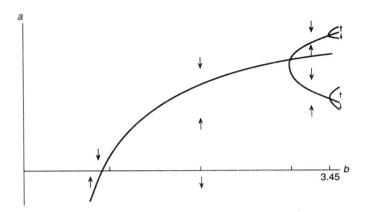

Fig. 45. Pitchfork bifurcation for the dynamical system of $A(n + 4) = f(f(f(f(A(n)))))$ where $f(x) = bx - bx^2$. The pair of pitchforks starting at $b = 3.45$ correspond to a 4-cycle for the logistic equation. The horizontal axis is $0 \leq b \leq 3.54$.

tracting 32-cycle, and so forth, as r approaches 3.57.

To review, since the values c_n approach 3.57, we get a series of period doubling bifurcations, each closer to 3.57 than the one before, as shown in Figures 46 and 47. All of the branches combine to give an attracting 2^n-cycle.

What happens when $r > 3.57$? At first the numbers $A(k)$ seem to have no pattern. But this is not exactly true. In Figure 48 (a) we can see $A(0)$, $A(1)$, $\ldots$, $A(100)$ plotted on a line with $a_0 = 0.1$ and $r = 3.58$. On Figure 48 (b), $A(101)$ through $A(200)$ are plotted. Though the behavior is not cyclic, all of the $A(k)$ values eventually fall into these four intervals.

The mathematics needed to study the dynamical system (8) for $3.57 < r < 4$ is beyond the level of this book, but I will sketch some of the results that have been found. More details will be given later in this text. Also see Devaney (1989) for an elementary introduction to this topic and Devaney (1986) for a more advanced discussion.

Suppose we have a set of points S. Then we say that the sequence of numbers $A(k)$ converges to S, denoted

$$\lim_{k \to \infty} |A(k) - S| = 0,$$

if, for every $\epsilon > 0$, there exists an integer K such that $A(k)$ is within ϵ of some point in S when $k > K$. For example, if $r = 3.5$ in equation (8), then S is the attracting 4-cycle, and we know that, for large values of k,

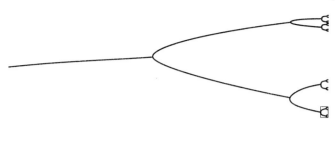

2.5   3   3.57 b

Fig. 46. Bifurcation diagram consisting of the attracting cycles for the dynamical system $A(n+1) = bA(n) - bA^2(n)$. Note as b increases towards 3.57 the period of the cycles keeps doubling. The horizontal axis is $2.5 \leq b \leq 3.57$ and vertical axis is $0 \leq a \leq 1$.

$A(k)$ is close (within ϵ) to one of those four points. The particular point that $A(k)$ is close to depends on the particular value of k.

Definition 4.24

*A set of points S is called an attracting set or simply an **attractor** for a dynamical system $A(n+1) = f(A(n))$ if there is a number δ such that if $|a_0 - s| < \delta$ for some point $s \in S$, then*

$$\lim_{k \to \infty} |A(k) - S| = 0.$$

Example 4.25

When $r = 2.5$, the dynamical system,

$$A(n+1) = 2.5A(n)[1 - A(n)]$$

has $a = 0.6$ as an attracting fixed point. Thus, the set $S = \{0.6\}$, consisting of this one value, is an attractor.

In fact, the set of **all** attracting fixed points is an attractor.

Example 4.26

The dynamical system

$$A(n+1) = 1.25A(n) - A^3(n)$$

has $a = 0.5$ and $a = -0.5$ as its two attracting fixed points. Thus, an attractor consists of the two numbers, $S = \{-0.5, 0.5\}$.

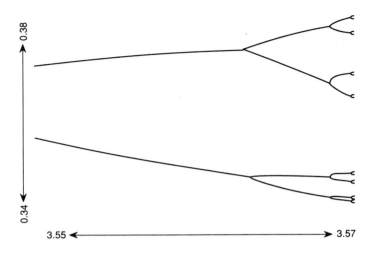

Fig. 47. Magnification of bifurcation diagram for the dynamical system $A(n+1) = bA(n) - bA^2(n)$. The two curves coming in from the left correspond to two points of an 8-cycle. The horizontal axis is $3.55 \leq b \leq 3.57$ and vertical axis is $0.34 \leq a \leq 0.38$.

Example 4.27

The dynamical system

$$A(n+1) = 3.2A(n)[1 - A(n)]$$

has an attracting 2-cycle consisting of the numbers $a = 1.16$ and $b = 0.746$. Thus, the set $S = \{1.16, 0.746\}$ is an attractor.

Example 4.28

The dynamical system

$$A(n+1) = 3.58A(n)[1 - A(n)]$$

has the four intervals of Figure 48 (b) as an attractor. (Actually, the attractor S for this equation consists of a subset of these four intervals, but we will ignore this problem.)

In Figure 49 is a bifurcation diagram for the dynamical system

$$A(n+1) = rA(n)[1 - A(n)], \quad \text{for} \quad 2.5 < r < 4.$$

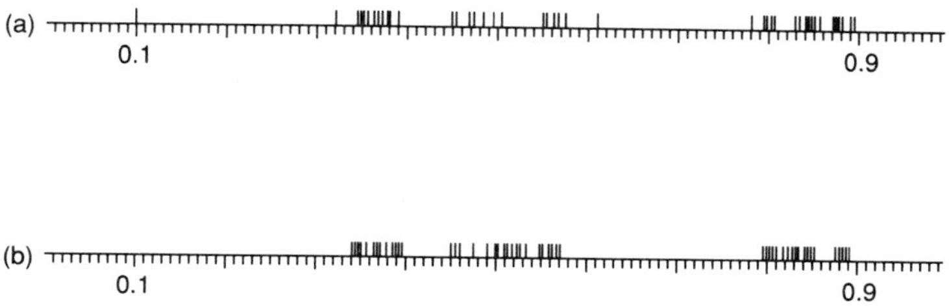

Fig. 48. (a) Plots of $A(0)$ through $A(100)$ above the axis and (b) plots is $A(101)$ through $A(200)$ for the dynamical system $A(n+1) = bA(n) - bA^2(n)$.

Draw a vertical line over some value of r. The points at which that line intersect the points of this graph form the attractor for that value of r. Notice that the vertical line over a value between 2.5 and 3 intersects this graph at one point, the attracting fixed point.

Definition 4.29

*A dynamical system is said to be **transitive** if, when a_0 is close to some point in an attractor S, then for every point s in the attractor there is a subsequence $A(k_j)$ of the $A(k)$ values that converge to s, that is,*

$$\lim_{k_j \to \infty} A(k_j) = s.$$

Essentially, a dynamical system is transitive if, when a_0 is 'close' to some value of S, the $A(k)$ values get 'close' to every point in S.

In Example 4.25, the attractor is the attracting fixed point, $S = \{0.6\}$. Since, when a_0 is close to 0.6, $A(k)$ gets closer to 0.6, it follows that the dynamical system

$$A(n+1) = 2.5A(n)[1 - A(n)]$$

is transitive.

In Example 4.26, the dynamical system

$$A(n+1) = 1.25A(n) - A^3(n)$$

has the attractor $S = \{-0.5, 0.5\}$, where each of these numbers is an attracting fixed point. If a_0 is close to 0.5, then $A(k)$ goes to 0.5, so $A(k)$ is **never** close to -0.5 for any value of k. This dynamical system is **not transitive**.

In Example 4.27 we saw that the attractor S consisted of an attracting 2-cycle. We know that, for even values of k, $A(k)$ gets close to one point of the 2-cycle, and for odd values of k, it gets close to the other point of

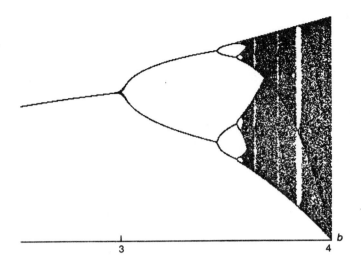

Fig. 49. Diagram of attractors for each value of b ($2.5 \le b \le 4$) for the dynamical system $A(n+1) = bA(n) - bA^2(n)$. The horizontal axis is $2.5 \le b \le 4$ and vertical axis is $0 \le a \le 1$.

the 2-cycle. Thus, if you pick any point in the attractor S, some $A(k)$ value (even or odd k) will be close to that point. This dynamical system is transitive.

In Example 4.28, the attractor S consists of (a subset of) the four intervals of Figure 48. No matter what value you pick for a_0 (near the attractor S), it can be shown that $A(k)$ values will be 'close' to every point in the four intervals. So this dynamical system is transitive.

In other words, a dynamical system is **transitive** if every solution 'gets close to' every point in the attractor. Pick any place in the attractor that you want to be and at some point in time, k, you will be there (almost). Thus, pick any point in the four intervals of the last example. You can predict that your solution $A(k)$ will be close to that point, although you cannot predict when.

Definition 4.30

*A dynamical system has **sensitive dependence on the initial values** if, whenever you take two initial values, a_0 and b_0, which are close together, then $A(k)$ and $B(k)$ eventually get further apart. To be more precise, there exists a number ϵ such that, whenever $0 < |a_0 - b_0| < \epsilon$, then there exists a value K such that $|A(K) - B(K)| > \epsilon$.*

Even though $A(k)$ and $B(k)$ get further than ϵ from each other, at a later point in time they may be less than ϵ apart (only to get further apart again).

For the dynamical system

$$A(n+1) = 2.5A(n)[1 - A(n)]$$

of Example 4.25, take two initial values, a_0 and b_0, close to each other (and also close to the attracting fixed point, $a = 0.6$). Since both $A(k)$ and $B(k)$ get close to 0.6, they must get close to each other. Thus, this dynamical system **does not have sensitive dependence on the initial values**.

Since the fixed points of Example 4.26 and the 2-cycle of Example 4.27 are attracting, for the same reason as in the above example, those dynamical systems do not have sensitive dependence on the initial values.

Example 4.31

Consider the dynamical system

$$A(n+1) = 2A(n).$$

A solution is $A(k) = 2^k a_0$. Given another initial value close to a_0, say b_0, the solution is $B(k) = 2^k b_0$. Thus,

$$|A(k) - B(k)| = |2^k a_0 - 2^k b_0| = 2^k |a_0 - b_0| \to \infty$$

no matter how close the initial values a_0 and b_0 are to each other. Thus, this system has sensitive dependence on the initial values. But notice that it does not have an attractor S.

It can be shown that the dynamical system

$$A(n+1) = 3.58A(n)[1 - A(n)]$$

of Example 4.28 has sensitive dependence on the initial values. In table 1 are two solutions in which the initial values are close together (within 0.001). Notice that the corresponding $A(k)$ and $B(k)$ values remain in the same intervals (of the four intervals of Figure 48), but they do not get closer to each other. They remain 'far' apart (over 0.1 when $k = 45$), considering they both have to be in the same intervals.

This means that if we are modeling a population with $r = 3.58$, and we measure $a_0 = 0.2$, whereas the actual value is $b_0 = 0.2001$, then our predictions $A(k)$ will not accurately describe the real behavior of the population $B(k)$.

Table 3. Selected values for the dynamical system $A(n+1) = 3.58A(n)[1 - A(n)]$ for two initial values.

$A(0)$	$=$	0.2	$B(0)$	$=$	0.2001
$A(1)$	$=$	0.5728	$B(1)$	$=$	0.5730148
$A(2)$	$=$	0.8760266	$B(2)$	$=$	0.8579145
$A(3)$	$=$	0.3888024	$B(3)$	$=$	0.3891041
$A(4)$	$=$	0.8507335	$B(4)$	$=$	0.8509735
$A(5)$	$=$	0.4546099	$B(5)$	$=$	0.4540071
$A(15)$	$=$	0.3721781	$B(15)$	$=$	0.3739662
$A(30)$	$=$	0.8917337	$B(30)$	$=$	0.888388
$A(45)$	$=$	0.4570562	$B(45)$	$=$	0.5735197
$A(60)$	$=$	0.7996981	$B(60)$	$=$	0.8417188
$A(75)$	$=$	0.3774491	$B(75)$	$=$	0.3847466
$A(90)$	$=$	0.8788545	$B(90)$	$=$	0.8878317

Definition 4.32

Suppose a dynamical system (1) is transitive on its attractor S, (2) has sensitive dependence of initial values, and (3) has repelling cycles that are 'close' to the attractor S. Then this dynamical system exhibits **chaos**.

We know that the dynamical system

$$A(n + 1) = 3.58A(n)[1 - A(n)]$$

of Example 4.28 is transitive and has sensitive dependence on its initial data. We also know that there is a repelling 2-cycle, since $r = 3.58 > 3.45$. There is also a repelling 4-cycle, since $r = 3.58 > 3.54$. In fact, since $3.58 > c_n$, there is a repelling 2^n-cycle for every value of n. These cycles 'fill up' our attractor of four intervals. Thus, this dynamical system exhibits **chaos**.

It can be shown that the dynamical system (8) exhibits chaos for every value of r such that $3.57 < r \leq 4$. Even though we have chaos for $r > 3.57$, the behavior of $A(k)$ can be quite different for different values of r. The complete behavior of equation (8) for $3.57 < r < 4$ is still unknown.

Intuitively, a dynamical system exhibits **chaos** if in one sense there is **unpredictability** (sensitive dependence on initial values says we can't make precise predictions), but in another sense there is **predictability** (transitivity says we will be at a point, we just don't know when). We also have **order out of chaos** in the sense that we have lots of cycles (nice solutions that repeat every 2^n time periods).

What this seems to imply is that for **some** real world situations (such as the study of weather, where chaos was first discovered), we are helpless in attempting to predict the future. No matter how much we know about the world, we cannot predict when things will happen (sensitive dependence), but we can predict that certain things will happen at some point in time (transitivity).

As a word of encouragement, the concept of chaos is new and is not completely understood by the mathematicians and scientists working in this field. The simple nonlinear dynamical system

$$A(n+1) = rA(n)[1 - A(n)],$$

whose cobweb is given by a **parabola**, is not completely understood for all values of r. In fact, there is still some disagreement as to what the precise definition of chaos should be, so you should not be discouraged if you didn't completely understand this section.

Hopefully, you have a feel for what mathematicians do for a living. In the case of this section, we have seen that mathematicians cannot completely describe the behavior of the solutions to a simple model of population growth. Therefore, there is much work to be done if we are to be able to study more complex and realistic models of the world.

Higher order linear dynamical systems

5.1 An introduction to second order linear equations

In Example 2.43, we considered a dynamical system that models the amount of pollution in two of the Great Lakes. Specifically, letting $A(n)$ and $B(n)$ be the amount of pollution in Lake Erie and Lake Ontario, respectively, in year n, we developed the equations

$$A(n + 1) = 0.62A(n) \tag{1}$$

and

$$B(n + 1) = 0.87B(n) + 0.38A(n). \tag{2}$$

The method we used to solve this system of equations was to find that $A(k) = c\,(0.62)^k$, and then to substitute that into the second equation giving the nonhomogeneous equation

$$B(n + 1) = 0.87B(n) + c\,(0.38)\,(0.62)^n,$$

whose solution is of the form

$$B(k) = c_1\,(0.87)^k + c_2\,(0.62)^k.$$

An alternate approach is to solve for $A(n)$ in equation (2), giving

$$A(n) = \frac{B(n + 1)}{0.38} - \frac{0.87B(n)}{0.38}.$$

Substituting this into equation (1) gives

$$\frac{B(n + 2)}{0.38} - \frac{0.87B(n + 1)}{0.38} = 0.62 \left(\frac{B(n + 1)}{0.38} - \frac{0.87B(n)}{0.38} \right).$$

Simplification gives the second order linear dynamical system

$$B(n + 2) = (0.87 + 0.62)B(n + 1) - (0.87)(0.62)B(n).$$

The solution still must be of the form

$$B(k) = c_1\,(0.87)^k + c_2\,(0.62)^k.$$

Observe that the numbers 0.87 and 0.62 are roots of the equation

$$x^2 = (0.87 + 0.62)x - (0.87)(0.62).$$

This should lead us to the idea that the general solution to a second order linear dynamical system

$$A(n + 2) = a\, A(n + 1) + b\, A(n)$$

might be of the form

$$A(k) = c_1\, r^k + c_2\, s^k$$

for some constants r and s, where c_1 and c_2 depend on the initial values $A(0)$ and $A(1)$.

Example 5.1

Let's see if the solution to the dynamical system,

$$A(n + 2) = -\tfrac{7}{2}A(n + 1) + 2A(n)$$

is of the form

$$A(k) = c_1\, r^k + c_2\, s^k.$$

Substituting our guess at a solution into the dynamical system gives

$$c_1\, r^{n+2} + c_2\, s^{n+2} = -\tfrac{7}{2}(c_1\, r^{n+1} + c_2\, s^{n+1}) + 2\,(c_1\, r^n + c_2\, s^n).$$

Bringing all terms to the left, collecting terms involving r and terms involving s, and factoring gives

$$c_1\, r^n(r^2 + \tfrac{7}{2}r - 2) + c_2\, s^n(s^2 + \tfrac{7}{2}s - 2) = 0.$$

We have equality if r and s are both roots of the equation

$$x^2 + \tfrac{7}{2}x - 2 = 0.$$

Since the two roots of this quadratic are 0.5 and -4, we will let $r = 0.5$ and $s = -4$ giving the general solution as

$$A(k) = c_1\, (0.5)^k + c_2\, (-4)^k.$$

Let's find the particular solution when $A(0) = 3$ and $A(1) = -3$. In this case, we must solve the system of equations

$$A(0) = c_1\, (0.5)^0 + c_2\, (-4)^0 = c_1 + c_2 = 3$$

and

$$A(1) = c_1\, (0.5)^1 + c_2\, (-4)^1 = 0.5c_1 - 4c_2 = -3.$$

In this case, $c_1 = 2$ and $c_2 = 1$, and the particular solution is

$$A(k) = 2\, (0.5)^k + (-4)^k.$$

Let's now develop a method for finding both general and particular solutions to arbitrary second order linear dynamical systems.

**Definition
5.2**

The **characteristic equation** *for the second order linear dynamical system*

$$A(n+2) = a\,A(n+1) + b\,A(n)$$

is

$$x^2 = a\,x + b.$$

As we saw in the discussion of the Great Lakes and in Example 5.1, the roots of the characteristic equation help determine the general solution to a second order linear dynamical system.

**Theorem
5.3**

Consider the second order dynamical system

$$A(n+2) = aA(n+1) + bA(n).$$

Suppose that the roots of the corresponding characteristic equation

$$x^2 - ax - b = 0$$

are $x = r$ and $x = s$, where $r \neq s$. Then the general solution of the second order dynamical system is

$$A(k) = c_1\,r^k + c_2\,s^k.$$

The numbers c_1 and c_2 depend on the initial values. In particular, if we are given $A(0)$ and $A(1)$ then

$$c_1 = \frac{A(1) - sA(0)}{r - s} \quad and \quad c_2 = \frac{A(1) - rA(0)}{s - r}.$$

Proof: Consider the dynamical system

$$A(n+2) = a\,A(n+1) + bA(n),$$

with characteristic equation

$$x^2 = ax + b.$$

Suppose that r and s are two distinct roots of this equation, that is,

$$r^2 = ar + b \quad and \quad s^2 = as + b.$$

We need to show that
$$A(k) = c_1\,r^k + c_2\,s^k$$

is a solution to the dynamical system. In this case,

$$A(n + 1) = c_1\, r^{n+1} + c_2\, s^{n+1} \quad \text{and} \quad A(n + 2) = c_1\, r^{n+2} + c_2\, s^{n+2}.$$

Substitution into the dynamical system gives

$$c_1\, r^{n+2} + c_2\, s^{n+2} = a\,(c_1\, r^{n+1} + c_2\, s^{n+1}) + b\,(c_1\, r^n + c_2\, s^n).$$

If this equation is balanced, then our formula for $A(k)$ is a solution.

Bring all the terms involving r to the left of the equation and all the terms involving s to the right. This gives

$$c_1\, r^{n+2} - a\, c_1\, r^{n+1} - b\, c_1\, r^n = -c_2\, s^{n+2} + a\, c_2\, s^{n+1} + b\, c_2\, s^n.$$

Factoring $c_1 r^n$ out of the left side and $-c_2\, s^n$ out of the right side, gives

$$c_1\, r^n (r^2 - ar - b) = -c_2\, s^n (s^2 - as - b).$$

Our assumption that r and s were roots of the characteristic equation gives

$$c_1\, r^n\,(0) = -c\, s^n\,(0), \quad \text{or} \quad 0 = 0.$$

Thus,

$$A(k) = c_1\, r^k + c_2\, s^k$$

is a solution to the dynamical system.

If we are given $A(0)$ and $A(1)$, then solving the two equations

$$A(0) = c_1\, r^0 + c_2\, s^0 = c_1 + c_2 \quad \text{and} \quad A(1) = c_1\, r + c_2\, s$$

for the two unknowns c_1 and c_2 gives

$$c_1 = \frac{A(1) - sA(0)}{r - s} \quad \text{and} \quad c_2 = \frac{A(1) - rA(0)}{s - r}.$$

For any given $A(0)$ and $A(1)$, a particular solution to the dynamical system satisfying this set of initial values is given by this choice of c_1 and c_2. Also, given $A(0)$ and $A(1)$, it is clear that $A(2)$, $A(3)$, ..., are uniquely determined, so there can be only one particular solution, and this choice of c_1 and c_2 must be it. Since

$$A(k) = c_1\, r^k + c_2\, s^k$$

gives every particular solution for appropriate choices of c_1 and c_2, it must be the general solution, and the proof is complete.

Remark: The problem of unique solutions is easy for discrete dynamical systems, but is nontrivial for differential equations.

Example 5.4

Consider the second order dynamical system

$$A(n + 2) = -A(n + 1) + 6A(n),$$

with $A(0) = 7$ and $A(1) = -6$. The characteristic equation is

$$x^2 = -x + 6.$$

Bringing all the terms to the left and factoring gives

$$x^2 + x - 6 = (x + 3)(x - 2) = 0,$$

so the roots are $x = 2$ and $x = -3$. The general solution is then

$$A(k) = c_1 \, 2^k + c_2 \, (-3)^k.$$

Using the formulas in Theorem 5.3 with $r = 2$ and $s = -3$, we again find that

$$c_1 = \frac{-6 - (-3)7}{2 - (-3)} = 3 \quad \text{and} \quad c_2 = \frac{-6 - (2)7}{-3 - 2} = 4,$$

and so the particular solution is

$$A(k) = 3 \, (2)^k + 4 \, (-3)^k.$$

Instead of using the above formulas, let's solve for c_1 and c_2 using the initial conditions. We get the two equations

$$A(0) = c_1 \, 2^0 + c_2 \, (-3)^0 = c_1 + c_2 = 7 \text{ and } A(1) = 2c_1 - 3c_2 = -6.$$

From the first equation, $c_1 = 7 - c_2$. Substitution into the second equation gives $2(7 - c_2) - 3c_2 = -6$, or, after simplifying, $c_2 = 4$. It follows that $c_1 = 7 - c_2 = 3$, giving the same answers as before.

Example 5.5

Consider the second order dynamical system

$$A(n + 2) = 0.5A(n + 1) + 0.5A(n).$$

The characteristic equation is, after bringing all the terms to the left,

$$x^2 - 0.5x - 0.5 = (x + 0.5)(x - 1) = 0,$$

so the roots are $x = 1$ and $x = -1/2$. Since $1^k = 1$, the general solution is then

$$A(k) = c_1 + c_2(-\tfrac{1}{2})^k.$$

Suppose we are given that $A(0) = 8$ and $A(1) = -1$. From the above formulas with $r = 1$ and $s = -1/2$, we get $c_1 = 2$ and $c_2 = 6$. Therefore, the particular solution is

$$A(k) = 2 + 6(-\tfrac{1}{2})^k.$$

Observe that, as k goes to infinity, $A(k)$ goes to 2.

Let's see how a second order dynamical system might come up in 'real life'. Actually, this is an interesting but artificial application. More realistic applications will be considered in later sections.

Consider a child who has a row of n blocks. The child starts at the left of the row and picks up one or two blocks and puts them into a toy box. The child continues picking up one or two blocks at a time until all the blocks have been picked up. How many ways can the child pick up the n blocks?

If the child has three blocks, there are three ways. Way 1 is to pick up the first block and then the next two, denoted $(1, 2)$; way 2 is to pick up the first two and then the third, denoted $(2, 1)$; and way 3 is to pick up the first then the second then the third, denoted $(1, 1, 1)$. If $n = 4$ then there are five ways, denoted $(1, 1, 1, 1)$, $(1, 1, 2)$, $(1, 2, 1)$, $(2, 1, 1)$, and $(2, 2)$.

Let $A(n)$ be the number of ways to pick up n blocks, one or two at a time. Note that $A(1) = 1$, $A(2) = 2$, $A(3) = 3$, and $A(4) = 5$. We see for the numbers computed that

$$A(3) = A(1) + A(2) \quad \text{and} \quad A(4) = A(2) + A(3).$$

We then might think that

$$A(n + 2) = A(n) + A(n + 1), \quad \text{for } n = 1, 2, \ldots. \tag{3}$$

Let us first justify our answer for $n = 5$, that is, $A(5) = 8$. We consider two cases. The first case is that the child picks up one block initially, denoted $(1, a)$. The second case is that the child picks up two blocks initially, denoted $(2, b)$.

To count the number of ways to accomplish the first case, that is, to pick up a total of five blocks and pick up one block first, we consider two stages. The first stage is to pick up the first block which can be done one way. The second stage is to pick up the remaining four blocks which can be done in $A(4) = 5$ ways. Thus, the first case can be done in $(1)A(4) = A(4) = 5$ ways. These ways are $(1,\mathbf{1,1,1,1})$, $(1,\mathbf{1,1,2})$, $(1,\mathbf{1,2,1})$, $(1,\mathbf{2,1,1})$, and $(1,\mathbf{2,2})$. Note that the numbers in boldface are the five ways listed above that four blocks can be picked up.

To count the number of ways to accomplish the second case, that is, to pick up a total of five blocks and pick up two blocks first, we also consider two stages. The first stage is to pick up the first two blocks which can be done one way. The second stage is to pick up the remaining three blocks which can be done in $A(3) = 3$ ways. Thus, the second case can be done in $(1)A(3) = A(3) = 3$ ways. These three ways are $(2,\mathbf{1},2)$, $(2,\mathbf{2},1)$, and $(2,\mathbf{1},1,1)$.

Thus, since every way of picking up five blocks must be one of these ways, we have

$$A(5) = A(4) + A(3).$$

Now we see the general argument. Suppose there are $n + 2$ blocks to pick up. We have two cases. The first case is that the child picks up one block first and then picks up the remaining $n + 1$ blocks. Since there are $A(n + 1)$ ways to pick up the $n + 1$ remaining blocks, there are $A(n + 1)$ ways to pick up $n+2$ blocks by picking up one block first. The second case is that the child picks up two blocks first and then picks up the remaining n blocks. There are $A(n)$ ways to do this.

Thus the $A(n + 2)$ ways of picking up $n + 2$ blocks must be one of the $A(n+1)$ ways in the first case or one of the $A(n)$ ways in the second case, giving the second order linear dynamical system (3),

$$A(n + 2) = A(n + 1) + A(n).$$

The numbers $A(1)$, $A(2)$, ... are 1, 2, 3, 5, 8, 13, ... This sequence of numbers is called a Fibonacci sequence and dynamical system (3) is called a Fibonacci relation. These numbers arise both in applied mathematics and in biology.

We now attempt to find the general solution to the Fibonacci relation. Our first step is to find the roots of the characteristic equation

$$x^2 = x + 1.$$

From the quadratic formula, we obtain the roots

$$r = \frac{1 + \sqrt{5}}{2} \quad \text{and} \quad s = \frac{1 - \sqrt{5}}{2}.$$

Thus the general solution to the above second order dynamical system is

$$A(k) = c_1 \left(\frac{1 + \sqrt{5}}{2}\right)^k + c_2 \left(\frac{1 - \sqrt{5}}{2}\right)^k.$$

This is amazing. The **integer** $A(k)$, which gives the number of ways to do something (and also forms a Fibonacci sequence), is given in terms of the irrational number $\sqrt{5}$.

We could solve for c_1 and c_2 by using the initial conditions that $A(1) = 1$ and $A(2) = 2$. If we say that there is 1 way of picking up 0 toys (which is not to pick them up), then we can use $A(0) = 1$ and $A(1) = 1$ as our initial values. This simplifies our algebra. Note that, using this convention, we do get $A(2) = A(1) + A(0)$. Using these initial conditions gives, after a little algebra,

$$c_1 = 0.5 + 0.1\sqrt{5} \quad \text{and} \quad c_2 = 0.5 - 0.1\sqrt{5}.$$

The particular solution, which gives the Fibonacci numbers, is

$$A(k) = (0.5 + 0.1\sqrt{5}) \left(\frac{1 + \sqrt{5}}{2}\right)^k + (0.5 - 0.1\sqrt{5}) \left(\frac{1 - \sqrt{5}}{2}\right)^k.$$

This is quite a complicated formula for what appears to be a simple sequence of integers.

Let's consider an example that appears to be even more amazing.

Example 5.6

Find the particular solution to the dynamical system

$$A(n + 2) = 2A(n + 1) - 5A(n),$$

with $A(0) = 2$ and $A(1) = 6$. Note that since the initial values are integers, $A(k)$ must be an integer for every value of k.

The characteristic equation is

$$x^2 - 2x + 5 = 0.$$

From the quadratic formula, we get that the two roots are

$$x = \frac{2 \pm \sqrt{4 - 20}}{2} = 1 \pm 2\sqrt{-1} = 1 \pm 2i,$$

where $i = \sqrt{-1}$. Thus, the general solution is

$$A(k) = c_1 (1 + 2i)^k + c_2 (1 - 2i)^k.$$

We are using complex numbers to compute the real solution to the above dynamical system.

To find the particular solution, we have

$$c_1 = \frac{A(1) - sA(0)}{r - s} = \frac{6 - (1 - 2i)2}{1 + 2i - (1 - 2i)} = \frac{4 + 4i}{4i}.$$

Rationalizing the denominator by multiplying numerator and denominator by $i = \sqrt{-1}$ gives

$$c_1 = \frac{4i - 4}{-4} = 1 - i.$$

Similarly, $c_2 = 1 + i$, and the particular solution is

$$A(k) = (1 - i)(1 + 2i)^k + (1 + i)(1 - 2i)^k.$$

It seems amazing that the solution which gives the integers, $A(0) = 2$, $A(1) = 6$, $A(2) = 2$, $A(3) = -24$, $A(4) = -58$, $A(5) = 4$, ..., involves complex numbers. Later, we will see real applications that involve complex numbers.

5.1.1 Problems

1. For each of the following dynamical systems, find the characteristic equation, find the roots of the characteristic equation, give the general solution of the dynamical system, and give the particular solution of the dynamical system for the given values of $A(0)$ and $A(1)$.

(a) $A(n + 2) = A(n + 1) + 2A(n)$, with $A(0) = 3$ and $A(1) = 3$.

(b) $A(n + 2) = 2A(n + 1) + A(n)$, with $A(0) = 2$ and $A(1) = 8$.

(c) $A(n + 2) = -2A(n + 1) + 15A(n)$, with $A(0) = 1$ and $A(1) = 11$.

(d) $A(n + 2) = -6A(n + 1) - 16A(n)$, with $A(0) = 2$ and $A(1) = 4$.

(e) $A(n + 2) = 4A(n + 1) - 5A(n)$, with $A(0) = 2$ and $A(1) = 4$.

(f) $A(n + 2) = -4A(n + 1) - 13A(n)$, with $A(0) = 6$ and $A(1) = -6$.

2. Suppose you have a pile of bubblegum which cost 1 cent each, a pile of licorice sticks which cost 1 cent each, and a pile of mints which cost 2 cents each. You pick n cents worth of candy, one piece at a time. Let $A(n)$ be the number of ways this can be done. For example, $A(1) = 2$ (bubblegum or licorice, denoted b and l), and $A(2) = 5$ denoted (b, b), (b, l), (l, b), (l, l), and (m). Notice that the order the candy is chosen is important.

(a) Find a dynamical system to model this problem.

(b) Find the general solution to this dynamical system.

(c) Using $A(0) = 1$ and $A(1) = 2$, find the particular solution to this dynamical system.

3. Suppose that the general solution to a dynamical system is

$$A(k) = c_1\, r^k + c_2\, s^k,$$

where $r \neq s$.

(a) Suppose that $A(1)$ and $A(2)$ are given. Find a formula for c_1 and c_2 in terms of $A(1)$ and $A(2)$.

(b) Suppose that $A(0)$ and $A(N)$ are given, where N is a given integer greater than 1. Find a formula for c_1 and c_2 in terms of $A(0)$ and $A(N)$.

5.2 Multiple roots

Suppose we have a car that gets 20 miles per gallon of gas and that we start driving with 15 gallons. Let $A(n)$ be the amount of gas we have left after driving n miles. Observe that $A(0) = 15$. Since we use 0.05 gallons of gas in driving 1 mile, we have

$$A(n + 1) = A(n) - 0.05,$$

that is, if we drive one more mile, we have 0.05 fewer gallons of gas. We know that the particular solution to this first order affine dynamical system is

$$A(k) = 15 - 0.05k.$$

Notice that $A(k)$ depends linearly on k, that is, if we plotted the points $(k, A(k))$, they would lie on a straight line.

More generally, the dynamical system that describes the amount of gas left in a car after going n miles is

$$A(n + 1) = A(n) - c,$$

where c is the amount of gas used in going 1 mile. The solution is

$$A(k) = c_1 + c_2\, k,$$

where c_1 depends on the amount of gas we start with and $c_2 = -c$.

Another way to approach this problem is to write the dynamical system

$$A(n + 2) - A(n + 1) = A(n + 1) - A(n).$$

This system says that the gas used in going any one mile (from $n + 1$ to $n + 2$ miles) is the same as the gas used in going any other mile (from n to $n + 1$ miles). Simplification gives

$$A(n + 2) = 2A(n + 1) - A(n).$$

The solution must still be

$$A(k) = c_1 + c_2 k$$

since we already know that this describes the amount of gas left after going k miles.

The characteristic equation for this second order dynamical system is

$$x^2 = 2x - 1, \quad \text{or} \quad (x - 1)^2 = 0.$$

Thus, $x = 1$ is a double root. We thus see that when $x = 1$ is a double root, the solution is of the form

$$A(k) = c_1 + c_2\, k.$$

Let's check that $A(k) = c_1 + c_2\, k$ is a solution to the dynamical system

$$A(n + 2) = 2A(n + 1) - A(n)$$

for every choice of c_1 and c_2. Substitution of $A(n + 2) = c_1 + c_2\,(n + 2)$, $A(n + 1) = c_1 + c_2\,(n + 1)$, and $A(n) = c_1 + c_2\, n$ gives

$$c_1 + c_2\,(n + 2) = 2\,[c_1 + c_2\,(n + 1)] - (c_1 + c_2\, n).$$

All the terms cancel and we get equality, so this is a solution. If we are given $A(0)$ and $A(1)$, then solving the equations

$$A(0) = c_1 + c_2\,(0) \quad \text{and} \quad A(1) = c_1 + c_2$$

gives $c_1 = A(0)$ and $c_2 = A(1) - A(0)$ (the amount of gas used in going 1 mile) so the particular solution is

$$A(k) = A(0) + [A(1) - A(0)]k.$$

We thus see that if $x = 1$ is a double root, that is, when the dynamical system is

$$A(n + 2) = 2A(n + 1) - A(n),$$

then the general solution is

$$A(k) = c_1 + c_2\, k.$$

What happens if $x = r$ is a double root of the characteristic equation, that is, when the characteristic equation is

$$(x - r)^2 = 0 \quad \text{or} \quad x^2 = 2\, r\, x - r^2?$$

In this case, the dynamical system is

$$A(n + 2) = 2r\, A(n + 1) - r^2\, A(n),$$

where r is a fixed constant. There is a clever trick for solving this dynamical system and that is to substitute

$$A(n) = r^n\, B(n)$$

into the dynamical system. This substitution gives

$$r^{n+2}\, B(n + 2) = 2r\, [r^{n+1}\, B(n + 1)] - r^2\, [r^n\, B(n)],$$

or, after dividing both sides by r^{n+2},

$$B(n + 2) = 2\, B(n + 1) - B(n).$$

From the above discussion, we know that the general solution to this dynamical system is

$$B(k) = c_1 + c_2\, k.$$

By substitution, it follows that

$$A(k) = r^k\, B(k) = r^k\, (c_1 + c_2\, k)$$

is the general solution to the original dynamical system. We summarize this result with the following theorem.

Theorem 5.7

Consider the dynamical system

$$A(n + 2) = 2\, r\, A(n + 1) - r^2\, A(n)$$

which has $x = r$ as a double root of the corresponding characteristic equation. Then the general solution is

$$A(k) = (c_1 + c_2\, k)r^k.$$

If $A(0)$ and $A(1)$ are known, then the particular solution is given when

$$c_1 = A(0) \quad \text{and} \quad c_2 = \frac{A(1) - r A(0)}{r}.$$

Example 5.8

Find the particular solution to the dynamical system

$$A(n + 2) = 4A(n + 1) - 4A(n),$$

given that $A(0) = 3$ and $A(1) = 4$. Factoring the characteristic equation

$$x^2 = 4x - 4$$

gives

$$(x - 2)^2 = 0,$$

so that $x = 2$ is a double root of the equation. Thus, the general solution is of the form

$$A(k) = (c_1 + c_2\, k)\, 2^k.$$

The initial values give $c_1 = 3$ and $c_2 = -1$, so the particular solution is

$$A(k) = (3 - k)\, 2^k.$$

5.2.1 Problems

1. Find the particular solution to each of the following dynamical systems.

   (a) $A(n + 2) = 2A(n + 1) - A(n)$, with $A(0) = 5$ and $A(1) = 4$.

   (b) $A(n + 2) = -2A(n + 1) - A(n)$, with $A(0) = 2$ and $A(1) = 5$.

   (c) $A(n + 2) = -2A(n + 1) - 2A(n)$, with $A(0) = 1$ and $A(1) = 0$.

   (d) $A(n + 2) = -A(n + 1) - 0.25A(n)$, with $A(0) = 1$ and $A(1) = 1$.

2. Suppose that the general solution to a dynamical system is

$$A(k) = (c_1 + c_2\, k)\, r^k.$$

   (a) Suppose that $A(1)$ and $A(2)$ are given. Find a formula for c_1 and c_2 in terms of $A(1)$ and $A(2)$.

   (b) Suppose that $A(0)$ and $A(N)$ are given, where N is a given integer greater than 1. Find a formula for c_1 and c_2 in terms of $A(0)$ and $A(N)$.

5.3 The gambler's ruin

We wish to consider a problem which is of interest to anyone who is planning to visit Las Vegas, Atlantic City, or Monte Carlo to gamble, namely the **gambler's ruin**.

Being a sensible person, you set aside a certain amount of money which you can afford to lose. Once this money is gone, you will quit gambling. Some people continue gambling until their money is gone. Being more intelligent than that, you set a goal for yourself of, say, N dollars. If you reach this total, you will take your winnings and go home.

You have decided always to bet **1 dollar** on the same game, in which your probability of winning a dollar is p while the probability of losing your dollar is $1 - p = q$. The question is, what is your probability of quitting a winner, that is, quitting with a total of N? Conversely, what is your probability of being ruined, that is, of losing all your money?

Suppose you start the above game with n dollars, where $0 \leq n \leq N$. The question is, 'what is the probability that you will eventually go broke under the conditions just described, **given** that you presently have n dollars?' We will denote the answer to this question by $P(n)$.

Suppose the game is the tossing of a fair coin. For each toss, the bet is 1 dollar, that is, you win 1 dollar if heads comes up and you lose 1 dollar if tails comes up. You will quit the game if you have a total of either 0 or 3 dollars. What is your probability of quitting broke if you started with 0, 1, 2, or 3 dollars?

Let $P(n)$ be the probability you will eventually go broke given that you presently have n dollars. Clearly $P(0) = 1$ and $P(3) = 0$ since you quit when you have 0 or 3 dollars. What are $P(1)$ and $P(2)$?

To compute $P(1)$, you have to compute the probability of quitting a loser, given that you presently have 1 dollar? There are two cases: case 1 is that you lose your dollar on this flip and thus are ruined; and case 2 is that you win a dollar on this flip and then eventually lose all your money. Since one of these cases must occur, we will compute the probability of each case happening and then $P(1)$ must be the sum of these two probabilities, that is,

$$P(1) = P(\text{case } 1) + P(\text{case } 2).$$

In case 1 for $P(1)$, the probability that you lose your dollar is the probability that tails comes up, which is 0.5. You are then broke, so $P(\text{case } 1) = 0.5$.

To compute the probability of case 2 for $P(1)$ happening, we notice that two things must happen: first we must flip a coin and get heads, and second we must then **eventually** go broke. The probability that we flip heads is $P(H) = 0.5$. Since we have flipped heads, we have won 1 dollar and now have 2 dollars. Thus, the probability that we now eventually go broke is, by our notation, $P(2)$. The probability that both of these occur (flipping heads then going broke) is, by the multiplication principle (first introduced in Section 2.3), the product of each of these probabilities, that is,

$$P(\text{case } 2) = P(H)P(2) = 0.5P(2).$$

So by the addition principle,

$$P(1) = 0.5 + 0.5P(2). \tag{4}$$

To compute $P(2)$, we must again consider two cases. In this part, we are assuming we have 2 dollars and want to know the probability we will eventually go broke. Case 1 now is that we get heads and eventually go broke, while case 2 is that we get tails and eventually go broke.

In case 1, if we get heads, we win a dollar, and thus quit playing and cannot go broke. Thus the probability of flipping heads and going broke is 0, since we cannot flip heads and go broke. So $P(\text{case } 1) = 0$.

Case 2 for $P(2)$ is computed similarly to case 2 for $P(1)$ above, that is, we consider a two-stage event in which the first stage is that we flip tails T, and the second stage is that we eventually go broke. Again, the probability of the first stage is $P(T) = 0.5$. Since we have now lost 1 dollar and only have 1 dollar left, the probability of the second stage is the probability we eventually go broke given we presently have 1 dollar, $P(1)$. By the multiplication principle,

$$P(\text{case } 2) = 0.5P(1).$$

Now by the addition principle,

$$P(2) = P(\text{case } 1) + P(\text{case } 2) = 0 + 0.5P(1) = 0.5P(1). \tag{5}$$

We now have two equations involving $P(1)$ and $P(2)$. From equation (5), we can substitute $0.5P(1)$ into equation (4) for $P(2)$, giving

$$P(1) = 0.5 + 0.5(0.5P(1)), \quad \text{or} \quad P(1) = \tfrac{2}{3}.$$

Consequently,

$$P(2) = \tfrac{1}{3}.$$

This was relatively easy because our goal of $N = 3$ dollars was relatively low. But if we decide to quit with either 0 or 1000 dollars, we would have 999 equations to solve simultaneously. A simpler method is to use the theory of second order linear dynamical systems.

We now consider the general gambler's ruin, that is, when the probability we win a dollar is p, the probability we lose a dollar is $q = 1 - p$, and we quit when we have a total of 0 or N dollars. (We can assume we are flipping an unfair coin, in which the probability p of heads occurring is not necessarily one-half.)

Let $P(n)$ be the probability we will **eventually** quit with 0 dollars if we presently have n dollars. Then $P(0) = 1$ and $P(N) = 0$ are our two 'initial' values. Note that the initial conditions are a bit unusual. Usually, we are given $P(0)$ and $P(1)$. But we will soon see that this causes no additional problems.

Let's now try to compute $P(n + 1)$, that is, the probability that we eventually go broke given that we presently have $n+1$ dollars. We assume that $0 < n + 1 < N$, that is, $n = 0, 1, \ldots, N - 2$. There are two cases. Case 1 is the case in which we win a dollar on the next flip and eventually go broke, while case 2 is the case in which we lose a dollar on the next flip and eventually go broke. By the addition principle,

$$P(n + 1) = P(\text{case } 1) + P(\text{case } 2).$$

Let H be the event we win a dollar on our next flip and let T be the event we lose a dollar on our next flip.

Case 1 is a two-stage process. We are given that the probability of the first stage occurring is $P(H) = p$. Now that we have won a dollar, we have a total of $n + 2$ dollars, so the probability of the second stage is the probability we eventually go broke given that we have $n + 2$ dollars, that is, $P(n + 2)$. Thus, by the multiplication principle,

$$P(\text{case } 1) = pP(n + 2).$$

Case 2 is also a two-stage process. The probability of the first stage occurring is $P(T) = q$. Since we have now lost a dollar, the second stage is the event that we eventually go broke given that we have n dollars, $P(n)$. By the multiplication principle,

$$P(\text{case } 2) = qP(n).$$

By the addition principle,

$$P(n + 1) = pP(n + 2) + qP(n), \quad \text{for } n = 0, 1, \ldots, N - 2.$$

Rearranging and dividing by p gives

$$P(n + 2) = \tfrac{1}{p}P(n + 1) - \tfrac{q}{p}P(n).$$

The characteristic equation is

$$x^2 = \tfrac{1}{p}x - \tfrac{q}{p}.$$

The two roots are $x = 1$ and $x = q/p$. Note that if $p \neq q$ then we have two distinct roots and can use Theorem 5.3 to find a solution. But if $p = q = 1/2$, then we have a double root and we have to use Theorem 5.7 to find a solution.

Suppose $p \neq 0.5$, that is, $p \neq q$. Then $q/p \neq 1$ and we have two roots. For simplicity, let $q/p = r$. Thus

$$P(k) = c_1 (1)^k + c_2 r^k = c_1 + c_2 r^k.$$

Since

$$P(0) = c_1 + c_2 = 1 \quad \text{and} \quad P(N) = c_1 + c_2 r^N = 0,$$

we can solve these equations for c_1 and c_2, giving

$$c_2 = \frac{1}{1 - r^N} \quad \text{and} \quad c_1 = \frac{-r^N}{1 - r^N}.$$

Thus

$$P(k) = \frac{-r^N}{1 - r^N} + \frac{r^k}{1 - r^N} = \frac{r^k - r^N}{1 - r^N}.$$

For example, suppose you start with $k = 20$ dollars, the probability you will win a dollar is $p = 0.48$, the probability you lose a dollar is $q = 0.52$, and you will quit when you go broke or have a total of $N = 40$. Then $r = 0.52/0.48 = 1.083$, and the probability you will go broke is

$$P(20) = \frac{r^{20} - r^{40}}{1 - r^{40}} = 0.832.$$

Observe that, **on each flip**, your probability of losing a dollar is only slightly more than 0.5. Also observe that you are playing double or nothing, that is, since $N = 40$ and $n = 20$ you quit if you win or lose a net of 20 dollars. Intuition might suggest that your probability of going broke would be only slightly greater than 0.5. But instead, your probability of going broke is 0.832, while your probability of quitting a winner with a profit of 20 dollars is only $1 - 0.832 = 0.168$. This is not too good for you.

Let's now compute the formula for $P(k)$ under the condition that we are playing a fair game, that is, $p = q = 0.5$. In this case $q/p = 1$ and 1 is a double root. Thus

$$P(k) = (c_1 + c_2 k) 1^k = c_1 + c_2 k.$$

Since $P(0) = c_1 = 1$ and $P(N) = c_1 + Nc_2 = 0$, it follows that $c_1 = 1$, $c_2 = -1/N$, and

$$P(k) = 1 - \frac{k}{N} = \frac{N-k}{N}.$$

For example, suppose you flip a fair coin and with heads you win a dollar and with tails you lose a dollar. Thus $p = q = 0.5$. Suppose you start with $n = 20$ and quit when you are ruined or when you have $N = 40$. Then your probability of ruin is $P(20) = (40 - 20)/40 = 0.5$, a much better result then when $p = 0.48$.

Moral: Don't gamble when $p < 0.5$. In the above, we used the same amounts of money but the probabilities were even money $p = 0.5$, and slightly against us $p = 0.48$. A difference of 0.02 in a game wouldn't seem to make much difference, but in reality it changed our chances of being ruined from 0.5 to 0.832. If you try these computations for larger amounts of money the results are even more dramatic. If $k = 100$, $N = 200$, and $p = 0.5$, our chances of ruin are 0.5, while if $p = 0.48$, our chance of ruin is over 0.999.

The result is that the more you gamble (when the odds are against you), the more likely it is that you will be ruined. In fact if you must gamble, your best chance to double your money is to place all your money on one bet. If you win, quit. If you lose, don't say you weren't warned.

5.3.1 Problems

1. Suppose you are in a game in which the probability of winning any particular bet is 0.49, while the probability of losing is 0.51. You start with 50 dollars and will quit when you have 100 dollars. What is your probability of ruin,

   (a) if you make 1 dollar bets,

   (b) if you make 5 dollar bets (Hint: Let 5 dollars equal one unit. Thus, you begin with 10 units, and quit when you have 20 units.),

   (c) if you make 10 dollar bets,

   (d) if you make 25 dollar bets, and

   (e) if you make 50 dollar bets?

2. Suppose you are in a game in which the probability of winning any particular bet is 0.49, while the probability of losing is 0.51. You will quit when you have 100 dollars.

   (a) What amount of money k do you need to start with so that you have at least a 50 per cent chance of quitting a winner?

(b) Same question as part (a) except that the probability of winning any one bet is 0.48.

3. Suppose you are in a game in which, on each play, there is a probability of 0.1 that you will win 2 dollars, there is a probability of 0.3 that you will win 1 dollar, and there is a probability of 0.6 that you will lose 1 dollar. You will quit when you are broke or when you have at least N dollars.

   (a) Suppose you quit if you have 3 or more dollars. What is $P(0)$, $P(1)$, $P(2)$, $P(3)$, and $P(4)$, where $P(n)$ is the probability of eventually going broke if you presently have n dollars?

   (b) Suppose you will quit when you are broke or when you have at least N dollars. Write a third order dynamical system to model this situation. What are the three 'initial' values?

5.4 Sex-linked genes

As was discussed earlier, many inherited traits of individuals are determined by a pair of alleles. If one allele A is dominant, while another allele a is recessive, then an individual has the recessive trait only if the pair of alleles are both recessive, that is, (a, a). For certain traits, women have a pair of alleles, but men have only one allele, which they inherit from their mother. Such traits are called **sex-linked traits**. Therefore, if a man inherits an A-allele, he will have the dominant trait, but if he inherits an a-allele, he will have the recessive trait. Color blindness and hemophilia are two such traits. In these cases, the alleles which cause problems are recessive. In the following, we will show why it is much more common for a man to exhibit a sex-linked trait than a woman.

Consider a sex-linked trait (in which women have a pair of alleles, but men have a single allele). Suppose that a woman has the pair of alleles (A, a), and a man has the allele A. Thus, both the man and the woman exhibit the dominant trait. Suppose these two individuals have an offspring. If the child is a boy, he will inherit either the A- or a-allele from his mother. Thus the boy has a probability of 0.5 of inheriting the a-allele and thus having the recessive trait. But if the child is a girl, she will inherit the A-allele from her father, and either the A- or a-allele from her mother. Therefore, the girl will have either the pair of alleles (A, a) or (A, A), and so she is certain to exhibit the dominant trait.

To study this problem, we must keep the alleles of the males separate from the alleles of the females. Thus, we will let $p(n)$ and $q(n)$ represent the proportion of A-alleles and a-alleles among the women of generation n, respectively. Likewise, we will let $P(n)$ and $Q(n)$ represent the proportion of A-alleles and a-alleles among the men of generation n, respectively.

Let u, v, and w represent the proportion of dominant homozygotes, heterozygotes, and recessive homozygotes, respectively, among the population of women in generation $n + 1$. To be a dominant homozygote, a girl must inherit an A-allele from her mother and an A-allele from her father. To compute the probability of this happening, we consider a two-stage process. The first stage is to draw an A-allele from the population of women of generation n, and the probability of this happening is $p(n)$. The second stage is to draw an A-allele from the population of men of generation n, and the probability of this happening is $P(n)$. Thus, by the multiplication principle,

$$u = p(n)P(n).$$

To compute the probability that a woman is a heterozygote, we must consider two cases. The first case is that she inherits an A-allele from her mother and an a-allele from her father. The probability of this happening is $p(n)Q(n)$. The second case is that she inherits an a-allele from her mother and an A-allele from her father, which by the multiplication principle is $q(n)P(n)$. Adding the probabilities of these two cases, we find that the probability a woman is a heterozygote is

$$v = p(n)Q(n) + P(n)q(n).$$

Similarly, the probability that a woman is a recessive homozygote is

$$w = q(n)Q(n).$$

Suppose the total number of women in generation $n + 1$ is W. Then the total number of alleles in the population of women of generation $n + 1$ is $2W$, since each woman has two alleles. The total number of A-alleles in the population of women of generation $n+1$ is: the total number of dominant homozygotes (which is uW) times 2 (since each dominant homozygote has two A-alleles) plus the total number of heterozygotes (which is vW) times 1 (since each heterozygote has one A-allele). Recall that the recessive women have no A-alleles. Thus the total number of A-alleles in the women of generation $n + 1$ is

$$
\begin{aligned}
W(2u + v) &= W[2p(n)P(n) + p(n)Q(n) + P(n)q(n)] \\
&= W[p(n)P(n) + p(n)Q(n) + p(n)P(n) + P(n)q(n)],
\end{aligned}
$$

after rearranging terms. Since $p(n) + q(n) = 1$ and $P(n) + Q(n) = 1$, it follows that

$$p(n)P(n) + p(n)Q(n) = p(n)[P(n) + Q(n)] = p(n),$$

and

$$p(n)P(n) + P(n)q(n) = P(n).$$

Thus, it follows that the total number of A-alleles in the women of generation $n + 1$ is

$$W(2u + v) = W[p(n) + P(n)].$$

The proportion of A-alleles in the women of generation $n + 1$ is the total number of the A-alleles divided by the total number of alleles, which gives

$$p(n + 1) = \frac{W[p(n) + P(n)]}{2W} = 0.5p(n) + 0.5P(n).$$

We now turn our attention to the men of generation n. Since men only have one allele, they are either dominant or recessive, and the proportion of men that are of each of these genotypes is the same as the proportion of alleles of type A and a among the men of generation n. Thus, the proportion of dominant men in generation n is $P(n)$, while the proportion of recessive men in generation n is $Q(n)$.

To compute the proportion of dominant men in generation $n + 1$, we must compute the probability that a man will inherit an A-allele. Since a man in generation $n + 1$ inherits his allele from a woman of generation n, the probability that a boy in generation $n + 1$ inherits an A-allele is

$$P(n + 1) = p(n).$$

Likewise, $Q(n + 1) = q(n)$.

To review, the proportions of A-alleles among women and among men satisfy the dynamical systems

$$p(n + 1) = 0.5p(n) + 0.5P(n) \quad \text{and} \quad P(n + 1) = p(n),$$

respectively. Let us substitute $n + 1$ for n in the first of these dynamical systems to get

$$p(n + 2) = 0.5p(n + 1) + 0.5P(n + 1).$$

Since we know from above that $P(n + 1) = p(n)$, we can substitute $p(n)$ for $P(n + 1)$ in the previous equation to get

$$p(n + 2) = 0.5p(n + 1) + 0.5p(n)$$

as the second order linear dynamical system that gives the relationship for the proportion of A-alleles among the women of generation n.

The characteristic equation for this dynamical system is

$$x^2 = 0.5x + 0.5.$$

The two roots are $x = 1$ and $x = -0.5$. Thus, the general solution to this equation is

$$p(k) = c_1 + c_2 (-0.5)^k,$$

where c_1 and c_2 depend on the initial values.

As k goes to infinity, $(-0.5)^k$ goes to zero and so $p(k)$ goes to c_1. Since the current population of women today is obviously the result of many previous generations, we can assume that k is large, that is, we can assume that $p(k) = c_1$, where $p(k)$ is the proportion of a-alleles among women today.

Since $P(k) = p(k-1) = c_1 + c_2 (-0.5)^{k-1}$, which is also close to c_1, we can assume that the proportion of A-alleles in the male population is $P(k) = c_1$ also.

To review, the proportion of A-alleles in the male and in the female populations is stable at some level $c_1 = p$, and thus the proportion of a-alleles in the male and female populations is $q = 1 - p$. Thus, the proportion of dominant homozygotes, heterozygotes, and recessive homozygotes among the population of women in any generation is

$$u = p^2, \quad v = 2pq, \quad w = q^2,$$

respectively, while the proportion of dominant and recessive men in any generation is

$$p \quad \text{and} \quad q,$$

respectively.

Color blindness is a sex-linked trait in which the proportion of men that are color blind is $q = 0.01$, which, as we have seen above, is also the proportion of a-alleles. Thus, we expect the proportion of women that are color blind to be $w = (0.01)^2 = 0.0001$, so that only 1 out of $10\,000$ women will exhibit this recessive trait.

5.4.1 Problems

1. Suppose that for a certain sex-linked trait we know that $p = 0.7$. What proportion of women and of men will exhibit the recessive trait? What proportion of the women are heterozygotes?

2. Answer Problem 1 with $p = 0.98$.

3. Suppose a recessive sex-linked allele, a, has recently appeared in the population, and so has not reached equilibrium. At present, we estimate that the proportion of a-alleles in women is $q(0) = 0.1$, and that the proportion of this allele in men is $Q(0) = 0.2$. This means that $p(0) = 0.9$ and $P(0) = 0.8$.

   (a) Using the dynamical system

$$p(n+1) = 0.5p(n) + 0.5P(n),$$

   find $p(1)$.

   (b) Using $p(1)$ from part (a), find the particular solution to this dynamical system.

   (c) What is the equilibrium value for the dynamical system in part (a)?

4. Repeat Problem 3 using $q(0) = 0.98$ and $Q(0) = 0.99$.

5. Suppose that a trait is sex-linked. Let $p(n)$ and $P(n)$ represent the proportion of A-alleles among the adult women and men, respectively, of generation n. Let $p'(n)$ and $P'(n)$ represent the proportion of A-alleles among the female and male children, respectively, of generation n. Suppose that a fraction μ of the A-alleles in children mutate to a-alleles in adults. Develop a second order linear dynamical system for $p(n+2)$ and find the solution to that system.

6. Suppose we have a fatal sex-linked trait in which all recessive individuals die before adulthood. Thus, all adult males contain one A-allele. Let $p(n)$ and $q(n)$ be the proportion of A- and a-alleles in the adult women of generation n.

   (a) Compute $p(n+1)$, the proportion of A-alleles among the females of generation $n+1$?

   (b) Solve the dynamical system in part (a) and find the stable equilibrium value.

   (c) Suppose that the fraction of males born with this trait is 10^{-2}. Use this information to find the particular solution to the dynamical system in part (a).

5.5 Second order nonhomogeneous equations

In this section, we study equations of the form

$$A(n+2) = aA(n+1) + bA(n) + f(n),$$

where a and b are given constants and f is a function of n. The results are similar to those of first order nonhomogeneous equations, discussed in Section 2.6. You might review that section before proceeding.

Example 5.9

Suppose we wish to find the general solution to the (affine) nonhomogeneous equation

$$A(n+2) = 5A(n+1) - 6A(n) + 4. \tag{6}$$

(From now on, we will consider an affine dynamical system to be a type of nonhomogeneous equation.) First, consider the corresponding linear dynamical system

$$A(n+2) = 5A(n+1) - 6A(n).$$

The two roots of the characteristic equation are $x = 2$ and $x = 3$. Therefore, the general solution of the linear dynamical system is

$$A(k) = c_1\, 2^k + c_2\, 3^k,$$

where c_1 and c_2 depend on the initial values.

Hence, we might expect the general solution to the original nonhomogeneous dynamical system (6) to be of the form

$$A(k) = c_1\, 2^k + c_2\, 3^k + a,$$

where c_1 and c_2 depend on the initial values, and a depends on the term added on to the linear equation, that is, on $f(n) = 4$. To determine the number a, we can substitute

$$
\begin{aligned}
A(n) &= c_1\, 2^n + c_2\, 3^n + a \\
A(n+1) &= c_1\, 2^{n+1} + c_2\, 3^{n+1} + a \\
A(n+2) &= c_1\, 2^{n+2} + c_2\, 3^{n+2} + a
\end{aligned}
$$

into the dynamical system. After canceling the 2^n and 3^n terms and solving for the unknown a, we get $a = 2$. Thus, the general solution to the above nonhomogeneous equation is

$$A(k) = c_1\, 2^k + c_2\, 3^k + 2.$$

The computation can be simplified by omitting the terms $c_1\, 2^n$ and $c_2\, 3^n$. This can be done because these terms depend only on the initial conditions. Therefore we only need to substitute

$$A(n) = a, \quad A(n+1) = a, \quad A(n+2) = a$$

into the dynamical system, giving

$$a = 5a - 6a + 4,$$

again getting $a = 2$.

You can check that the above value is a solution by substituting it back into the nonhomogeneous dynamical system. You will see that everything cancels, giving a balanced equation.

You can see that the above is the general solution by solving

$$A(0) = c_1 + c_2 + 2 \quad \text{and} \quad A(1) = 2c_1 + 3c_2 + 2$$

for c_1 and c_2.

Example 5.10

Now consider the equation

$$A(n+2) = 5A(n+1) - 6A(n) + 2n + 1. \tag{7}$$

From the previous example, we know that the roots of the corresponding linear dynamical system

$$A(n+2) = 5A(n+1) - 6A(n)$$

are $x = 2$ and $x = 3$. Therefore, we expect the general solution to the nonhomogeneous dynamical system (7) to be of the form

$$A(k) = c_1\, 2^k + c_2\, 3^k + a + b\,k,$$

where c_1 and c_2 depend on the initial values, while a and b depend on the function $f(n) = 2n + 1$. As in the previous example we omit the 2^n and 3^n terms, since they will cancel each other out, anyway. To find a and b, we substitute

$$
\begin{aligned}
A(n) &= a + bn \\
A(n+1) &= a + b(n+1) = a + bn + b \\
A(n+2) &= a + b(n+2) = a + bn + 2b
\end{aligned}
$$

into the nonhomogeneous dynamical system, giving

$$a + 2b + bn = 5a + 5b + 5bn - 6a - 6bn + 2n + 1,$$

or

$$2a - 3b + 2bn = 2n + 1.$$

Now collect all the terms on the left, group the terms involving n together and factor out the n, and group the constant terms (not involving n) together, giving

$$(2b - 2)n + (2a - 3b - 1) = 0.$$

We want to choose a and b so that this equation is satisfied **for every value of** n. Notice that if $2b - 2$ (the coefficient of n) equals zero, and if the constant term, $2a - 3b - 1$, also equals zero, then we have $0 = 0$ and the equation is satisfied. Thus we want a and b to satisfy the equations

$$2b - 2 = 0 \quad \text{and} \quad 2a - 3b - 1 = 0.$$

Solving the first equation gives $b = 1$. Substituting this into the second equation gives $a = 2$. Therefore the general solution to the above nonhomogeneous dynamical system is

$$A(k) = c_1 \, 2^k + c_2 \, 3^k + 2 + k,$$

where c_1 and c_2 depend on the initial values.

Let's summarize the rule for finding the general solution to a nonhomogeneous second order linear dynamical system in which the nonhomogeneous term is a polynomial. Recall that, for first order nonhomogeneous equations, there was a special case when $r = 1$. For second order equations there are two roots of the characteristic equation, so there will be two special cases, exactly one root equals 1 and 1 is a double root.

Theorem 5.11

Nonhomogeneous dynamical systems in which $f(n)$ is a polynomial: *Consider the dynamical system*

$$A(n + 2) = aA(n + 1) + bA(n) + f(n),$$

where the roots of the characteristic equation $x^2 = ax + b$ are r and s, and $f(n)$ is an m-th order polynomial, that is,

$$f(n) = b_m n^m + b_{m-1} n^{m-1} + \ldots + b_1 n + b_0.$$

- If $r \neq 1$ and $s \neq 1$, then the general solution is of the form

$$A(k) = c_1\, r^k + c_2\, s^k + a_m\, k^m + a_{m-1}\, k^{m-1} + \ldots + a_1 k + a_0.$$

Replace $c_1\, r^k + c_2\, s^k$ with $(c_1 + c_2\, k)\, r^k$ if $r = s$, as was discussed in Section 5.2.

- If $r \neq 1$ and $s = 1$, then the general solution is of the form

$$A(k) = c_1\, r^k + c_2 + a_m\, k^{m+1} + a_{m-1}\, k^m + \ldots + a_1\, k^2 + a_0\, k.$$

- If $r = s = 1$, then the general solution is of the form

$$A(k) = c_1 + c_2\, k + a_m\, k^{m+2} + a_{m-1}\, k^{m+1} + \ldots + a_1\, k^3 + a_0\, k^2.$$

In all cases, c_1 and c_2 depend on the initial values, and the constants $a_m, a_{m-1}, \ldots, a_1,$ and a_0 can be found by substituting into the dynamical system and then solving $m+1$ equations for the $m+1$ unknowns by setting the coefficient of the n^m term, $\ldots$, the coefficient of the n term, and the constant term equal to zero.

Example 5.12

Consider the second order nonhomogeneous dynamical system

$$A(n + 2) = 4A(n + 1) - 4A(n) + 7 - 2n. \tag{8}$$

Since the characteristic equation for the corresponding linear dynamical system

$$A(n + 2) = 4A(n + 1) - 4A(n)$$

has $x = 2$ as a double root, it follows from Theorem 5.11 part 1 that the general solution is of the form

$$A(k) = (c_1 + c_2\, k)\, 2^k + a + b\, k,$$

where c_1 and c_2 depend on the initial values, and a and b depend on the function $f(n) = 7 - 2n$. (We are using a and b instead of a_1 and a_2 to avoid subscripts.) Omitting the term $(c_1 + c_2\, k)\, 2^k$ so as to simplify our computations, we substitute

$$
\begin{aligned}
A(n) &= a + bn \\
A(n + 1) &= a + b\,(n + 1) \\
A(n + 2) &= a + b\,(n + 2)
\end{aligned}
$$

into the dynamical system, giving

$$(a + bn + 2b) = 4(a + b + bn) - 4(a + bn) + 7 - 2n,$$

or, after collecting terms on the left and simplifying,

$$(b + 2)n + (a - 2b - 7) = 0.$$

Solving the two equations

$$b + 2 = 0 \quad \text{and} \quad a - 2b - 7 = 0$$

gives $b = -2$ and $a = 3$.

Thus the general solution to the second order nonhomogeneous dynamical system (8) is

$$A(k) = (c_1 + c_2 \, k) \, 2^k + 3 - 2k,$$

where c_1 and c_2 depend on the initial values.

Suppose $A(0) = 2$ and $A(1) = 9$. To find the particular solution, we solve

$$2 = A(0) = (c_1 + 0)2^0 + 3 - 2(0) = c_1 + 3$$

and

$$9 = A(1) = (c_1 + c_2)2^1 + 3 - 2 = 2c_1 + 2c_2 + 3 - 2.$$

The first equation gives $c_1 = -1$. Substitution into the second equation gives $c_2 = 5$, so the particular solution is

$$A(k) = (-1 + 5k) \, 2^k + 3 - 2k.$$

Example 5.13

Consider the dynamical system

$$A(n + 2) = 2A(n + 1) - A(n) + 6. \tag{9}$$

We see that $r = 1$ is a double root of the characteristic equation and $f(n) = 6$ is a zeroth order polynomial so that $m = 0$. Therefore, from Theorem 5.11 part 3 we know that the general solution is of the form

$$A(k) = c_1 + c_2 \, k + a \, k^2,$$

where c_1 and c_2 depend on the initial values, while a depends on the nonhomogeneous term, 6. Substituting

$$A(n) = a \, n^2, \quad A(n + 1) = a \, (n + 1)^2, \quad A(n + 2) = a \, (n + 2)^2$$

into the dynamical system gives

$$a\,n^2 + 4an + 4a = 2a\,n^2 + 4an + 2a - a\,n^2 + 6.$$

Canceling the n and the n^2 terms gives $2a = 6$, or

$$a = 3.$$

The general solution to the dynamical system is then

$$A(k) = c_1 + c_2\,k + 3\,k^2.$$

If $A(0) = 2$ and $A(1) = 1$, then solving

$$2 = c_1 \quad \text{and} \quad 1 = c_1 + c_2 + 3$$

gives the particular solution as

$$A(k) = 2 - 4\,k + 3\,k^2.$$

Observe that this solution is quadratic in the sense that the points $(k, A(k))$ lie on a parabola.

Let's now study dynamical systems in which the nonhomogeneous term is an exponential of the form $b_0\,p^n$. The general solution is of the same form as in Section 2.6 except that there is an additional special case.

Theorem 5.14

Nonhomogeneous dynamical systems in which $f(n)$ is an exponential: *Consider the second order nonhomogeneous dynamical system*

$$A(n + 2) = a\,A(n + 1) + b\,A(n) + b_0\,p^n,$$

where b_0 and p are given constants. Suppose the roots of the characteristic equation for the corresponding linear dynamical system are $x = r$ and $x = s$. The general solution is of the following forms:

- *If $r \neq p$ and $s \neq p$, then*

$$A(k) = c_1\,r^k + c_2\,s^k + a_0\,p^k \quad \text{if } r \neq s$$

   or

$$A(k) = (c_1 + c_2\,k)\,r^k + a_0\,p^k \quad \text{if } r = s.$$

- *If $r = p$ and $s \neq p$, then*

$$A(k) = c_2\,s^k + (c_1 + a_0\,k)\,r^k.$$

- *If $r = s = p$, that is, p is a double root of the characteristic equation, then*

$$A(k) = (c_1 + c_2\, k + a_0\, k^2)\, r^k.$$

In each part, c_1 and c_2 depend on the initial values while a_0 can be obtained by substitution into the dynamical system.

Example 5.15

Consider the nonhomogeneous equation

$$A(n + 2) = 5A(n + 1) - 6A(n) + 6\,(4)^n. \tag{10}$$

We know that the roots of the characteristic equation are 2 and 3. Thus we expect the general solution to be of the form

$$A(k) = c_1\, 2^k + c_2\, 3^k + a\, 4^k,$$

where c_1 and c_2 depend on the inital values, while a depends on the non-homogeneous term. Substituting $A(n) = a\, 4^n$ into the dynamical system gives

$$a\, 4^{n+2} = 5a\, 4^{n+1} - 6a\, 4^n + 6\,(4)^n.$$

Dividing by 4^n gives

$$16a = 20a - 6a + 6, \quad \text{or} \quad a = 3.$$

Thus, the general solution to the dynamical system (10) is

$$A(k) = c_1\, 2^k + c_2\, 3^k + 3\,(4)^k,$$

where c_1 and c_2 depend on the initial values.

Example 5.16

Consider the dynamical system

$$A(n + 2) = 4A(n + 1) - 4A(n) + 8\,(2)^n. \tag{11}$$

Here, $r = 2$ is a double root of the characteristic equation and is also involved in the nonhomogeneous term. From Theorem 5.14 part 3, the general solution is of the form

$$A(k) = (c_1 + c_2\, k + a\, k^2)\, 2^k,$$

where c_1 and c_2 depend on the initial values, while a depends on the term $8\,(2)^n = 2^{n+3}$. Substituting

$$
\begin{aligned}
A(n) &= a\, n^2\, 2^n \\
A(n + 1) &= a\, (n + 1)^2\, 2^{n+1} \\
A(n + 2) &= 4a\, (n^2 + 4n + 4)\, 2^n
\end{aligned}
$$

into the dynamical system (11) and then dividing by 2^n gives

$$4a\left(n^2 + 4n + 4\right) = 8a\left(n^2 + 2n + 1\right) - 4a\,n^2 + 8.$$

Since the n^2 terms and the n terms cancel, we obtain

$$16a = 8a + 8, \quad \text{or} \quad a = 1.$$

Thus, the general solution to the dynamical system (11) is

$$A(k) = (c_1 + c_2\,k + k^2)\,2^k.$$

We must make a comment concerning the proofs of Theorems 5.11 and 5.14. The proof in each case is a matter of actually substituting the claimed form of the general solution into the dynamical system and solving for the constants $a_0, \ldots$ in terms of the given constants $b_0, \ldots$. The algebra involved in the proof of each part of Theorem 5.14 is relatively easy as can be seen below in the proof of part 3. The algebra involved in the proof of each part of Theorem 5.11 is more difficult and will be omitted.

Proof of Theorem 5.14 part 3: We are assuming that r is a double root of the characteristic equation, that is, the characteristic equation is

$$(x - r)^2 = 0, \quad \text{or} \quad x^2 - 2rx + r^2 = 0.$$

But this is the characteristic equation for the dynamical system

$$A(n + 2) = 2rA(n + 1) - r^2 A(n).$$

Thus, we are trying to find the general solution to the dynamical system

$$A(n + 2) = 2rA(n + 1) - r^2 A(n) + b_0\,r^n.$$

Substituting $A(n) = (c_1 + c_2\,n + a_0\,n^2)\,r^n$ into the dynamical system gives

$$[c_1 + c_2\,(n + 2) + a_0(n + 2)^2]r^{n+2} =$$
$$2r[c_1 + c_2(n + 1) + a_0(n + 1)^2]r^{n+1} - r^2(c_1 + c_2 n + a_0 n^2)r^n + b_0\,r^n.$$

The terms involving c_1 and c_2 cancel out, leaving

$$a_0\left(n + 2\right)^2 = 2a_0\left(n + 1\right)^2 - a_0\,n^2 + b_0\,r^{-2}$$

after dividing both sides by r^{n+2}. The $a_0 n^2$ and $a_0 n$ terms cancel leaving

$$4a_0 = 2a_0 - b_0\, r^{-2}, \quad \text{or} \quad a_0 = \frac{b_0}{2r^2}.$$

We see not only that the general solution to the equation

$$A(n+2) = 2r\, A(n+1) - r^2 A(n) + b_0\, r^n$$

is of the form

$$A(n) = (c_1 + c_2\, k + a_0\, k^2) r^k$$

but that

$$a_0 = \frac{b_0}{2r^2}.$$

We could now solve for c_1 and c_2 in terms of $A(0)$ and $A(1)$ to complete the proof.

5.5.1   Problems

1. Find the general solution for the following second order dynamical systems.

   (a) $A(n+2) = A(n+1) + 6A(n)$

   (b) $A(n+2) = A(n+1) + 6A(n) - 19\,(5)^n$

   (c) $A(n+2) = A(n+1) + 6A(n) - 12n + 8$

   (d) $A(n+2) = A(n+1) + 6A(n) + 4\,(2)^n$

   (e) $A(n+2) = A(n+1) + 6A(n) - 10\,(3)^{n+1}$

2. Find the general solution for the following second order dynamical systems.

   (a) $A(n+2) = -2A(n+1) - A(n)$

   (b) $A(n+2) = -2A(n+1) - A(n) + 8$

   (c) $A(n+2) = -2A(n+1) - A(n) + 9\,(2)^n$

   (d) $A(n+2) = -2A(n+1) - A(n) + 4\,(-1)^n$

3. Find the general solution for the following second order dynamical systems.

   (a) $A(n+2) = -A(n+1) + 2A(n)$

   (b) $A(n+2) = -A(n+1) + 2A(n) - 2^{n+2}$

   (c) $A(n+2) = -A(n+1) + 2A(n) + 6\,(-2)^n$

(d) $A(n+2) = -A(n+1) + 2A(n) + 9$

(e) $A(n+2) = -A(n+1) + 2A(n) - 12n - 10$

4. Find the general solution for the following second order dynamical systems.

(a) $A(n+2) = 2A(n+1) - A(n)$

(b) $A(n+2) = 2A(n+1) - A(n) - 6$

(c) $A(n+2) = 2A(n+1) - A(n) + 2^n$

(d) $A(n+2) = 2A(n+1) - A(n) + 6n + 4$

5. Find the particular solution to the dynamical system

(a) in Problem 1 (b) given that $A(0) = 2$ and $A(1) = 5$

(b) in Problem 2 (d) given that $A(0) = -3$ and $A(1) = -3$

(c) in Problem 3 (d) given that $A(0) = 1$ and $A(1) = -11$

(d) in Problem 4 (b) given that $A(0) = 7$ and $A(1) = 6$

6. See if you can combine Theorems 5.11 and 5.14 to find the general solution to the dynamical systems

(a) $A(n+2) = A(n+1) + 6A(n) + (30n + 33) 3^n$

(b) $A(n+2) = 2A(n+1) - A(n) - 6 + 2^n$

7. Find the general solution to the following third order nonhomogeneous dynamical systems

(a) $A(n+3) = 5A(n+2) - 8A(n+1) + 4A(n) + 3^n$

(b) $A(n+3) = 5A(n+2) - 8A(n+1) + 4A(n) + 1$

(c) $A(n+3) = 5A(n+2) - 8A(n+1) + 4A(n) - 8 (2)^n$

8. Suppose that the solution to a dynamical system is

$$A(n) = (c_1 + c_2 k + a_0 k^2) r^k.$$

Find c_1 and c_2 in terms of a_0, $A(0)$, and $A(1)$.

9. The roots of the characteristic equation for the dynamical system

$$A(n+2) = (r + s)A(n+1) - rsA(n) + b_0 r^n$$

are r and s. Show that the general solution is of the form

$$A(k) = (c_1 + a_0\,k)\,r^k + c_2\,s^k$$

by substituting this solution into the dynamical system and solving for a_0 in terms of b_0.

5.6 Applications of nonhomogeneous equations

In this section, we consider two applications. The first is a variation on the gambler's ruin, while the second is a study of the effects of inbreeding in genetics.

5.6.1 Gambler's ruin revisited

First, as in Section 5.3, assume we are playing a game in which the probability of winning a dollar on any particular try is p, while the probability of losing a dollar on any particular try is $1 - p = q$. We quit the game when we have a total of N dollars or when we are broke. The question we now wish to answer is, 'Given that we now have n dollars, on the average how many bets will we make?' Notice that we are not interested in whether we quit as a winner or a loser.

Suppose we now have n dollars. Let $E(n)$ represent the average number of bets we will make before the game is over. Notice that $E(0) = 0$ and $E(N) = 0$ since in these two cases, we quit playing. These are our 'initial' values.

Suppose $0 < n < N$. Then we have not yet quit and therefore expect to play the game at least one more time. So

$$E(n) = 1 + \text{how many more bets?}$$

We play the game and one of two things happens. Case 1 is that we win a dollar and continue playing if possible, and case 2 is that we lose a dollar and continue playing if possible. The trick is to find the average number of bets we will make in each of these two cases. We then use a weighted average of these two cases by using the likelihood of each of these cases occurring.

If case 1 occurs, that is, if we win the next bet, we will have $n + 1$ dollars and will make an average of $E(n + 1)$ more bets. If case 2 occurs, we will have only $n - 1$ dollars and will make an average of $E(n - 1)$ more bets. Since p is the fraction of the time that case 1 occurs and q is the fraction of the time that case 2 occurs, the weighted average of the two cases is

$$pE(n + 1) + qE(n - 1).$$

(If you make 12 bets one-third of the time and you make 9 bets two-thirds of the time, then on the average you will make

$$\tfrac{1}{3}(12) + \tfrac{2}{3}(9) = 10$$

more bets, that is if you play three more times, you will on the average make 12 bets once and 9 bets twice for an average of 10 bets.)

Thus, $E(n)$, the expected number of times to play before quitting, is 1 (since we now play the game once), plus the weighted average given above, that is,

$$E(n) = pE(n+1) + qE(n-1) + 1.$$

To solve this equation, we first substitute $n+1$ for n, giving

$$E(n+1) = pE(n+2) + qE(n) + 1.$$

Dividing by p and rearranging gives

$$E(n+2) = \tfrac{1}{p}E(n+1) - \tfrac{q}{p}E(n) - \tfrac{1}{p}.$$

The two roots of the characteristic equation for the linear part of the equation are $x = 1$ and $x = q/p$.

If $p \neq q$, that is, if $p \neq 0.5$, then we have two distinct roots. But if $p = q = 0.5$, we have $r = 1$ as a double root.

First, let's assume that $p \neq q$, so that $q/p \neq 1$, and we have two distinct roots. Since $f(n) = -1/p$, which is a zeroth order polynomial, and $r = 1$ is one of the roots, by Theorem 5.11 part 1, the solution to the nonhomogeneous equation is of the form

$$E(k) = c_1 + c_2 \left(\frac{q}{p}\right)^k + a\,k,$$

where c_1 and c_2 depend on the initial values, while a depends on the nonhomogeneous term, $-1/p$. Substituting into the second order non-homogeneous dynamical system gives

$$a\,(n+2) = \frac{a\,(n+1)}{p} - \frac{qan}{p} - \frac{1}{p}.$$

Multiplying both sides by p, substituting $1-p$ for q, and canceling the n terms gives

$$2ap = a - 1, \quad \text{or} \quad a = \frac{-1}{2p-1} = \frac{1}{q-p}.$$

using the fact that $2p - 1 = p - q$.

The general solution to the dynamical system is then

$$E(k) = c_1 + c_2 \left(\frac{q}{p}\right)^k + \frac{k}{q - p}.$$

Since

$$E(0) = 0 = c_1 + c_2 \quad \text{and} \quad E(N) = 0 = c_1 + c_2 \left(\frac{q}{p}\right)^N + \frac{N}{q - p},$$

we can solve these two equations for c_1 and c_2 to get

$$c_1 = \frac{N}{(q - p)[(q/p)^N - 1]} = -c_2,$$

and the particular solution to the nonhomogeneous equation is

$$E(k) = \frac{N[1 - (q/p)^k]}{(q - p)[(q/p)^N - 1]} + \frac{k}{q - p},$$

after collecting terms.

For example, suppose $p = 0.49$, $N = 20$, and $n = 1$, that is, we have 1 dollar left and will play until we are broke or have 20 dollars. In this case, $E(1) = 16.7$, that is, on the average, we will play 16.7 times before quitting. Notice this is an average, since about half the time we lose our dollar on the first try and quit. But there are times when we play for long periods, so that the average is 16.7.

Many gamblers have the best intentions about quitting, but once they reach their goal they are unable to quit. Under these conditions, they will eventually go broke. How long will they play before going broke? To rephrase the above more precisely, suppose a gambler has n dollars, the probability of winning any (1 dollar) bet is $p < 0.5$, and the gambler plays until broke. On the average, how many bets will the gambler make?

The solution is easy. Suppose the gambler makes an unrealistically high goal, say $N = 1\,000\,000$, but presently has $n = 50$. Then the gambler is (almost) certain to go broke and $E(50)$ would be a reasonably accurate answer to our question. To get the exact answer, let N go to infinity, that is, the expected number of bets would be

$$\lim_{N \to \infty} E(n) = \lim_{N \to \infty} \left(\frac{N[1 - (q/p)^n]}{(q - p)[(q/p)^N - 1]} + \frac{n}{q - p} \right).$$

While it will not be proved here, when $r > 1$,

$$\lim_{N \to \infty} \frac{N}{r^N} = 0.$$

This is essentially because N grows linearly, but r^N grows exponentially. Since $p < 0.5$, it follows that $q/p > 1$, so

$$\lim_{N \to \infty} \frac{N[1 - (q/p)^n]}{(q-p)[(q/p)^N - 1]} = 0$$

and

$$\lim_{N \to \infty} E(n) = \frac{n}{q-p}.$$

Thus if $p = 0.49$ and we have $n = 1$ dollar, we expect to make $1/(0.51 - 0.49) = 50$ bets before going broke, as compared to the 16.7 bets when we stop at 20 dollars.

Now let's consider a fair game, that is, $p = q = 0.5$. Our dynamical system then becomes

$$E(n+2) = 2E(n+1) - E(n) - 2,$$

and $x = 1$ is a double root. By Theorem 5.11 part 3, we know that the general solution is of the form

$$E(k) = c_1 + c_2 \, k + a \, k^2,$$

where c_1 and c_2 depend on the initial values, while a depends on the nonhomogeneous term, -2. Substituting into the dynamical system gives

$$a \, n^2 + 4an + 4a = 2a \, n^2 + 4an + 2a - a \, n^2 - 2, \quad \text{or} \quad a = -1.$$

Thus, the general solution is

$$E(k) = c_1 + c_2 \, k - k^2.$$

Since

$$E(0) = 0 = c_1 \quad \text{and} \quad E(N) = 0 = c_1 + c_2 \, N - N^2,$$

it follows that $c_1 = 0$ and $c_2 = N$, so that the particular solution is

$$E(k) = k \, N - k^2 = k \, (N - k).$$

In this case, if $n = 1$ and $N = 20$, then $E(n) = 19$ as compared with 16.7 when $p = 0.49$.

Notice that if we are in an honest game and decide to play until we go broke, then

$$\lim_{N \to \infty} E(n) = \lim_{N \to \infty} n(N - n) = \infty,$$

so we will be playing for a long time.

5.6.2   Inbreeding

We now wish to consider a simple example of inbreeding. Suppose there are four alleles for a trait, a, b, c, and d. Thus, there are four types of homozygotes, (a, a), (b, b), (c, c), and (d, d). We are not interested in the types of heterozygotes.

Suppose we start with a couple where the woman has allelic pair (a, b) while the man has allelic pair (c, d). These two individuals mate, producing a brother and a sister in generation 1. The brother and sister mate, producing a brother and a sister in generation 2, and so on. Pick an individual in generation n and let $P(n)$ be the probability that this individual is a homozygote, the type being unimportant.

Let $A(n)$ be the probability that, given a brother and a sister in generation n, if we pick one allele from each of them, these two alleles are of the same type. Notice that

$$P(n + 1) = A(n),$$

since the probability that an individual of generation $n+1$ is a homozygote is the same as the probability that this individual chose an allele from each of his parents (in generation n) and got alleles of the same type.

An individual of generation 1 takes an allele from the mother, who has alleles a and b, and an allele from the father, who has alleles c and d. Thus, an individual of generation 1 cannot be a homozygote, that is, $P(1) = 0$. Also, since neither of the original two parents are homozygote, $P(0) = 0$.

Let's compute the probability that an individual of generation 2 has allelic pair (a, a). This is a four-stage process. The first stage is that the grandmother (the original woman with allelic pair (a, b)) gave an a-allele to her daughter. This will happen with probability $1/2$. The second stage is that the grandmother gave her son an a-allele, which also has probability $1/2$. The third stage is that the woman in generation 1 now gives her a-allele to the individual in generation 2. This also happens with probability $1/2$. The fourth stage is that the male in generation 1 gives the individual in generation 2 his a-allele, which also happens with probability $1/2$. By the multiplication principle, the probability that an individual of generation 2 has allelic pair (a, a) is $(1/2)^4 = 1/16$. This can be seen graphically in the diagram of Figure 50.

Let's compute the probability that an individual of generation 2 is a homozygote. There are four cases. Case 1 is that the individual has allelic pair (a, a) which happens with probability $1/16$. Case 2 is the allelic pair (b, b) which, similarly to the above, has probability $1/16$. Similarly, the probabilities of the cases (c, c) and (d, d) are both $1/16$. By the addition

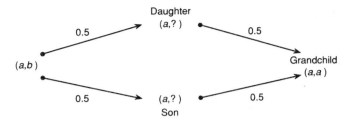

Fig. 50. Genetic relationship between generation 0 and generation 2.

principle,

$$P(2) = 4(\tfrac{1}{16}) = 0.25.$$

Let's now consider the ways that an individual can get a pair of alleles from the grandparents. There are three ways this can happen. First, both alleles can be copies of the same allele in one grandparent, (a, a), (b, b), (c, c), or (d, d) for the second generation. Second, the individual can get the same **pair** of genes that one of the grandparents had, (a, b) or (c, d) for the second generation. Third, the individual can get one allele from each grandparent, (a, c), (a, d), (b, c), or (b, d) for the second generation.

Let C_1 be the event that an individual in generation $n + 2$ has two copies of the same allele from one of the grandparents from generation n. The grandparents have four alleles between them. The probability that the individual gets two of the same allele from one grandparent, say allele x, is 1/16, for the same reason that the individual in generation 2 has a probability of 1/16 of being (a, a). Since the probability is 1/16 for each of the four alleles that the grandparents have, similarly to $P(2)$, it follows that

$$P(C_1) = 4(\tfrac{1}{16}) = \tfrac{1}{4}.$$

Let C_2 be the event that the individual has different genes from one grandparent. There are two ways in which these two genes can come from the grandmother. These cases are given graphically in Figure 51. Note that the multiplication principle is used in each case, and the two cases are then added together to get that the probability is $2(1/16) = 1/8$. Likewise, the probability of getting two different alleles from the grandfather is also 1/8. The two grandparents form two cases. Thus, to get $P(C_2)$, we add the probabilities, giving

$$P(C_2) = \tfrac{1}{8} + \tfrac{1}{8} = \tfrac{1}{4}.$$

Let C_3 be the event that the individual gets one allele from each grandparent. Since one of these three events must occur, it follows that

$$P(C_1) + P(C_2) + P(C_3) = 1, \quad \text{so that} \quad P(C_3) = 0.5.$$

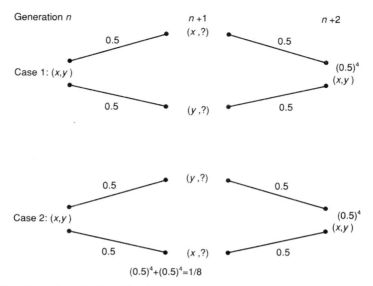

Fig. 51. Genetic relationship between generation n and generation $n + 2$.

The probability that a person in generation $n + 2$ is a homozygote is denoted by $P(n+2)$. To compute $P(n+2)$, we consider three cases. Case 1 is that event C_1 occurs and our individual is a homozygote. Likewise, cases 2 and 3 are that C_2 and C_3 occur, respectively, and our individual is a homozygote. To compute $P(n+2)$, we must compute the probability of each of these three cases and add them together. To do this, we again use the multiplication principle.

If an individual's two alleles are copies of the same allele from a grandparent, the individual must be a homozygote. Thus,

$$P(\text{case } 1) = P(C_1) = 0.25.$$

If an individual has one of each allele from a grandparent, this individual is a homozygote only if that grandparent (generation n) is a homozygote. But this is $P(n)$. Thus by the multiplication principle

$$P(\text{case } 2) = P(C_2)P(n) = 0.25P(n).$$

If an individual has an allele from each grandparent of generation n, the question is, what is the probability that these two alleles are the same? But the probability that two alleles, one chosen from the brother (the male grandparent) and one chosen from the sister (the female grandparent) in generation n, are the same was defined to be $A(n)$. Recall that $A(n) =$

$P(n + 1)$. Thus

$$P(\text{case } 3) = P(C_3)A(n) = P(C_3)P(n+1) = 0.5P(n+1).$$

Adding the three cases together gives the dynamical system for inbreeding as

$$P(n+2) = 0.5P(n+1) + 0.25P(n) + 0.25. \tag{12}$$

The two roots of the corresponding characteristic equation are $x = 1/4 + \sqrt{5}/4 = 0.809\ldots$, and $x = 1/4 - \sqrt{5}/4 = -0.309\ldots$. Therefore, the solution to this equation is of the form

$$P(k) = c_1 (0.809)^k + c_2 (-0.309)^k + a_0,$$

where c_1 and c_2 depend on the initial values, while a_0 depends on the nonhomogeneous term, 0.25. Substituting $P(k) = a_0$ into the nonhomogeneous dynamical system and solving, gives $a_0 = 1$. Therefore, the general solution is

$$P(k) = c_1 (0.809)^k + c_2 (-0.309)^k + 1.$$

While we could solve for c_1 and c_2 using $P(0) = 0$ and $P(1) = 0$, we observe that $(0.809)^k$ and $(-0.309)^k$ both go to zero as k goes to infinity. Thus, $P(k)$ goes to 1, and so the probability that an individual from the above type of inbreeding is a homozygote is approximately 1 for large k, that is, after many generations of inbreeding.

Note that $a_0 = 1$ is a stable equilibrium value since both roots satisfy $|r| < 1$, that is, $|0.809| < 1$ and $|-0.309| < 1$.

Since it is equally likely that the individual will be a homozygote of each of the four types, the probability that the individual is a homozygote of type (a, a) is approximately $1/4$. Suppose that allele a is a recessive allele in the population. Suppose one parent has this allele as one of the pair. Then, if the offspring are inbred, eventually approximately $1/4$ of the offspring will be recessive homozygotes of type (a, a), even though this trait is rare in the general population. If this allele causes an undesirable trait, the offspring from inbreeding have a high probability, $1/4$, of developing this undesirable, and possibly fatal, trait. This is why inbreeding among humans is discouraged. It has also caused genetic problems among the rulers of countries in which inbreeding was practiced, such as the ancient pharoahs of Egypt. (With all the different genes that make up a person's traits and all the types of alleles of each gene, it is highly likely that each person has some rare and undesirable allele.)

In the case where this allele is desirable, such inbreeding could be used to develop a breed of dogs or a superior strain of corn. But there is also a likelihood of an undesirable trait occurring. This is no problem with dogs or corn, since those that are undesirable can be destroyed or not bred. In humans, this cannot be done; therefore there is too much risk involved in inbreeding humans.

The study of inbreeding can also be combined with selection and mutation. Sometimes there is only partial inbreeding in which cousins mate instead of siblings. This leads to a concept called the **inbreeding coefficient** which represents the degree of inbreeding. This arises in the study of fatal or harmful traits that occur in small communities.

5.6.3 Problems

1. Find the expected number of bets to be made if the probability of winning 1 dollar is 0.49, you start with 50 dollars, and you quit if you go broke or reach a total of 100 dollars.

2. Repeat Problem 1 when

   (a) $p = 0.49$, $n = 1$, and $N = 100$

   (b) $p = 0.5$, $n = 50$, and $N = 100$

   (c) $p = 0.5$, $n = 1$, and $N = 100$

3. Suppose that there are two individuals with allelic pairs (a, b) and (a, c). Thus, $P(0) = 0$.

   (a) Find the probability, $P(1)$, that an individual of generation 1 is a homozygote.

   (b) Find $P(2)$, the probability that, with inbreeding, a grandchild will be a homozygote. Compute this answer using diagrams similar to Figures 50 and 51.

   (c) Using $P(0) = 0$ and $P(1)$ from part (a), compute the particular solution to the dynamical system for inbreeding (12).

4. Suppose that there are two individuals with allelic pairs (a, a) and (c, d). Thus, $P(0) = 1/2$ and $P(1) = 0$.

   (a) Find $P(2)$, the probability that, with inbreeding, a grandchild will be a homozygote. Compute this answer using diagrams similar to Figures 50 and 51.

   (b) Using $P(0) = 1/2$ and $P(1) = 0$, compute the particular solution to the dynamical system for inbreeding (12).

5. Assume we inbreed plants as described previously, except that we start with two heterozygotes, that is, the parents of generation 0 have alleles (a, b) and (a, b). Find $P(0)$, $P(1)$, and the particular solution to the dynamical system for inbreeding (12).

6. Let $A(n)$ be the distance traveled by a falling object after n seconds. Then the average velocity during the nth second is given by $V(n) = A(n) - A(n - 1)$. Observations indicate that the change in velocity during any second is constant and equals -32 feet per second squared, that is,

$$V(n + 1) - V(n) = -32.$$

(a) Develop a second order nonhomogeneous dynamical system for distance traveled, $A(n)$.

(b) Find the general solution to this dynamical system.

(c) Given that a falling object starts at $A(0) = 100$ feet and its average velocity for the first second is $V(1) = -16$ feet per second, find the particular solution for this falling object, and compute how long it will take to reach the ground.

5.7 Stability for second order affine equations

In this section, we are going to study the stability of fixed points for second order affine dynamical systems. First assume that **the two roots of the characteristic equation, r and s, are distinct (r is not a double root) and are not equal to 1**. Thus, we are assuming that the solution to the dynamical system

$$A(n + 2) = aA(n + 1) + bA(n) + c$$

(where a, b, and c are given constants) is of the form

$$A(k) = c_1 r^k + c_2 s^k + A,$$

where c_1 and c_2 depend on the initial values and the number A depends on the equation. The number A will be the fixed point for the equation.

Let's first find the fixed point for the dynamical system given above, that is, the constant solution. In other words, we want to find a number A such that if $A(0) = A$ and $A(1) = A$, then $A(2) = A$, $A(3) = A$, $\ldots$, that is,

$$A(k) = A$$

is a particular solution. We can find such a number A by substituting $A(n+2) = A$, $A(n+1) = A$, and $A(n) = A$ into the dynamical system, and then solving for A. In particular, we solve the equation

$$A = aA + bA + c$$

for A, giving

$$A = \frac{c}{1 - a - b}$$

as the fixed point (assuming that $a + b \neq 1$).

It is easy to check that if $a + b = 1$, then the two roots of the characteristic equation will be $r = 1$ and $s = -b$. But we are presently assuming that 1 is not a root of the characteristic equation.

Suppose we have two real distinct roots, r and s, of the characteristic equation and that they satisfy

$$|r| < 1 \quad \text{and} \quad |s| < 1.$$

Then, as k goes to infinity, $c_1 r^k$ and $c_2 s^k$ both go to zero, and so the solution satisfies

$$\lim_{k \to \infty} A(k) = \lim_{k \to \infty} (c_1 r^k + c_2 s^k + A) = A.$$

Therefore A is an attracting fixed point.

Now suppose that r is a double root of the characteristic equation and that $|r| < 1$. Then the general solution is of the form

$$A(k) = (c_1 + c_2 k) r^k + A.$$

We know that the term $c_1 r^k$ goes to zero as k goes to infinity. But the term $c_2 k r^k$ also goes to zero as k goes to infinity, a fact that was used in the last section. A brief sketch of the proof of this fact is as follows.

Proof: Let $B(k) = k r^k$. $B(k)$ satisfies the dynamical system

$$B(k+1) = \frac{(k+1)r}{k} B(k).$$

Thus each number is a (nonconstant) multiple of the previous number, that multiple being $(k+1)r/k$. Since $|r| < 1$, if k is large enough, then

$$\left| \frac{(k+1)r}{k} \right| < r_0 < 1.$$

So from that point on, each number is less than a constant fraction of the previous number, that is,

$$|B(n+m)| < r_0|B(n+m-1)| < r_0^2|B(n+m-2)| < \ldots < r_0^n|B(m)|.$$

Since $r_0 < 1$, it follows that

$$\lim_{n\to\infty}(n+m)r^{n+m} = \lim_{n\to\infty}|B(n+m)| < \lim_{n\to\infty}r_0^n|B(m)| = 0.$$

Thus,

$$\lim_{k\to\infty} kr^k = 0$$

and the proof is complete.

If either one of the roots, say r, is greater than 1 (in absolute value) then $|A(k)|$ goes to infinity (since $|r^k|$ goes to infinity) and the fixed point is repelling.

We have shown the following.

Theorem 5.17

Suppose that the dynamical system

$$A(n+2) = aA(n+1) + bA(n) + c$$

has two real roots r and s. If $|r| < 1$ and $|s| < 1$, then the fixed point is **attracting**. *If either $|r| > 1$ or $|s| > 1$, or both, then the fixed point is* **repelling**.

Suppose the roots of the dynamical system are complex. The fixed point is still $A = c/(1 - a - b)$. When is it attracting?

Before continuing, let us review complex numbers. Let a, b, c, and d be four real (not complex) numbers. Then

$$(a + bi)(c + di) = (ac - bd) + (ad + bc)i.$$

Using this formula, we get

$$(3 + 2i)(-1 + 5i) = (-3 - 10) + (15 - 2)i = -13 + 13i.$$

You can **visualize** a complex number, $a + bi$, as the point (a, b) in the xy plane. Note that the real part a is the x coordinate and the imaginary part b is the y coordinate. Observe that, by the Pythagorean theorem, the distance between the point (a, b) and the origin is given by $\sqrt{a^2 + b^2}$. From this idea, we can define the absolute value of a complex number as its distance from the origin.

**Definition
5.18**

The absolute value of an complex number $a + bi$ is

$$|a + bi| = \sqrt{a^2 + b^2}.$$

For example,

$$|3 + 4i| = \sqrt{9 + 16} = 5,$$

and

$$\left| \tfrac{1}{2} + \tfrac{\sqrt{3}}{2}i \right| = \sqrt{\tfrac{1}{4} + \tfrac{3}{4}} = 1.$$

Notice that $(1/2, \sqrt{3}/2)$ is a point on the unit circle.

Suppose that the root r to the characteristic equation for a second order dynamical system is complex, that is, $r = a + bi$. What we will see is that, if $|r| = |a + bi| < 1$, then $|r^k|$, the distance of the complex number r^k from the origin, will be 'small' for large k, that is, the real part of r^k will be close to zero and the complex part of r^k will be close to zero. We say that

$$\lim_{k \to \infty} r^k = 0.$$

So if both roots r and s satisfy $|r| < 1$ and $|s| < 1$, then r^k and s^k will both go to zero and the fixed point A will be attracting. Thus, we can restate Theorem 5.17 without the word 'real'.

**Theorem
5.19**

Suppose that the dynamical system

$$A(n + 2) = aA(n + 1) + bA(n) + c$$

has two roots r and s. If $|r| < 1$ and $|s| < 1$, then the fixed point is **attracting**. *If either $|r| > 1$ or $|s| > 1$, or both, then the fixed point is* **repelling**.

Proof: All we need to show is that, if $|r| = |a + bi| < 1$, then $|r^k|$ goes to zero. We **know**, since $|r| < 1$, that $|r|^k$ goes to zero. To prove the theorem, we will show that

$$|r^k| = |r|^k.$$

First we will show that if r and s are two complex numbers then $|rs| = |r||s|$, that is, you can multiply the numbers and then take the absolute value, or you can take the absolute value of each number and then multiply.

$$|rs| = |(a + bi)(c + di)| \quad \text{and} \quad |r||s| = |a + bi||c + di|.$$

We will see that they are equal. Since

$$(a + bi)(c + di) = (ac - bd) + (bc + ad)i,$$

it follows that

$$
\begin{aligned}
|(a + bi)(c + di)| &= \sqrt{(ac - bd)^2 + (bc + ad)^2} \\
&= \sqrt{(ac)^2 + (bd)^2 + (bc)^2 + (ad)^2}
\end{aligned}
$$

after multiplying out and canceling the $2abcd$ terms. Also,

$$
\begin{aligned}
|a + bi||c + di| &= \sqrt{a^2 + b^2}\sqrt{c^2 + d^2} \\
&= \sqrt{(a^2 + b^2)(c^2 + d^2)} \\
&= \sqrt{(ac)^2 + (bd)^2 + (bc)^2 + (ad)^2}.
\end{aligned}
$$

So we see that $|rs| = |r||s|$.

Now, let $A(n) = |r^n|$, where r is an complex number. Note that $|r^0| = 1$. We have just shown in the above argument that

$$A(2) = |r^2| = |r\,r| = |r||r| = |r|A(1)$$

and that

$$A(3) = |r^3| = |r\,r^2| = |r||r^2| = |r|A(2).$$

In fact,

$$A(n + 1) = |r^{n+1}| = |rr^n| = |r||r^n| = |r|A(n).$$

The solution to this first order linear dynamical system is

$$A(k) = |r|^k A(0) = |r|^k.$$

Thus, if $|r| < 1$, then

$$\lim_{k\to\infty} A(k) = \lim_{k\to\infty} |r^k| = \lim_{k\to\infty} |r|^k = 0$$

and the proof is complete.

Example 5.20

Consider the dynamical system

$$A(n + 2) = -0.25A(n) + 5. \tag{13}$$

The roots of the characteristic equation for the linear dynamical system

$$A(n + 2) = -0.25A(n)$$

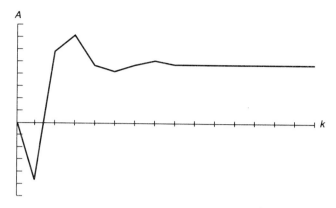

Fig. 52. A solution $(k, A(k))$ for the dynamical system $A(n + 2) = -0.25A(n) + 5$.

are $x = 0.5i$, and $x = -0.5i$. Therefore, the general solution of the nonhomogeneous equation is of the form

$$A(k) = c_1 (0.5i)^k + c_2 (-0.5i)^k + A,$$

where c_1 and c_2 depend on the initial values, while A depends on the equation. Substituting $A(n) = A$ into the dynamical system gives

$$A = -0.25A + 5, \quad \text{or} \quad A = 4.$$

Therefore, the general solution to the dynamical system is

$$A(k) = c_1 (0.5i)^k + c_2 (-0.5i)^k + 4.$$

Notice that $A = 4$ is the fixed point for this nonhomogeneous dynamical system. Since $|\pm 0.5i| = 0.5 < 1$, it follows that $c_1 (0.5i)^k$ and $c_2 (-0.5i)^k$ go to zero as k goes to infinity, so that $A(k)$ goes to 4. Thus, $A = 4$ is an attracting fixed point for this dynamical system. See Figure 52, in which the solution to this dynamical system is plotted with $A(0) = 0$ and $A(1) = -4$.

Example 5.21

Consider the second order dynamical system

$$A(n + 2) = 2A(n + 1) - 2A(n). \tag{14}$$

Note that the fixed point is $A = 0$. From the quadratic formula, the roots of the characteristic equation are

$$x = 1 \pm i,$$

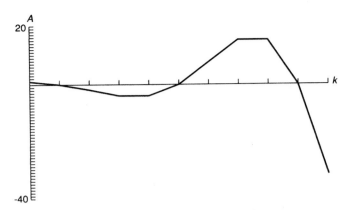

Fig. 53. A solution $(k, A(k))$ for the dynamical system $A(n+2) = 2A(n+1) - 2A(n)$.

and the general solution is

$$A(k) = c_1 (1 + i)^k + c_2 (1 - i)^k.$$

Since

$$|1 \pm i| = \sqrt{1^2 + 1^2} = \sqrt{2} > 1,$$

$A = 0$ is a repelling fixed point. This can be seen in Figure 53, where the particular solution is plotted with $A(0) = 1$ and $A(1) = 0$. Notice that $A(k)$ oscillates with increasing amplitude.

If $|a \pm bi| = 1$, then $|(a \pm bi)^k| = 1$ for all k, and so the 'size' of the solution remains constant in the sense that the solution oscillates. But we will see that the solution can behave in quite a strange manner.

Example 5.22

Consider the dynamical system

$$A(n + 2) = A(n + 1) - A(n). \tag{15}$$

The fixed point is again $A = 0$. The characteristic equation is

$$x^2 = x - 1.$$

From the quadratic formula, the roots are

$$x = \tfrac{1}{2} \pm \tfrac{\sqrt{3}}{2} i$$

The general solution is

$$A(k) = c_1 \left(\tfrac{1}{2} + \tfrac{\sqrt{3}}{2} i \right)^k + c_2 \left(\tfrac{1}{2} - \tfrac{\sqrt{3}}{2} i \right)^k.$$

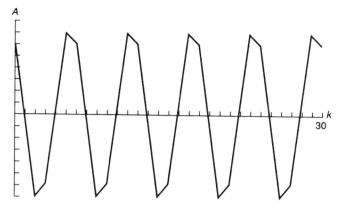

Fig. 54. A solution $(k, A(k))$ for the dynamical system $A(n + 2) = A(n + 1) - A(n)$.

Since $|1/2 \pm (\sqrt{3}/2)i| = \sqrt{1/4 + 3/4} = 1$, the fixed point is neither attracting nor repelling. This can be seen in Figure 54, in which the particular solution is plotted for $A(0) = 6$ and $A(1) = -1$. If you compute several values of $A(k)$, you will find that $A(2) = -7$, $A(3) = -6$, $A(4) = 1$, and $A(5) = 7$. You then find that these six numbers keep repeating, that is, $A(k)$ forms a **6-cycle**.

In fact, for any initial values $A(0)$ and $A(1)$, the solution to this dynamical system will form a 6-cycle. We will see why in a moment.

Let's see one more example in which the roots of the characteristic equation equal 1 in absolute value. The behavior of the solution will be quite interesting.

Example 5.23

Consider

$$A(n + 2) = 1.2A(n + 1) - A(n). \qquad (16)$$

The roots of the characteristic equation are

$$x = \tfrac{3}{5} \pm \tfrac{4}{5}i,$$

which satisfy $|3/5 \pm 4i/5| = 1$. In Figure 55, $A(k)$ is plotted with $A(0) = 1$ and $A(1) = -2$. Is it periodic? It doesn't appear to be, although it almost is (the peaks are slightly different).

This solution is what mathematicians call 'almost period'. We will not give a precise definition of almost period. Intuitively, a solution is almost period if it looks periodic (as this solution does), but it never repeats itself exactly.

You might wonder why solutions involving complex numbers tend to oscillate. The reason is that complex numbers are closely connected with

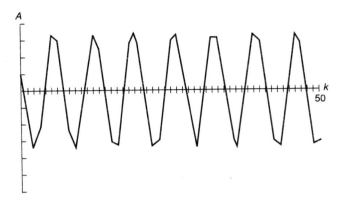

Fig. 55. A solution $(k, A(k))$ for the dynamical system $A(n+2) = 1.2A(n+1) - A(n)$.

trigonometric functions, specifically the sin and cos functions. Recall that the point (a, b) in the plane corresponds to the complex number $a + bi$. But a point in the plane can also be written in polar coordinates, that is, as $r \cos \theta + ir \sin \theta$, where $r = \sqrt{a^2 + b^2}$ and θ is the angle that the line from the origin to the point (a, b) makes with the positive x axis. Thus, by substitution, a solution involving complex numbers can be rewritten as

$$
\begin{aligned}
A(k) &= c_1 (a + bi)^k + c_2 (a - bi)^k \\
&= c_1 (r \cos \theta + ir \sin \theta)^k + c_2 (r \cos \theta - ir \sin \theta)^k \\
&= c_1 r^k (\cos \theta + i \sin \theta)^k + c_2 r^k (\cos \theta - i \sin \theta)^k.
\end{aligned}
$$

It happens that

$$(\cos \theta + i \sin \theta)^k = \cos k\theta + i \sin k\theta \tag{17}$$

and

$$(\cos \theta - i \sin \theta)^k = \cos k\theta - i \sin k\theta. \tag{18}$$

Substitution of equations (17) and (18) into the general solution and then simplification gives

$$A(k) = r^k (c_3 \cos k\theta + c_4 \sin k\theta),$$

where $c_3 = c_1 + c_2$ and $c_4 = i(c_1 - c_2)$.

Proof of equation (17): We know that the particular solution to the dynamical system

$$A(n + 1) = (\cos \theta + i \sin \theta)A(n)$$

with $A(0) = 1$ is

$$A(k) = (\cos \theta + i \sin \theta)^k.$$

We will now show that the particular solution also is given by

$$A(k) = \cos k\theta + i \sin k\theta. \tag{19}$$

Since there is only one particular solution, these two solutions must be equal and we have equation (17). From equation (19), we have by the formulas for addition of angles that

$$
\begin{aligned}
A(n+1) &= \cos(n+1)\theta + i \sin(n+1)\theta \\
&= \cos n\theta \cos \theta - \sin n\theta \sin \theta + i(\sin n\theta \cos \theta + \cos n\theta \sin \theta) \\
&= (\cos \theta + i \sin \theta)(\cos n\theta + i \sin n\theta) \\
&= (\cos \theta + i \sin \theta)A(n).
\end{aligned}
$$

Thus, equation (19) satisfies the dynamical system. Since it satisfies the initial condition, it is also the particular solution and our claim is proved.

Put another way, if the characteristic equation for a second order linear dynamical system has $x = a \pm bi$ as its two roots, the general solution can be written as

$$A(k) = r^k (c_3 \cos k\theta + c_4 \sin k\theta),$$

where $r = \sqrt{a^2 + b^2}$ and θ is the angle between the line $y = bx/a$ and the x axis. From this it can be seen that solutions involving complex numbers will oscillate.

In the case of the dynamical system (13),

$$A(n+2) = -0.25A(n) + 5,$$

of Example 5.20, the roots of the characteristic equation are $x = \pm i/2$. In this case, $r = 1/2$ and $\theta = \pi/2$, so the general solution can be written as

$$A(k) = \left(\tfrac{1}{2}\right)^k \left(c_3 \cos \frac{k\pi}{2} + c_4 \sin \frac{k\pi}{2}\right) + 4.$$

Now it is clear that $A(k)$ converges to 4 since $(0.5)^k$ goes to zero. It is also clear that the solution oscillates, each oscillation requiring 4 units of time since $\cos 0.5(k+4)\pi = \cos 0.5k\pi$.

In the case of the dynamical system (14)

$$A(n+2) = 2A(n+1) - 2A(n)$$

of Example 5.21, the roots of the characteristic equation are $x = 1 \pm i$, so that $r = \sqrt{2}$ and $\theta = \pi/4$. In this case, the general solution is

$$A(k) = (\sqrt{2})^k \left(c_3 \cos \frac{k\pi}{4} + c_4 \sin \frac{k\pi}{4} \right).$$

This clearly oscillates to infinity, each oscillation requiring 8 units of time since $\pi/4$ is one-eighth of 2π.

In the case of the dynamical system (15),

$$A(n + 2) = A(n + 1) - A(n),$$

of Example 5.22, the roots of the characteristic equation are $x = 0.5 \pm 0.5\sqrt{3}i$, so that $r = 1$ and $\theta = \pi/3$. In this case, the general solution is

$$A(k) = c_3 \cos \frac{k\pi}{3} + c_4 \sin \frac{k\pi}{3}.$$

This solution is periodic with period 6 since $\cos(k + 6)\theta = \cos k\theta$.

In the case of the dynamical system (16),

$$A(n + 2) = 1.2A(n + 1) - A(n),$$

of Example 5.22, the roots of the characteristic equation are $x = 3/5 \pm 4i/5$, so that $r = 1$ and $\theta = \arctan 4/3$. The general solution is

$$A(k) = c_3 \cos k\theta + c_4 \sin k\theta.$$

If some multiple m of θ equals some multiple of 2π, then the general solution is periodic with that period m. But, in this example, θ is an irrational multiple of 2π, so the solution never **exactly** repeats itself, although it comes very close to doing so.

5.7.1 Problems

1. Compute the following:

   (a) $(2 + 3i)(7 - 2i)$

   (b) $(-1 + 3i)(5 + 4i)$

   (c) $(2 - 7i)^2$

   (d) $|2 - 7i|$

   (e) $|2 + i|$

2. Consider the dynamical system

$$A(n + 2) = 4A(n + 1) - 5A(n).$$

    (a) Find the general solution using complex numbers.

    (b) Is $A = 0$ an attracting or repelling fixed point?

    (c) Given that $A(0) = 2$ and $A(1) = 6$, plot the particular solution from $(0, A(0))$ through $(5, A(5))$.

3. Consider the dynamical system

$$A(n + 2) = -A(n + 1) - 0.5A(n).$$

    (a) Find the general solution using complex numbers.

    (b) Find the general solution in terms of $\sin k\theta$ and $\cos k\theta$.

    (c) Is zero an attracting or repelling fixed point?

    (d) Given that $A(0) = 0$ and $A(1) = -1$, find the particular solution using complex numbers.

    (e) Given that $A(0) = 0$ and $A(1) = -1$, find the particular solution using trigonometric functions.

4. Consider the dynamical system

$$A(n + 2) = 4A(n + 1) - 5A(n) + 6.$$

    (a) Find the general solution using complex numbers.

    (b) Find the fixed point and determine if it is attracting or repelling.

5. Consider the dynamical system

$$A(n + 2) = -A(n + 1) - 0.5A(n) - 5.$$

    (a) Find the general solution using complex numbers.

    (b) Find the fixed point and determine if it is attracting or repelling.

5.8 A model of a national economy

In this section, we show how dynamical systems can be used in economics by presenting a simplified model of a nation's economy. To do this, we make four assumptions.

    Assumption 1: The national income is composed of three elements: income from consumer expenditures, private investment, and government expenditures, denoted by C, I, and G, respectively. The total national income, denoted by T, is the sum of these three parts, that is,

$$T = C + I + G.$$

While consumption, investment, and government expenditures are being done continuously, they are only known at discrete periods of time, for example, quarterly reports issued by the government. We shall assume that these components depend on a time period, n. Thus, the total national income during time period n is

$$T(n) = C(n) + I(n) + G(n). \tag{20}$$

The above components of national income could be subdivided into more components and other components could be added, to give a more complex model of the economy.

Assumption 2: We assume that individuals (companies, and the government) save a certain fixed proportion of their income, and therefore spend a fixed proportion of their incomes. This money is spent in the time period after it is earned, that is, consumption in time period $n+1$ is proportional to the total income in time period n. Mathematically, this is

$$C(n + 1) = aT(n). \tag{21}$$

Again, we realize this is a gross over-simplification. We could have assumed, for example, that there is a certain fixed consumption, C, and that a certain fixed proportion of the excess income, $T(n) - C$, is saved. This would give $C(n + 1) = aT(n) + b$.

Assumption 3: Private investment (in buying new machines or building new factories) depends on the **change** in consumption, that is, if consumption increases, more factories will be needed to produce the material being consumed, so investment must be high. But if consumption decreases, then existing factories are sufficient to produce materials, so investment will be small. Thus, an investor, in time period $n + 1$, compares the present consumption, $C(n+1)$, to the past consumption, $C(n)$, and looks at the change in consumption, $C(n + 1) - C(n)$. If this is a large positive number, people are spending more, and thus the investment, $I(n + 1)$, should be large. If $C(n+1) - C(n)$ is small, the investment is small. In short, investment in time period $n + 1$ is proportional to the **change** in consumption from time period n to time period $n + 1$, that is

$$I(n + 1) = b(C(n + 1) - C(n)). \tag{22}$$

One might argue that by the time the investors know $C(n + 1)$ and $C(n)$, it is one time period later before they can act on this information.

Thus, we would have $I(n + 2) = b[C(n + 1) - C(n)]$. But we could also argue that investors tend to watch current trends and have a good idea of what $C(n+1)$ will be ahead of its publication, and therefore we keep our original assumption. (Also, the equation given in this paragraph would lead to a third order dynamical system which would lead to more difficult analysis.)

Assumption 4: Let's assume that government expenditures are constant. Whatever this amount, we let it represent one unit of money, that is,

$$G(n) = 1 \tag{23}$$

for all n.

While this last assumption seems unrealistic, it is more reasonable if we are assuming that all units of money are based on today's value of money, that is, the government's increases in expenditures equal the inflation rate. Thus, the **value** of the government's expenditures remains constant. While there are other equally valid assumptions about governmental expenditures, such as a proportion of the taxes, which is a proportion of total income, we will keep our relatively simple assumption 4.

Thus, our assumptions translate into the four equations (20), (21), (22), and (23).

The constant a in equation (21) is known as the **marginal propensity to consume**, or MPC. Since what is not spent is saved, $1-$MPC is called the **marginal propensity to save**, or MPS. The constant b in equation (22) is called the **constant of adjustment**.

We substitute 1 for $G(n)$, and then $n + 2$ for n in equation (20), to get

$$T(n + 2) = C(n + 2) + I(n + 2) + 1.$$

From the third assumption, equation (22), we make the substitution of $I(n + 2) = b[C(n + 2) - C(n + 1)]$ into our last equation, giving

$$\begin{aligned} T(n + 2) &= C(n + 2) + b(C(n + 2) - C(n + 1)) + 1 \\ &= (1 + b)C(n + 2) - bC(n + 1) + 1. \end{aligned}$$

From equation (21), we make the substitutions $C(n+2) = aT(n+1)$, and $C(n + 1) = aT(n)$, giving the second order nonhomogeneous dynamical system

$$T(n + 2) = (1 + b)aT(n + 1) - baT(n) + 1 \tag{24}$$

as our model for the national economy. This dynamical system is a variation of the Samuelson (1939) accelerator-multiplier model.

Example 5.24

Consider the case in which $a = 0.9$ and $b = 0.5$. Dynamical system (24) becomes

$$T(n + 2) = 1.35T(n + 1) - 0.45T(n) + 1.$$

The roots of the characteristic equation are, from the quadratic formula, $r = 0.75$ and $r = 0.6$. Thus, the general solution is of the form

$$T(k) = c_1 (0.75)^k + c_2 (0.6)^k + T,$$

where c_1 and c_2 depend on the initial values, while the constant T depends on the dynamical system. Substituting $T(n) = T$ into the non-homogeneous equation and solving gives the equilibrium value as $T = 10$. Thus, the general solution is

$$T(k) = c_1 (0.75)^k + c_2 (0.6)^k + 10.$$

Since $0.75 < 1$ and $0.6 < 1$, the equilibrium value is stable.

In this section, we will use the terminology 'stable and unstable equilibrium' instead of 'attracting and repelling fixed point'. The reason is that we are describing an economy, so it makes sense to refer to an economy that is in equilibrium. We would then call the economy in Example 5.24, a stable economy (not an attracting economy). As discussed before, the terminology you use depends on what you are doing.

Example 5.25

Consider the case in which $a = 0.9$ and $b = 1$. Dynamical system (24) becomes

$$T(n + 2) = 1.8T(n + 1) - 0.9T(n) + 1.$$

The roots of the characteristic equation are, by the quadratic formula, $r = 0.9 + 0.3i$ and $r = 0.9 - 0.3i$. Thus, the general solution is of the form

$$T(k) = c_1 (0.9 + 0.3i)^k + c_2 (0.9 - 0.3i)^k + T.$$

Substituting $T(n) = T$ into the nonhomogeneous equation and solving gives $T = 10$. Thus, the general solution is

$$T(k) = c_1 (0.9 + 0.3i)^k + c_2 (0.9 - 0.3i)^k + 10.$$

Since

$$|0.9 \pm 0.3i| = \sqrt{(0.9)^2 + (0.3)^2} = \sqrt{0.9} = 0.9487 < 1,$$

the equilibrium value is stable. Recall from the previous section that the complex roots cause the solution to oscillate to equilibrium. See Figure 56, in which $T(0) = 4$ and $T(1) = 5$ for one such solution.

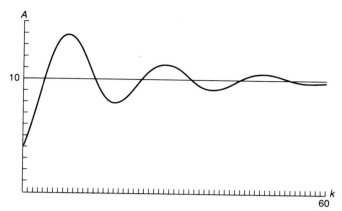

Fig. 56. One solution $(k, T(k))$ for the dynamical system $T(n + 2) = 1.8T(n + 1) - 0.9T(n) + 1$.

Example 5.26

Consider the case in which $a = 0.9$ and $b = 1.5$. Dynamical system (24) becomes

$$T(n + 2) = 2.25T(n + 1) - 1.35T(n) + 1$$

in this case. The roots of the corresponding characteristic equation are, from the quadratic formula, $r = 1.125 \pm 0.29i$, and so the general solution is

$$T(k) = c_1 (1.125 + 0.29i)^k + c_2 (1.125 - 0.29i)^k + T.$$

By substituting $T(n) = T$ into the nonhomogeneous equation and solving, we again find that $T = 10$. Thus, the general solution is

$$T(k) = c_1 (1.125 + 0.29i)^k + c_2 (1.125 - 0.29i)^k + 10.$$

Since

$$|1.125 \pm 0.29i| = \sqrt{1.35} = 1.16 > 1$$

the equilibrium value is unstable. The complex roots cause the solution to oscillate away from equilibrium.

Let's now consider the general case of equation (24)

$$T(n + 2) = a(1 + b)T(n + 1) - abT(n) + 1.$$

Let's first find the equilibrium value, which is also the constant term added to the general solution to the dynamical system. Substituting $T(n) = T$ into the equation gives

$$T = a(1 + b)T - abT + 1, \quad \text{or} \quad (1 - a - ab + ab)T = 1.$$

Canceling the ab terms and then dividing by $(1 - a)$ gives

$$T = \frac{1}{1 - a} = \frac{1}{\text{MPS}}$$

as the equilibrium value. Notice that the economy's equilibrium value depends only on the value of a, the marginal propensity to consume.

We now know that the general solution to the dynamical system is

$$T(k) = c_1 (r_1)^k + c_2 (r_2)^k + \frac{1}{1 - a},$$

where r_1 and r_2 are the roots of the characteristic equation

$$r^2 - a(1 + b)r + ab = 0.$$

Using the quadratic formula, the roots are

$$r_1 = \tfrac{1}{2} \left(a(1 + b) + \sqrt{a^2(1 + b)^2 - 4ab} \right)$$

and

$$r_2 = \tfrac{1}{2} \left(a(1 + b) - \sqrt{a^2(1 + b)^2 - 4ab} \right).$$

We need to find out when the roots are real and when they are complex. The roots are complex when the discriminant is negative, that is, when

$$a^2(1 + b)^2 - 4ab < 0.$$

Since $a > 0$, we can divide both sides by a, giving

$$a(1 + b)^2 < 4b, \quad \text{or} \quad a < \frac{4b}{(1 + b)^2}.$$

The curve $a = 4b/(1 + b)^2$ is plotted in Figure 57. All points (a, b) below that curve give rise to complex roots, while all points above that curve give rise to real roots. (Using calculus to plot this curve is an interesting exercise.)

When the roots are complex, that is, $a^2(1 + b)^2 - 4ab < 0$, we have

$$\left| \frac{a(1 + b)}{2} \pm \frac{i}{2}\sqrt{4ab - a^2(1 + b)^2} \right| = \tfrac{1}{2}\sqrt{a^2(1 + b)^2 + 4ab - a^2(1 + b)^2}$$

$$= \sqrt{ab}.$$

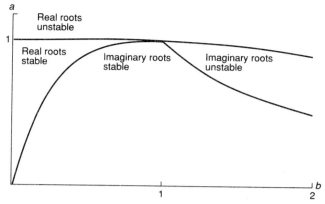

Fig. 57. Regions of stability and instability for an economy satisfying $T(n+2) = a(1+b)T(n+1) - abT(n) + 1$.

The equilibrium value is therefore stable when $\sqrt{ab} < 1$. Squaring both sides and dividing by b gives the condition that the equilibrium value is stable if

$$a < \frac{1}{b}.$$

Thus, points (a,b) which are below this curve and below the curve $a = 4b/(1+b)^2$ give rise to complex roots (which cause oscillations) and cause the equilibrium value to be stable. One such point is $a = 0.9$ and $b = 1$, which we studied in Example 5.25. See Figure 57, in which this region is labeled.

Also in Figure 57, we have labeled the region in which points are above the curve $a = 1/b$ and below the curve $a = 4b/(1+b)^2$, which correspond to complex roots (or oscillations) but an unstable equilibrium value. An example of this is $a = 0.9$ and $b = 1.5$, which was studied in Example 5.26.

In the case where $a > 4b/(1+b)^2$, we have real roots, the largest of which is

$$r = \frac{a(1+b) + \sqrt{a^2(1+b)^2 - 4ab}}{2}.$$

The question is, when is $r > 1$ and when is $r < 1$? The inequality

$$\frac{a(1+b) + \sqrt{a^2(1+b)^2 - 4ab}}{2} < 1$$

is a bit tricky, but the solution, which is plotted in Figure 57, consists of the points (a,b) such that $a < 1$, $b < 1$, and the point (a,b) is above the curve $a = 4b/(1+b)^2$. An example of such a point is $a = 0.9$ and $b = 0.5$.

This was considered in Example 5.24. You should check that, when $a = 0.9$ and $b = 2$, the root r_1 is real and greater than 1, so the equilibrium value is unstable.

Notice that in most applications $a < 1$, for otherwise people would be spending **more** than the country's income. Also, it is reasonable that $b < 1$, since otherwise the investment would be more than could be made from the increase in sales or consumption C. Thus, in reality, an unstable equilibrium will only occur from complex roots. Thus the economy is unstable when

$$a > \frac{1}{b},$$

that is, when the marginal propensity to spend is greater than the inverse of the constant of adjustment.

Let's discuss this result. The constant b is a measure of how the investors react to good and bad news. Thus, the larger b, the more sensitive the investors are to consumption. Likewise, a is a measure of how consumers react to the economy, that is, the larger a, the more the consumers spend. Our result that we need $a < 1/b$ to have a stable economy says that if one of these constants is large, the other must be small.

Suppose that the government has found that we are in an unstable economy. What can be done? They need to reduce either a or b. One possible method would be to increase taxes to reduce the amount available for spending, which would reduce a and make the economy stable. Another method would be to encourage saving by not taxing certain savings accounts. But a reduction in a would mean an increase in $1 - a$, the marginal propensity to save. Recall that the equilibrium value was $T = 1/(1 - a)$, so this policy would **reduce** the total national economy and possibly lead to a recession.

Another possible solution would be for the government to change from having constant expenditures to having variable expenditures. Thus, as the economy oscillates with increasing amplitude, the government could have a one or two time change in expenditures to try to bring the $T(k)$ values closer to equilibrium. This would require constant supervision since as soon as the economy is brought close to equilibrium, it will start oscillating away. Also, if the government is not careful, this change might cause worse oscillations instead of better ones. Also, since there is usually a time delay before the government reacts, we might have $G(n + 1) = cT(n)$ or $G(n + 2) = cT(n)$. This would lead to a new dynamical system and its stability needs to be studied. One such analysis is in Baumol (1961).

Economists often make models of a nation's economy, such as this one. They also use these models to help them make policy decisions to keep a prosperous economy. But just as we saw in the previous discussion, there is often no perfect solution, and they must choose between the least of many evils.

As a last mathematical comment, notice that points on the curve $a = 4b/(1+b)^2$ give rise to the double root

$$r = \frac{a(1+b)}{2}.$$

In this case, the general solution is

$$T(k) = (c_1 + c_2 k) \left(\frac{a(1+b)}{2} \right)^k + \frac{1}{1-a},$$

and the equilibrium value is stable when

$$\frac{a(1+b)}{2} < 1, \quad \text{or} \quad a < \frac{2}{1+b}.$$

Values of a and b that are on the line $a = 4b/(1+b)^2$, with $b < 1$ satisfy this condition, and so the line separating the real stable roots from the complex stable roots also gives rise to a stable equilibrium value. Points on that curve with $b > 1$ correspond to unstable equilibrium so the line separating unstable real roots from unstable complex roots also corresponds to an unstable equilibrium.

5.8.1 Problems

1. Suppose the government spends 2 units in each time period instead of 1 unit. What is the equilibrium value?

2. Suppose that investment is made according to the formula $I(n+2) = b[C(n+1)-C(n)]$. With the other assumptions remaining the same, develop a third order dynamical system that models this economy.

3. Suppose that, instead of the government having fixed expenditures, it increases its expenditures by 5 per cent each time period, that is, $G(n) = (1.05)^n$. Assuming that $a = 0.9$ and $b = 0.5$, find a second order nonhomogeneous dynamical system to model the economy and then find the general solution to that equation.

4. Consider the model of the economy in which $a = 0.9$ and $b = 2$.

   (a) Find the general solution to the equation. Observe that the equilibrium value 10 is unstable.

(b) Suppose we develop the strategy that when $T(n) < 9$ the government increases its expenditures by 1 unit in the next time interval (to a total of 2), that is, $G(n+1) = 3$, and when $T(n) > 11$ then $G(n + 1) = 0$. To see if this will stablize the economy, use this strategy to compute $T(2)$ through $T(10)$ when $T(0) = 9.6$ and $T(1) = 9.4$.

(c) Repeat part (b), except that the government has a two time period delay, that is, when $T(n) < 9$ then $G(n + 2) = 3$, and when $T(n) > 11$ then $G(n + 2) = 0$.

5. Suppose that the dynamical system

$$T(n + 2) = abT(n + 1) - aT(n) + 3$$

models our economy.

(a) What is the equilibrium value?

(b) What are the two roots of the characteristic equation corresponding to the linear second order dynamical system?

(c) Find a curve $a = f(b)$ such that if the point (a, b) is below that curve then the roots are complex.

(d) Assuming that the values for a and b are such that the roots are complex. Find a condition that implies the equilibrium value is stable.

6. Suppose that the dynamical system

$$T(n + 2) = abT(n + 1) - ab^2T(n) + 1$$

models our economy.

(a) What is the equilibrium value?

(b) What are the two roots of the characteristic equation?

(c) Find a curve $a = f(b)$ such that if the point (a, b) is below that curve then the roots are complex.

(d) Assuming that the values for a and b are such that the roots are complex, find a condition that implies the equilibrium value is stable.

5.9 Dynamical systems with order greater than two

We now know how to handle first and second order linear dynamical systems. Higher order (third, fourth, and so on) linear equations require nothing new.

Example 5.27

Consider the third order dynamical system

$$A(n + 3) = 6A(n + 2) - 11A(n + 1) + 6A(n). \qquad (25)$$

The first step for finding the general solution is to substitute $A(n) = r^n$ into this equation, and then divide by r^n, to get the characteristic equation

$$r^3 = 6r^2 - 11r + 6.$$

The second step is to bring all the terms to one side, say the left, and factor, giving

$$(r - 1)(r - 2)(r - 3) = 0.$$

Thus, the roots of the characteristic equation are $r = 1$, 2, and 3. Since there are no multiple roots, the general solution is

$$A(k) = a + b\,2^k + c\,3^k,$$

since $1^n = 1$.

If we are given three initial values such as $A(0) = 2$, $A(1) = 3$, and $A(2) = 7$, we can then find the particular solution by solving the system of three equations

$$
\begin{aligned}
A(0) &= a + b2^0 + c3^0 = a + b + c = 2,\\
A(1) &= a + b2^1 + c3^1 = a + 2b + 3c = 3,\\
A(2) &= a + b2^2 + c3^2 = a + 4b + 9c = 7.
\end{aligned}
$$

It is easy to see that the solution to these equations is $a = 2$, $b = -1$, and $c = 1$. The particular solution to dynamical system (25) is

$$A(k) = 2 - 2^k + 3^k.$$

As before, when r is a multiple root for the characteristic equation, the general solution contains terms of the form r^n, nr^n, n^2r^n, and so forth, until we have the same number of terms as the multiplicity of r.

Example 5.28

The fourth order dynamical system

$$A(n + 4) = 4A(n + 3) - 16A(n + 1) + 16A(n)$$

has characteristic equation

$$r^4 - 4r^3 + 16r - 16 = 0.$$

By a lucky guess, we see that $r = 2$ is a root of this equation. Dividing $(r - 2)$ into the characteristic equation gives

$$r^3 - 2r^2 - 4r + 8 = 0.$$

Another lucky guess of $r = 2$ tells us that 2 is (at least) a double root of the characteristic equation. Again, we divide the last equation by $(r - 2)$, giving

$$r^2 - 4 = 0.$$

Factoring this into $(r - 2)(r + 2)$, we see that the original characteristic equation factors into

$$r^4 - 4r^3 + 16r - 16 = (r - 2)^3(r + 2) = 0.$$

Since 2 is a triple root of the equation, the general solution has terms of the form 2^n, $n2^n$, and $n^2 2^n$ (three terms), as well as the term $(-2)^n$ (since -2 is also a root). Thus, the general solution is, after factoring out a 2^n from the first three terms,

$$A(k) = 2^k(a + bk + ck^2) + d(-2)^k,$$

where a, b, c, and d are four constants which depend on the initial values $A(0)$, $A(1)$, $A(2)$, and $A(3)$.

The main difficulty with higher order equations is that it may be difficult or impossible to factor the characteristic equation. Often other techniques, such as Newton's method (Section 3.4), must be used.

Let's consider an application of higher order dynamical systems to the study of population growth. To make things easy, we will assume that growth rates are constant and not dependent on population size. This will make the equations linear. Things are hard enough without working with nonlinear higher order equations. Consider a species which can be broken into three equal age groups, 0–1 years, 1–2 years, and 2–3 years. Instead of years we could have said decades, etc. Let $A(n)$ represent the number of individuals in the 0–1 age group in year n. Likewise, let $B(n)$ and $C(n)$ represent the individuals in the 1–2 and 2–3 age groups, respectively, in year n.

There are two pieces of information we need: the survival rate for each age group, and the fertility rate for each age group.

First, consider the survival rate. Suppose half of the individuals in the 0–1 age group survive a year, that is, $B(n + 1) = 0.5A(n)$. Also suppose two-thirds of the individuals in the 1–2 age group survive to the next year, that is, $C(n + 1) = (2/3)B(n)$.

Second, consider the fertility rate. Suppose that each year, on the average, each individual in the 0–1 age group has 0.5 offspring, each individual in the 1–2 age group has 5 offspring, and each individual in the 2–3 age group has 3 offspring. Since individuals in the 0–1 age group in year $n + 1$ are offspring of some individual in year n, it follows that

$$A(n + 1) = 0.5A(n) + 5B(n) + 3C(n).$$

We now need to derive a dynamical system involving only one age group. Since $B(n + 1) = 0.5A(n)$, we can make the substitutions $A(n) = 2B(n + 1)$ and $A(n + 1) = 2B(n + 2)$ in the above equation, giving

$$2B(n + 2) = B(n + 1) + 5B(n) + 3C(n).$$

Since $C(n + 1) = (2/3)B(n)$, we can make the substitutions $B(n) = (3/2)C(n + 1)$, $B(n + 1) = (3/2)C(n + 2)$, and $B(n + 2) = (3/2)C(n + 3)$ into the above equation, giving

$$2 \times \tfrac{3}{2} \times C(n + 3) = \tfrac{3}{2}C(n + 2) + 5 \times \tfrac{3}{2} \times C(n + 1) + 3C(n).$$

After dividing both sides by 3 and simplifying, we get

$$C(n + 3) = 0.5C(n + 2) + 2.5C(n + 1) + C(n).$$

The characteristic equation for this dynamical system is

$$r^3 - 0.5r^2 - 2.5r - 1 = 0,$$

which factors into

$$(r + 0.5)(r + 1)(r - 2) = 0.$$

It then follows that the general solution for the 2–3 age group is

$$C(k) = a(-0.5)^k + b(-1)^k + c(2)^k.$$

Since $B(n) = (3/2)C(n + 1)$, it follows that

$$
\begin{aligned}
B(k) &= \tfrac{3}{2}C(k + 1) \\
&= \tfrac{3}{2}a(-0.5)^{k+1} + \tfrac{3}{2}b(-1)^{k+1} + \tfrac{3}{2}c(2)^{k+1} \\
&= -\tfrac{3}{4}a(-0.5)^k - \tfrac{3}{2}b(-1)^k + 3c(2)^k.
\end{aligned}
$$

Similarly, we find that

$$
\begin{aligned}
A(k) &= 2B(k+1) = 2\left[-\tfrac{3}{4}a(-0.5)^{k+1} - \tfrac{3}{2}b(-1)^{k+1} + 3c(2)^{k+1}\right] \\
&= -\tfrac{3}{2}a(-0.5)^{k+1} - 3b(-1)^{k+1} + 6c(2)^{k+1} \\
&= \tfrac{3}{4}a(-0.5)^{k} + 3b(-1)^{k} + 12c(2)^{k}.
\end{aligned}
$$

Because of the $(2)^k$ term, the population grows exponentially. To get more information from our model, divide $A(k)$, $B(k)$, and $C(k)$ by $c\,(2)^k$. In this case,

$$
\begin{aligned}
\frac{A(k)}{c2^k} &= \frac{3a}{4c}(-0.25)^k + \frac{3b}{c}(-0.5)^k + 12, \\
\frac{B(k)}{c2^k} &= \frac{-3a}{4c}(-0.25)^k - \frac{3b}{2c}(-0.5)^k + 3, \\
\frac{C(k)}{c2^k} &= \frac{a}{c}(-0.25)^k + \frac{b}{c}(-0.5)^k + 1.
\end{aligned}
$$

Since $(-0.25)^k$ and $(-0.5)^k$ go to zero, it follows that for large k,

$$
\lim_{k\to\infty}\frac{A(k)}{c2^k} = 12, \quad \lim_{k\to\infty}\frac{B(k)}{c2^k} = 3, \quad \lim_{k\to\infty}\frac{C(k)}{c2^k} = 1.
$$

In other words, for large k, the three age groups are in the ratio

$$
(A(k) : B(k) : C(k)) = (12 : 3 : 1).
$$

Thus, we have seen from this model that populations may grow exponentially, but that the ratios of the different age groups may become stable.

Some species reproduce in a continuous manner, so this would not be a good model. One species for which this model seems to work reasonably well is the blue whale. The blue whale mates between June 20 and August 20. The gestation period is 1 year and they nurse for 7 more months, so they only reproduce every 2 years.

When we break a population into m age groups, this approach leads to an mth order linear dynamical system which means we must factor an mth order polynomial. If we were considering humans, we could break the (reproductive) age of the population into five age groups, 0–10, 10–20, $\ldots$, 40–50, or we could break the population into 50 age groups, 0–1, 1–2, $\ldots$, 49–50. The first grouping would be easier to work with; the second might give more information.

Suppose we have m roots to the characteristic equation, r_1, r_2, $\ldots$, r_m. Suppose that $r_1 > |r_j|$ for $j = 2, 3, \ldots, m$. Then by dividing the size of each age group by $(r_1)^k$, as we divided $A(k)$, $B(k)$, and $C(k)$ by 2^k, we can find the relative age distribution of the population $((12{:}3{:}1)$ in the above discussion). There are mathematical techniques that enable us to find this value of r_1. They will be discussed in Section 6.9.

In some cases, the largest value of $|r_j|$ occurs when r_j is a complex number. As we remember, r^k, when r is complex, causes cycles. In this case we find that each age group has cyclic behavior, that is, the size of each age group rises and falls, causing what is known as population waves. This may explain occurences such as the baby boom population and the offspring of this generation. See Hoppensteadt (1982) for further details.

Sometimes a species has a low reproductive rate until it reaches adulthood. For example, the American bison does not reproduce for the first 2 years. Once it reaches adulthood, the birth rate and death rate are approximately constant for the 2–3, 3–4, etc., age groups. We could develop a large number of equations that would reduce to one high order dynamical system. But there is a trick that will keep the number of equations to a minimum. Suppose that we have 'three' age groups 0–1, 1–2, and adults. The number of each age group present at the beginning of the nth year is denoted $A(n)$, $B(n)$, and $C(n)$, respectively. Suppose that the fraction of each age group that survives to the next year is 0.8, 0.5, and 0.8, respectively. Since those in the 0–1 age group that survive a year will be in the 1–2 age group, and those in the 1–2 age group and in the adult age group that survive the year will then be in the adult age group, we can summarize these results with the two equations

$$B(n+1) = 0.8A(n) \quad \text{and} \quad C(n+1) = 0.5B(n) + 0.8C(n).$$

Suppose that the reproductive rates for the three age groups are 1.2, 10.2625, and 23.92, respectively. Since the offspring in each group during one time period will be in the 0–1 age group at the beginning of the next time period, we get the reproductive equation

$$A(n+1) = 1.2A(n) + 10.2625B(n) + 23.92C(n).$$

From the first two equations we get

$$A(n) = 1.25B(n+1) \quad \text{and} \quad B(n) = 2C(n+1) - 1.6C(n).$$

Using these two equations to substitute into the reproductive equation, we find (after some simplification) that

$$C(n+3) = 2C(n+2) + 7.25C(n+1) + 3C(n).$$

Factoring the characteristic equation gives

$$r^3 - 2r^2 - 7.25r - 3 = (r-4)(r+1.5)(r+0.5) = 0,$$

so the general solution is

$$C(k) = a4^k + b(-1.5)^k + c(-0.5)^k.$$

Thus,

$$\lim_{k \to \infty} \frac{C(k)}{a4^k} = \lim_{k \to \infty} 1 + \frac{b}{a}\left(-\frac{3}{8}\right)^k + \frac{c}{a}\left(-\frac{1}{8}\right)^k = 1.$$

As a note, by substituting $k+1$ for k, we also have

$$\lim_{k \to \infty} \frac{C(k+1)}{a4^{k+1}} = 1.$$

From the formulas $B(n) = 2C(n+1) - 1.6C(n)$ and $A(n) = 1.25B(n+1)$, we have

$$\lim_{k \to \infty} \frac{B(k)}{a4^k} = \lim_{k \to \infty} \left(\frac{2C(k+1)}{a4^k} - \frac{1.6C(k)}{a4^k}\right)$$

$$= \lim_{k \to \infty} \left(8\frac{C(k+1)}{a4^{k+1}} - 1.6\frac{C(k)}{a4^k}\right)$$

$$= (8(1) - 1.6(1)) = 6.4$$

and

$$\lim_{k \to \infty} \frac{A(k)}{a4^k} = \lim_{k \to \infty} \frac{1.25B(k+1)}{a4^k} = \lim_{k \to \infty} 6\frac{B(k+1)}{a4^{k+1}} = 5(6.4) = 32.$$

From this, we find that eventually the relative ratios of the three age groups will be approximately $(A : B : C) = (32 : 6.4 : 1)$.

One species to which this model has been applied is the American bison. Bison break down into three groups: calves (0–1 age group), yearlings (1–2 age group), and adults. The calves have a survival rate of 0.6, the yearlings have a survival rate of 0.75, and the adults have a survival rate of 0.95. Only adults reproduce, with a reproduction rate of 0.42. Only females are counted in these rates.

5.9.1 Problems

1. Suppose a species has two age groups. Suppose that the survival rate for the 0–1 age group is 0.8 and the reproductive rate is 2, while the reproductive rate for the 1–2 age group is 3.75. Find a second order dynamical system to model this population and find the long term ratio of the 0–1 age group to the 1–2 age group.

2. Suppose a species has two age groups. Suppose that the survival rate for the 0–1 age group is 0.91 and the reproductive rate is 0.6, while the reproductive rate for the 1–2 age group is 1.0. Find a second order dynamical system to model this population and find the long term ratio of the 0–1 age group to the 1–2 age group.

3. Suppose a species has two age groups: 0–1 and adults. Suppose that the survival rate for the 0–1 age group is 0.5 and the reproductive rate is 1.8, while the survival rate of the adults is 0.8 and the reproductive rate is 4. Find a second order dynamical system to model this population and find the long term ratio of the 0–1 age group to the adults.

4. Consider the following dynamical system of three equations:

$$\begin{aligned}
A(n+1) &= 2B(n), \\
B(n+1) &= 3C(n), \\
C(n+1) &= A(n) - \tfrac{11}{3}B(n) + 6C(n).
\end{aligned}$$

   (a) Rewrite these as a third order equation in terms of C.

   (b) Find the general solution.

   (c) Find the long term ratios $(A : B : C)$.

5. Find the long term ratios of calves to yearlings to adults among American bison. You will need to use Newton's method to find a root of the characteristic equation.

Dynamical systems of several equations

6.1 Introduction to dynamical systems of several equations

In Section 5.9, we developed a model for population growth in which the population was divided into three age groups. With $a(n)$, $b(n)$, and $c(n)$ representing the first, second, and third age groups, respectively, in time period n, we derived the following dynamical system of three equations:

$$
\begin{aligned}
a(n+1) &= 0.5a(n) + 5b(n) + 3c(n) \\
b(n+1) &= 0.5a(n) \\
c(n+1) &= \tfrac{2}{3}b(n).
\end{aligned}
$$

In this chapter we will learn how to use matrix algebra to study dynamical systems of several equations such as this one. Note that we are using small letters instead of capital letters to write these equations.

To understand how the population modeled by the above three equations behaves, we need to compute solutions for $a(k)$, $b(k)$, and $c(k)$. For shorthand, we construct the 3-vector $A(n)$ and matrix R as

$$
A(n) = \begin{pmatrix} a(n) \\ b(n) \\ c(n) \end{pmatrix} \quad \text{and} \quad R = \begin{pmatrix} 0.5 & 5 & 3 \\ 0.5 & 0 & 0 \\ 0 & \tfrac{2}{3} & 0 \end{pmatrix}. \tag{1}
$$

(Throughout this chapter, capital letters will represent vectors and matrices; the context will make it clear which.) Using the notation (1), the previous dynamical system of three equations can be rewritten in the form

$$
A(n+1) = RA(n). \tag{2}
$$

If we are given $a(0)$, $b(0)$, and $c(0)$, that is, we are given $A(0)$, then we can formally compute $A(1) = RA(0)$. Since the order of multiplication is important when dealing with matrices, we carefully compute that

$$
A(2) = RA(1) = R[RA(0)] = (RR)A(0) = R^2 A(0),
$$

and we see that for dynamical systems of several equations we have the same result as we did for first order linear dynamical systems of a single equation, that is, the solution is

$$
A(k) = R^k A(0).
$$

The problem is that matrix multiplication is time consuming and not very illuminating. Thus, for this population model, knowing that $A(100) = R^{100} A(0)$ does not help much in learning about the long term behavior of the population, which we discovered in Section 5.9. The goal of this chapter is to develop methods (using matrix algebra) for studying the solutions to dynamical systems of several equations.

6.1.1   Problem

1. In Section 5.4 we developed the dynamical system of two equations

$$p(n + 1) = 0.5p(n) + 0.5a(n) \quad \text{and} \quad a(n + 1) = p(n)$$

to model a sex-linked gene. (In that section, P was used instead of a.) Rewrite this equation in matrix notation, carefully specifying the vector $P(n)$ and the matrix R.

6.2   Characteristic values

It is assumed that the reader is familiar with matrix addition and multiplication. A matrix with one column will be called a **vector**. Vectors usually are the answer to some problem; for example, in Section 6.1 vector $A(n)$ represented the size of the three different age groups after n generations.

By using vectors and matrices, we can rewrite a first order dynamical system of several equations as one first order linear dynamical system relating a vector at time $n + 1$ to the vector at time n. For example, the dynamical system $a(n + 1) = 0.5a(n) + 5b(n) + 3c(n)$, $b(n + 1) = 0.5a(n)$, and $c(n + 1) = (2/3)b(n)$, which we used to model population growth, was rewritten as

$$A(n + 1) = RA(n)$$

where

$$A(n) = \begin{pmatrix} a(n) \\ b(n) \\ c(n) \end{pmatrix} \quad \text{and} \quad R = \begin{pmatrix} 0.5 & 5 & 3 \\ 0.5 & 0 & 0 \\ 0 & \frac{2}{3} & 0 \end{pmatrix}.$$

Since the solution to this equation is

$$A(k) = R^k A(0),$$

in order to compute $A(10)$, for instance, we would need to compute the tenth power of the matrix R. It is clear that this would require quite a bit of tedious work. Our goal in this section is to reduce this work considerably.

Let's consider two examples. Specifically, let's compute $R^3 A$ and $R^3 B$, where

$$R = \begin{pmatrix} 1 & -1 \\ 2 & 4 \end{pmatrix}, \quad A = \begin{pmatrix} 2 \\ 1 \end{pmatrix}, \quad B = \begin{pmatrix} 1 \\ -1 \end{pmatrix}.$$

In this case,

$$RA = \begin{pmatrix} 1 & -1 \\ 2 & 4 \end{pmatrix} \begin{pmatrix} 2 \\ 1 \end{pmatrix} = \begin{pmatrix} 1(2) - 1(1) \\ 2(2) + 4(1) \end{pmatrix} = \begin{pmatrix} 1 \\ 8 \end{pmatrix}.$$

Therefore,

$$R^2 A = R(RA) = \begin{pmatrix} 1 & -1 \\ 2 & 4 \end{pmatrix} \begin{pmatrix} 1 \\ 8 \end{pmatrix} = \begin{pmatrix} -7 \\ 34 \end{pmatrix},$$

and

$$R^3 A = R(R^2 A) = \begin{pmatrix} 1 & -1 \\ 2 & 4 \end{pmatrix} \begin{pmatrix} -7 \\ 34 \end{pmatrix} = \begin{pmatrix} -41 \\ 122 \end{pmatrix}.$$

As you can see, it would take some time to compute $R^{20} A$.

Now, let's compute $R^3 B$.

$$RB = \begin{pmatrix} 1 & -1 \\ 2 & 4 \end{pmatrix} \begin{pmatrix} 1 \\ -1 \end{pmatrix} = \begin{pmatrix} 1(1) - 1(-1) \\ 2(1) + 4(-1) \end{pmatrix}$$

$$= \begin{pmatrix} 2 \\ -2 \end{pmatrix} = 2 \begin{pmatrix} 1 \\ -1 \end{pmatrix}.$$

Notice that $RB = 2B$ in this case. Therefore,

$$R^2 B = R(RB) = R(2)B = 2(RB) = 2(2B) = 4B = 4 \begin{pmatrix} 1 \\ -1 \end{pmatrix}.$$

Similarly,

$$R^3 B = R(R^2 B) = R(2^2 B) = 2^2 (RB) = 2^3 B.$$

In this case, it is easy to see that

$$R^{20} B = 2^{20} B = 2^{20} \begin{pmatrix} 1 \\ -1 \end{pmatrix}.$$

Try computing $R^3 C$, where

$$C = \begin{pmatrix} 1 \\ -2 \end{pmatrix}.$$

You should find that $RC = 3C$ and therefore $R^3 C = 3^3 C$.

We see from the above that, when R is an m-by-m matrix, there may be an m-vector A and a constant r such that

$$RA = rA.$$

Such a number r is called a **characteristic value** for the matrix R, and the vector A is called a **characteristic vector** corresponding to the characteristic value r. Specifically, the matrix

$$R = \begin{pmatrix} 1 & -1 \\ 2 & 4 \end{pmatrix}$$

has characteristic values $r = 2$ and $r = 3$. The vector B given above is a characteristic vector corresponding to $r = 2$, and the vector C given above is a characteristic vector corresponding to $r = 3$.

Any multiple of B will also be a characteristic vector corresponding to $r = 2$, that is, for a fixed constant b,

$$R(bB) = b(RB) = b(2B) = 2(bB),$$

and so bB is a characteristic vector corresponding to $r = 2$ also.

The question is, how do you find the characteristic values and corresponding characteristic vectors for a given matrix R?

Consider the matrix

$$R = \begin{pmatrix} 3 & 1 \\ 4 & 3 \end{pmatrix}.$$

We wish to find a constant r and a vector

$$A = \begin{pmatrix} x \\ y \end{pmatrix}$$

(where x and y are not both zero) such that

$$RA = rA,$$

that is,

$$\begin{pmatrix} 3 & 1 \\ 4 & 3 \end{pmatrix} \begin{pmatrix} x \\ y \end{pmatrix} = r \begin{pmatrix} x \\ y \end{pmatrix},$$

or

$$\begin{aligned} 3x + y &= rx \\ 4x + 3y &= ry. \end{aligned}$$

Collecting terms on the left yields

$$\begin{aligned} (3 - r)x + y &= 0, \\ 4x + (3 - r)y &= 0, \end{aligned}$$

or

$$\begin{pmatrix} 3-r & 1 \\ 4 & 3-r \end{pmatrix} \begin{pmatrix} x \\ y \end{pmatrix} = \begin{pmatrix} 0 \\ 0 \end{pmatrix}.$$

One solution to this system of equations is obviously $x = 0$ and $y = 0$. We are looking for a solution such that x and y are not both zero. But, in that case, there is **more than one solution** to this system of equations. Thus, the determinant of the matrix must be zero, that is,

$$\begin{vmatrix} 3-r & 1 \\ 4 & 3-r \end{vmatrix} = (3-r)(3-r) - (1)(4) = 0.$$

This simplifies to

$$r^2 - 6r + 5 = 0.$$

Factoring this equation gives $r = 1$ and $r = 5$, so the characteristic values for the matrix

$$R = \begin{pmatrix} 3 & 1 \\ 4 & 3 \end{pmatrix}$$

are $r = 1$ and $r = 5$.

Our next problem is to find a characteristic vector corresponding to the value of $r = 1$, that is, find values for x and y that satisfy the equations

$$(3-r)x + y = 0 \quad \text{and} \quad 4x + (3-r)y = 0$$

when $r = 1$. Substituting 1 for r in these equations gives us

$$2x + y = 0 \quad \text{and} \quad 4x + 2y = 0.$$

Since the second equation is a multiple of the first, any solution to the equation

$$2x + y = 0$$

will work. We can give any value we wish for y, and then solve for x. Thus, letting $y = 2$ (to avoid fractions) we get $x = -1$ and a characteristic vector is

$$A = \begin{pmatrix} -1 \\ 2 \end{pmatrix}.$$

We get other characteristic vectors by picking different values for y. Letting $y = 2a$, we get $x = -a$, and all characteristic vectors corresponding to $r = 1$ are of the form

$$a \begin{pmatrix} -1 \\ 2 \end{pmatrix}.$$

You should check the computations to see that

$$RA = A.$$

To find a characteristic vector corresponding to $r = 5$, we substitute 5 for r in the above equations, giving

$$-2x + y = 0 \quad \text{and} \quad 4x - 2y = 0.$$

Again the second equation is a multiple of the first, so we only need a solution to the equation

$$-2x + y = 0.$$

Thus we again see that we can pick any value for y, say $y = a$. Therefore, $x = y/2 = a/2$, and

$$a \begin{pmatrix} 0.5 \\ 1 \end{pmatrix}$$

is a characteristic vector for $r = 5$, for every value of a. In particular, picking $a = 2$ (to eliminate decimals), we get

$$B = \begin{pmatrix} 1 \\ 2 \end{pmatrix}.$$

Again you should compute RB to see that it equals $5B$.

Let's develop a systematic method for finding the characteristic values for an m-by-m matrix R. We are looking for a number r and a vector A (with at least one nonzero entry), such that

$$RA = rA.$$

Since $A = IA$, where I is the identity matrix, we have

$$RA = rIA, \quad \text{or} \quad (R - rI)A = 0.$$

We see that we are looking for a number r such that $(R - rI)A = 0$, where A is not all zeros. Since the vector containing all zeros is also a solution to this equation, we must have more than one solution (actually an infinite number) to this equation. Thus, the determinant of the m-by-m matrix $(R - rI)$, must be zero. This leads to the following conclusion.

Definition 6.1

*The **characteristic values** of an m-by-m matrix R are the values r such that the determinant of the matrix $(R - rI)$ is zero, that is, the solutions r to the equation*

$$|R - rI| = 0.$$

Example 6.2

Find the characteristic values for the matrix

$$R = \begin{pmatrix} 1 & 2 & 1 \\ -1 & 1 & 0 \\ 3 & -6 & -1 \end{pmatrix}.$$

First we construct the matrix

$$R - rI = \begin{pmatrix} 1 & 2 & 1 \\ -1 & 1 & 0 \\ 3 & -6 & -1 \end{pmatrix} - r \begin{pmatrix} 1 & 0 & 0 \\ 0 & 1 & 0 \\ 0 & 0 & 1 \end{pmatrix}$$

$$= \begin{pmatrix} 1 - r & 2 & 1 \\ -1 & 1 - r & 0 \\ 3 & -6 & -1 - r \end{pmatrix}.$$

The determinant is

$$\begin{aligned} |R - rI| &= (1 - r)(1 - r)(-1 - r) + (2)(0)(3) + (1)(-1)(-6) \\ &\quad - (1 - r)(0)(-6) - (2)(-1)(-1 - r) - (1)(1 - r)(3) \\ &= -r^3 + r^2 + 2r \end{aligned} \tag{3}$$

after simplification. To solve the equation

$$|R - rI| = -r^3 + r^2 + 2r = 0,$$

we only need to factor the polynomial, giving

$$r(-r + 2)(r + 1) = 0.$$

Thus, the characteristic values are

$$r = 0, \quad r = 2, \quad r = -1.$$

The idea behind finding characteristic values is easy, but in practice it may be difficult to accomplish since, for an m-by-m matrix, we need to factor an mth order polynomial. (We could use Newton's method to find the roots.)

Since the characteristic values are the roots of the polynomial $|R - rI|$ there will be times that the characteristic values are **complex numbers**. If r_0 is a double root of the above polynomial, that is, $(r - r_0)^2$ is a factor of the polynomial, we say that r_0 is a characteristic value of order

2. If $(r - r_0)^j$ is a factor of the polynomial $|R - rI|$, then r_0 is called a characteristic value of order j.

Once the characteristic values are found, we need to find corresponding characteristic vectors. To do this, we pick a characteristic value, say r_0, construct the matrix

$$R - r_0 I,$$

and then solve the system of equations

$$(R - r_0 I)A = 0$$

for the unknowns $a_1, a_2, \ldots, a_m$, where

$$A = \begin{pmatrix} a_1 \\ \vdots \\ a_m \end{pmatrix}.$$

Example 6.3

To find a characteristic vector corresponding to the characteristic value $r = 2$ for the matrix R of Example 6.2, we construct the matrix

$$R - 2I = \begin{pmatrix} 1 & 2 & 1 \\ -1 & 1 & 0 \\ 3 & -6 & -1 \end{pmatrix} - 2 \begin{pmatrix} 1 & 0 & 0 \\ 0 & 1 & 0 \\ 0 & 0 & 1 \end{pmatrix} = \begin{pmatrix} -1 & 2 & 1 \\ -1 & -1 & 0 \\ 3 & -6 & -3 \end{pmatrix}.$$

We then solve the equations

$$(R - 2I)A = \begin{pmatrix} -1 & 2 & 1 \\ -1 & -1 & 0 \\ 3 & -6 & -3 \end{pmatrix} \begin{pmatrix} x \\ y \\ z \end{pmatrix} = \begin{pmatrix} 0 \\ 0 \\ 0 \end{pmatrix},$$

or

$$-x + 2y + z = 0, \quad -x - y = 0, \quad 3x - 6y - 3z = 0.$$

The second equation gives $y = -x$. Substitution into the first equation gives $-3x + z = 0$ or $z = 3x$. Substitution for y and z into the third equation gives $3x + 6x - 9x = 0$ or $0 = 0$. Thus, x can be anything, say $x = 1$. Then $y = -1$, $z = 3$, and a characteristic vector is

$$A = \begin{pmatrix} 1 \\ -1 \\ 3 \end{pmatrix}.$$

Any multiple of this vector will also work.

To find a characteristic vector B for the value $r = 0$ we need to solve the system of equations

$$(R - 0I)B = RB = \begin{pmatrix} 1 & 2 & 1 \\ -1 & 1 & 0 \\ 3 & -6 & -1 \end{pmatrix} \begin{pmatrix} x \\ y \\ z \end{pmatrix} = \begin{pmatrix} 0 \\ 0 \\ 0 \end{pmatrix},$$

or

$$x + 2y + z = 0, \quad -x + y = 0, \quad 3x - 6y - z = 0.$$

You should find that a solution (or characteristic vector) is

$$B = \begin{pmatrix} 1 \\ 1 \\ -3 \end{pmatrix}$$

or any multiple of this vector.

Likewise, to find a characteristic vector C for $r = -1$ you need to solve the system of equations

$$(R + I)C = \begin{pmatrix} 2 & 2 & 1 \\ -1 & 2 & 0 \\ 3 & -6 & 0 \end{pmatrix} \begin{pmatrix} x \\ y \\ z \end{pmatrix} = \begin{pmatrix} 0 \\ 0 \\ 0 \end{pmatrix},$$

or

$$2x + 2y + z = 0, \quad -x + 2y = 0, \quad 3x - 6y = 0.$$

You should find that a characteristic vector is

$$C = \begin{pmatrix} 2 \\ 1 \\ -6 \end{pmatrix}$$

or any multiple of this vector.

If r is a characteristic value of order 2, we would expect to find two characteristic vectors, A and B, where B is not a multiple of A. Unfortunately this is not always true, but we will postpone a discussion of this.

To review the results of Examples 6.2 and 6.3, the matrix

$$R = \begin{pmatrix} 1 & 2 & 1 \\ -1 & 1 & 0 \\ 3 & -6 & -1 \end{pmatrix}$$

has the characteristic values $r = 2$, 0, and -1, and corresponding characteristic vectors

$$A = \begin{pmatrix} 1 \\ -1 \\ 3 \end{pmatrix}, \quad B = \begin{pmatrix} 1 \\ 1 \\ -6 \end{pmatrix}, \quad C = \begin{pmatrix} 2 \\ 1 \\ -6 \end{pmatrix}.$$

Thus, $RA = -A$, $RB = 0B = 0$, and $RC = 2C$.

We now wish to compute RX, where X is some vector other than one of the characteristic vectors. The idea is to write X as a sum of the characteristic vectors, say

$$X = aA + bB + cC$$

for some constants a, b, and c. If we can do this, then

$$\begin{aligned} RX &= R(aA + bB + cC) = aRA + bRB + cRC \\ &= a(2)A + b(0)B + c(-1)C = 2aA - cC. \end{aligned}$$

Then,

$$R^k X = aR^k A + bR^k B + cR^k C = a2^k A + c(-1)^k C.$$

Suppose that

$$X = \begin{pmatrix} 3 \\ -4 \\ 3 \end{pmatrix}.$$

We now wish to solve the system of equations

$$X = aA + bB + cC$$

for the constants a, b, and c, that is, solve

$$a \begin{pmatrix} 1 \\ -1 \\ 3 \end{pmatrix} + b \begin{pmatrix} 1 \\ 1 \\ -3 \end{pmatrix} + c \begin{pmatrix} 2 \\ 1 \\ -6 \end{pmatrix} = \begin{pmatrix} 3 \\ -4 \\ 3 \end{pmatrix}$$

or

$$a + b + 2c = 3, \quad -a + b + c = -4, \quad 3a - 3b - 6c = 3.$$

You should find it relatively simple to solve these three equations. If you do you will find that

$$a = 2, \quad b = -5, \quad c = 3.$$

Thus,

$$X = 2A - 5B + 3C$$

and

$$R^k X = R^k(2A - 5B + 3C) = 2(2^k)A + 3(-1)^k C$$

$$= 2^{k+1} \begin{pmatrix} 1 \\ -1 \\ 3 \end{pmatrix} + 3(-1)^k \begin{pmatrix} 2 \\ 1 \\ -6 \end{pmatrix},$$

(since $R^k B = 0B$).

To review, suppose we have an m-by-m matrix R, an m-vector B, and that we wish to compute $R^k B$. Then we follow these four steps.

1. **Compute the characteristic values:** Set the determinant of the matrix $R - rI$ equal to zero and solve, that is, find solutions r to the equation

$$|R - rI| = 0.$$

This means finding the m roots, r_1, r_2, ..., r_m, of an mth order polynomial. These roots are the m characteristic values of R. We will assume that these are all distinct.

2. **Compute the characteristic vectors:** To do this, solve the system of m equations

$$(R - r_1 I)A_1 = 0,$$

where the m unknowns are the m components of the vector A_1. Note that the solution to this system of equations will not be unique, that is, there will be one independent component, and the other components will be given in terms of this component. Repeat this process for r_2, r_3, ..., r_m, finding corresponding characteristic vectors A_2, A_3, ..., A_m. We now have m characteristic values and their corresponding characteristic vectors.

3. **Write B as a sum of characteristic vectors:** Remember that B and A_1, ..., A_m are all known at this point. Now solve the system of equations

$$x_1 A_1 + x_2 A_2 + \ldots + x_m A_m = B$$

for the unknowns, x_1, ..., x_m. This solution will be unique.

4. **Compute our answer, that is, compute $R^k B$:** To do this, we compute

$$R^k B = R^k(x_1 A_1 + \ldots + x_m A_m) = x_1 r_1^k A_1 + \ldots + x_k r_m^k A_m.$$

Remark: Observe that if we construct a matrix M that has the vector A_1 as its first column, A_2 as its second column, ..., and A_m as its mth column, and if we construct the vector

$$X = \begin{pmatrix} x_1 \\ \vdots \\ x_m \end{pmatrix},$$

then we can rephrase step 3 as follows.

3 Solve the system of equations

$$MX = B.$$

Let's demonstrate these steps by computing $R^3 B$, where

$$R = \begin{pmatrix} 1 & 2 \\ -1 & 4 \end{pmatrix} \quad \text{and} \quad B = \begin{pmatrix} 5 \\ 1 \end{pmatrix}.$$

First we find the characteristic values, that is, we solve

$$\begin{aligned} |R - rI| &= (1-r)(4-r) - (2)(-1) \\ &= r^2 - 5r + 6 = (r-3)(r-2) = 0, \end{aligned}$$

for r. Therefore, the characteristic values are $r = 3$ and $r = 2$.

Next, we find the characteristic vectors starting with a characteristic vector corresponding to $r = 3$. To do this we solve the system of equations $(R - 3I)A_1 = 0$, that is,

$$\begin{pmatrix} -2 & 2 \\ -1 & 1 \end{pmatrix} \begin{pmatrix} x \\ y \end{pmatrix} = \begin{pmatrix} 0 \\ 0 \end{pmatrix}.$$

This is in reality only a single equation, that is,

$$-x + y = 0.$$

Since we can let y be anything we want, let's pick $y = 1$. Then $x = 1$, and a characteristic vector corresponding to $r = 3$ is

$$A_1 = \begin{pmatrix} 1 \\ 1 \end{pmatrix}.$$

We could have let $x = 1$ in the above and then solved for y.

To find a characteristic vector corresponding to $r = 2$, solve the system of equations $(R - 2I)A_2 = 0$, that is,

$$\begin{pmatrix} -1 & 2 \\ -1 & 2 \end{pmatrix} \begin{pmatrix} x \\ y \end{pmatrix} = \begin{pmatrix} 0 \\ 0 \end{pmatrix}.$$

This is in reality only a single equation,

$$-x + 2y = 0.$$

Since we can let y be anything we want, let's pick $y = 1$. Then $x = 2$, and a characteristic vector corresponding to $r = 2$ is

$$A_2 = \begin{pmatrix} 2 \\ 1 \end{pmatrix}.$$

Our third step is to rewrite B in terms of A_1 and A_2, that is, solve

$$x \begin{pmatrix} 1 \\ 1 \end{pmatrix} + y \begin{pmatrix} 2 \\ 1 \end{pmatrix} = \begin{pmatrix} 5 \\ 1 \end{pmatrix},$$

or

$$x + 2y = 5 \quad \text{and} \quad x + y = 1.$$

You should find that the solution to these equations is $x = -3$ and $y = 4$. Thus,

$$B = -3A_1 + 4A_2.$$

Finally we can compute the answer. From the above calculations, we get

$$\begin{aligned} R^3 B &= R^3(-3A_1 + 4A_2) = -3(3^3)A_1 + 4(2^3)A_2 = -81A_1 + 32A_2 \\ &= -81 \begin{pmatrix} 1 \\ 1 \end{pmatrix} + 32 \begin{pmatrix} 2 \\ 1 \end{pmatrix} = \begin{pmatrix} -17 \\ -49 \end{pmatrix}. \end{aligned}$$

You should compute $R^3 B$ using matrix multiplication to check the answer.

Matrix multiplication is easier in this example. But if you were asked to compute $R^{20} B$, this procedure would easily give the answer

$$\begin{aligned} R^{20} B &= R^{20}(-3A_1 + 4A_2) = -3(3^{20})A_1 + 4(2^{20})A_2 \\ &= \begin{pmatrix} -3(3^{20}) + 8(2^{20}) \\ -3(3^{20}) + 4(2^{20}) \end{pmatrix}, \end{aligned}$$

while matrix multiplication would require long and tedious computations.

Notice that our procedure gives a relatively simple method for performing matrix multiplication without ever having to multiply a matrix.

6.2.1 Problems

1. Consider the matrix R and the vector B given as

$$R = \begin{pmatrix} -2 & 3 \\ 1 & 0 \end{pmatrix} \quad \text{and} \quad B = \begin{pmatrix} -2 \\ 6 \end{pmatrix}.$$

(a) Find the characteristic values for R.

(b) Find the corresponding characteristic vectors.

(c) Write B as a sum of the characteristic vectors.

(d) Compute $R^4 B$.

2. Consider the matrix R and the vector B given as

$$R = \begin{pmatrix} 3 & 4 \\ 2 & 1 \end{pmatrix} \quad \text{and} \quad B = \begin{pmatrix} 7 \\ 8 \end{pmatrix}.$$

(a) Find the characteristic values for R.

(b) Find the corresponding characteristic vectors.

(c) Write B as a sum of the characteristic vectors.

(d) Compute $R^3 B$.

3. Consider the matrix R and the vector B given as

$$R = \begin{pmatrix} 14 & -2 & 5 \\ 9 & -1 & 3 \\ -30 & 4 & -11 \end{pmatrix} \quad \text{and} \quad B = \begin{pmatrix} -3 \\ 1 \\ 9 \end{pmatrix}.$$

(a) Find the characteristic values for R.

(b) Find the corresponding characteristic vectors.

(c) Write B as a sum of the characteristic vectors.

(d) Compute $R^5 B$.

4. Consider the matrix R and the vector B given as

$$R = \begin{pmatrix} -4 & -4 & -23 \\ 2 & 2 & 11 \\ 0 & 0 & 2 \end{pmatrix} \quad \text{and} \quad B = \begin{pmatrix} -25 \\ 13 \\ 4 \end{pmatrix}.$$

(a) Find the characteristic values for R.

(b) Find the corresponding characteristic vectors.

(c) Write B as a sum of the characteristic vectors.

(d) Compute $R^5 B$.

6.3 First order dynamical systems of several equations

In Section 5.4 we derived two equations which described the process of sex-linked traits in genetics. Letting $p(n)$ be the proportion of A-alleles among women in generation n, and $p'(n)$ be the proportion of A-alleles among men in generation n, we derived the two equations

$$p(n + 1) = 0.5p(n) + 0.5p'(n) \quad \text{and} \quad p'(n + 1) = p(n).$$

Defining the vector $P(n)$ and the matrix R as

$$P(n) = \begin{pmatrix} p(n) \\ p'(n) \end{pmatrix} \quad \text{and} \quad R = \begin{pmatrix} 0.5 & 0.5 \\ 1 & 0 \end{pmatrix},$$

we can rewrite the above two equations as

$$P(n + 1) = RP(n).$$

The general solution to this first order system of equations is

$$P(k) = R^k P,$$

where P is a fixed vector that depends on the initial values $p(0)$ and $p'(0)$.

To compute $R^k P$, we use the four steps discussed in the previous section. First, we find the characteristic values for R, that is, we solve

$$|R - rI| = (0.5 - r)(-r) - 0.5(1) = r^2 - 0.5r - 0.5 = 0.$$

Factoring, we get

$$|R - rI| = (r - 1)(r + 0.5) = 0,$$

so the characteristic values are $r = 1$ and $r = -0.5$.

Second, we compute a characteristic vector corresponding to $r = 1$ and to $r = -0.5$. To compute the characteristic vector associated with $r = 1$, we solve the system of equations

$$(R - 1I)P_1 = 0$$

for the vector P_1, that is, solve

$$\begin{pmatrix} -0.5 & 0.5 \\ 1 & -1 \end{pmatrix} \begin{pmatrix} a \\ b \end{pmatrix} = \begin{pmatrix} 0 \\ 0 \end{pmatrix}.$$

Both of these equations reduce to

$$a - b = 0.$$

Since b can be anything, let $b = 1$. Then $a = 1$ and

$$P_1 = \begin{pmatrix} 1 \\ 1 \end{pmatrix}.$$

You should find that a characteristic vector corresponding to $r = -0.5$ is

$$P_2 = \begin{pmatrix} -1 \\ 2 \end{pmatrix}.$$

Third, since we wish to compute $R^k P$, we write P in terms of P_1 and P_2, that is, we find numbers a and b such that

$$P = aP_1 + bP_2.$$

Fourth, we find that the general solution is

$$P(k) = R^k P = a(1)^k P_1 + b(-0.5)^k P_2.$$

If we were given $P(0) = P$, we could compute the numbers a and b. But in this example, we assumed that genetics had been operating for many generations, and that presently we are in generation k where k is large. Since $|-0.5| < 1$, it follows that $(-0.5)^k$ goes to zero so that

$$\lim_{k \to \infty} P(k) = aP_1 = \begin{pmatrix} a \\ a \end{pmatrix}.$$

From this, we see that $p(k) = a$ and $p'(k) = a$ and we can draw the same conclusion that we did in Section 3.3, that is, the proportion of A-alleles is approximately the same in men and women. Note that a is the proportion of men with the trait determined by the A-allele, which can be easily determined through observation.

We note here that we actually have two methods for solving first order linear systems of several equations. The first method is to rewrite the equations as one higher order dynamical system and then solve by factoring the characteristic equation. The second is to solve the system by finding the roots of the determinant, that is, solving $|R - rI| = 0$. These two methods must give **the same results**, since they both give solutions to the same dynamical system, and there is only one solution to a first order linear dynamical system of several equations.

Since we must get the same results, the roots of the characteristic equation and the roots of the determinant $|R - rI| = 0$ must be the same. Therefore, the characteristic equation for the higher order system and the determinant of $|R - rI|$ **must be the same**. Because of this, we will call the equation

$$|R - rI| = 0,$$

the characteristic equation to the first order dynamical system

$$A(n + 1) = RA(n).$$

You might ask which method is better. In some sense, they are the same. On the other hand, the first order system is aesthetically more pleasing because systems of several equations arise naturally (as in sex-linked genes and populations with age structure) and they have a simple matrix notation.

We will see later that systems of equations are easier to deal with when we have a large number of equations, say a system of four or more equations. In these cases, it is often difficult to factor the characteristic equation, but we can use the system and our computer to estimate the roots (or at least one of the roots) of the characteristic equation. This will be enough to determine the behavior of the system.

Let's work some examples.

Example 6.4

Find the particular solution to the system of equations

$$a(n + 1) = a(n) + 2b(n) \quad \text{and} \quad b(n + 1) = -a(n) + 4b(n)$$

where $a(0) = 1$ and $b(0) = 2$.

Define the vector $A(n)$ and the matrix R as

$$A(n) = \begin{pmatrix} a(n) \\ b(n) \end{pmatrix} \quad \text{and} \quad R = \begin{pmatrix} 1 & 2 \\ -1 & 4 \end{pmatrix}.$$

Note that

$$A(0) = \begin{pmatrix} 1 \\ 2 \end{pmatrix}.$$

The above system of equations can now be written as

$$A(n + 1) = RA(n).$$

The general solution is $A(k) = R^k A$ and the particular solution is $A(k) = R^k A(0)$. The first step is to compute the roots of the characteristic equation, that is, the characteristic values for $|R - rI| = 0$. The characteristic equation is

$$(1 - r)(4 - r) - 2(-1) = 0, \quad \text{or} \quad (r - 2)(r - 3) = 0$$

after simplification. The roots are $r = 2$ and $r = 3$.

If A_1 and A_2 are characteristic vectors corresponding to $r = 2$ and $r = 3$, respectively, then the general solution is

$$A(k) = R^k A = R^k (a A_1 + b A_2) = a 2^k A_1 + b 3^k A_2,$$

where a and b are two unknown constants (corresponding to the initial conditions, $a(0)$ and $b(0)$).

The second step is to compute characteristic vectors corresponding to $r = 2$ and $r = 3$, respectively. For $r = 2$, solving the system of equations

$$(R - 2I)A_1 = \begin{pmatrix} -1 & 2 \\ -1 & 2 \end{pmatrix} \begin{pmatrix} x \\ y \end{pmatrix} = \begin{pmatrix} 0 \\ 0 \end{pmatrix}$$

(which reduces to the single equation $-x + 2y = 0$) gives the characteristic vector

$$A_1 = \begin{pmatrix} 2 \\ 1 \end{pmatrix}$$

(or any multiple of this vector).

Likewise, you should find that a characteristic vector corresponding to $r = 3$ is

$$A_2 = \begin{pmatrix} 1 \\ 1 \end{pmatrix}.$$

The third step is to write $A(0)$ in terms of A_1 and A_2. Thus, we need to solve

$$a A_1 + b A_2 = A(0),$$

that is, solve the two equations,

$$2a + b = 1 \quad \text{and} \quad a + b = 2.$$

You should get $a = -1$ and $b = 3$ as the solution. Thus,

$$A(0) = -A_1 + 3A_2.$$

The fourth step is to compute the particular solution. This is,

$$
\begin{aligned}
A(k) &= R^k A(0) = R^k (-A_1 + 3A_2) = -2^k A_1 + 3 (3)^k A_2 \\
&= \left(\begin{array}{c} -2(2)^k + 3(3)^k \\ -(2)^k + 3(3)^k \end{array} \right).
\end{aligned}
$$

Example 6.5

Let's find the general solution and then the particular solution to the dynamical system

$$A(n + 1) = RA(n),$$

given that

$$
R = \left(\begin{array}{cc} 0.5 & -0.25 \\ 1 & 0.5 \end{array} \right) \quad \text{and} \quad A(0) = \left(\begin{array}{c} 1 \\ 2 \end{array} \right).
$$

First, we find the roots of the characteristic equation

$$(0.5 - r)(0.5 - r) - (-0.25)(1) = r^2 - r + 0.5 = 0.$$

Using the quadratic formula, the roots are the complex numbers

$$r = 0.5 + 0.5i \quad \text{and} \quad r = 0.5 - 0.5i.$$

Thus, the general solution is

$$A(k) = a(0.5 + 0.5i)^k A_1 + b(0.5 - 0.5i)^k A_2,$$

where a and b are two unknown constants and A_1 and A_2 are the corresponding characteristic vectors.

To solve for the characteristic vector corresponding to $r = 0.5 + 0.5i$, we need to find a vector that satisfies the equations

$$
(R - (0.5 + 0.5i)I)A_1 = \left(\begin{array}{cc} -0.5i & -0.25 \\ 1 & -0.5i \end{array} \right) \left(\begin{array}{c} x \\ y \end{array} \right) = \left(\begin{array}{c} 0 \\ 0 \end{array} \right),
$$

which means solving the two equations

$$-0.5ix = 0.25y \quad \text{and} \quad x = 0.5iy.$$

After multiplying both sides of the second equation by $-0.5i$ it is seen that the second equation is a multiple of the first. Thus, we need to solve one of the equations, say

$$x = 0.5iy.$$

Since y can be any real (or complex) number, let $y = 2$. Then we get $x = i$, and a characteristic vector is

$$A_1 = \begin{pmatrix} i \\ 2 \end{pmatrix}.$$

A similar calculation gives the characteristic vector corresponding to $r = 0.5 - 0.5i$ as

$$A_2 = \begin{pmatrix} -i \\ 2 \end{pmatrix}.$$

Thus, the general solution to the real dynamical system is given by

$$
\begin{aligned}
A(k) &= R^k A = a A_1 + b A_2 \\
&= a(0.5 + 0.5i)^k \begin{pmatrix} i \\ 2 \end{pmatrix} + b(0.5 - 0.5i)^k \begin{pmatrix} -i \\ 2 \end{pmatrix},
\end{aligned}
$$

where a and b are arbitrary.

If we wish to find the particular solution, given $A(0)$ above, we need to solve for a and b in the equation

$$A(0) = a A_1 + b A_2,$$

that is, solve the equations

$$ia - ib = 1 \quad \text{and} \quad 2a + 2b = 2.$$

In the first equation, taking ib to the right side, dividing by i, and recalling that $1/i = -i$, we get

$$a = b - i.$$

Substitution into the second equation gives

$$2(b - i) + 2b = 2, \quad \text{or} \quad b = 0.5 + 0.5i.$$

Thus,

$$a = b - i = 0.5 - 0.5i.$$

The particular solution is then

$$A(k) = (0.5 - 0.5i)(0.5 + 0.5i)^k A_1 + (0.5 + 0.5i)(0.5 - 0.5i)^k A_2.$$

It seems amazing that such a complicated solution, when multiplied out for a given k, gives real numbers for answers (the complex numbers all canceling out). This must happen, though, since this is the solution, and when we observe the original dynamical system, it is clear that we always get real numbers for $a(k)$ and $b(k)$.

6.3.1 Problems

1. Find a general solution, by finding the characteristic values and their corresponding characteristic vectors, for the dynamical system

$$A(n + 1) = RA(n),$$

where R equals each of the following matrices.

(a) $\begin{pmatrix} -2 & 2 \\ 5 & 1 \end{pmatrix}$, (b) $\begin{pmatrix} 1.5 & 1 \\ 0.5 & 1 \end{pmatrix}$,

(c) $\begin{pmatrix} 2 & -5 \\ 1 & -2 \end{pmatrix}$, (d) $\begin{pmatrix} 2 & 5 & 1 \\ 0 & 1 & 4 \\ 0 & 0 & 3 \end{pmatrix}$.

2. Find the particular solution to the corresponding dynamical system in Problem 1, when $A(0)$ equals the following vectors.

(a) $\begin{pmatrix} -3 \\ 7 \end{pmatrix}$, (b) $\begin{pmatrix} 0 \\ -3 \end{pmatrix}$,

(c) i. $\begin{pmatrix} 4 \\ 2 \end{pmatrix}$, ii. $\begin{pmatrix} 10 \\ 4 \end{pmatrix}$, (d) $\begin{pmatrix} 7 \\ 3 \\ 1 \end{pmatrix}$.

3. Find the particular solution to the first order linear system of equations

$$\begin{aligned} a(n + 1) &= -0.5a(n) + 0.5b(n) \\ b(n + 1) &= -0.5a(n) + 0.75b(n) \end{aligned}$$

given that $a(0) = 6$ and $b(0) = 6$.

6.4 Behavior of solutions

In this section we will briefly analyze the behavior of the solutions to first order linear dynamical systems. We will study these results in more detail in the applications in the following sections.

To simplify our analysis, we will only consider systems in which there are **no double roots** of the characteristic equation $|R - rI| = 0$. Double roots will be considered later in this chapter.

Suppose we have the dynamical system of m equations,

$$A(n + 1) = RA(n),$$

where R is an m-by-m matrix, and $A(n)$ is an m-vector. The first step is to find the m (distinct) roots (or characteristic values) of the characteristic equation

$$|R - rI| = 0,$$

say

$$r_1, r_2, \ldots, r_m.$$

We then find m corresponding characteristic vectors

$$A_1, A_2, \ldots, A_m.$$

The general solution to this dynamical system can then be written as

$$A(k) = a_1(r_1)^k A_1 + a_2(r_2)^k A_2 + \ldots + a_m(r_m)^k A_m.$$

We now find $|r_1|, |r_2|, \ldots, |r_m|$. Recall that if r_j is complex then

$$|r_j| = |a + ib| = \sqrt{a^2 + b^2}.$$

We know that if

$$|r_1| < 1 \quad \text{then} \quad \lim_{k \to \infty} r_1^k = 0.$$

Thus, if

$$|r_j| < 1 \quad \text{for} \quad j = 1, 2, \ldots, m$$

then each of the terms that make up $A(k)$ goes to zero, and so

$$\lim_{k \to \infty} A(k) = 0.$$

To simplify the terminology, let's state the following definition.

Definition 6.6

Consider an m-by-m matrix R with m distinct characteristic values, r_1, $\ldots$, r_m. We define the **absolute value** *of R to be*

$$\|R\| = \text{maximum}\{|r_1|, |r_2|, \ldots, |r_m|\}.$$

Since $|R|$ represents the determinant of R, we use the notation $\|R\|$ to represent the absolute value of R. Mathematicians call this the **norm** of R.

Let's consider several of the matrices studied in the last section. The first matrix considered in Section 6.3 was the matrix

$$R = \begin{pmatrix} 0.5 & 0.5 \\ 1 & 0 \end{pmatrix}.$$

The characteristic values of R are $r = 1$ and $r = -0.5$. The maximum of 1 and $|-0.5| = 0.5$ is 1, so that $\|R\| = 1$. In Example 6.4, we found that the characteristic values for the matrix

$$R = \begin{pmatrix} 1 & 2 \\ -1 & 4 \end{pmatrix}$$

were $r = 2$ and $r = 3$. The maximum of these numbers is 3, so that $\|R\| = 3$. In Example 6.5, we found that the characteristic values for the matrix

$$R = \begin{pmatrix} 0.5 & -0.25 \\ 1 & 0.5 \end{pmatrix},$$

were $r = 0.5 + 0.5i$ and $r = 0.5 - 0.5i$. Since

$$|0.5 \pm 0.5i| = \sqrt{0.25 + 0.25} = \sqrt{0.5},$$

it follows that $\|R\| = \sqrt{0.5}$.

Theorem 6.7

Consider the dynamical system

$$A(n+1) = RA(n)$$

where R is an m-by-m matrix. If $\|R\| < 1$, then

$$\lim_{k \to \infty} A(k) = \mathbf{0},$$

where $\mathbf{0}$ means the vector with m zeros. In this case, the zero vector is called a **stable equilibrium vector** *or an* **attracting fixed point**.

Proof: If R has m distinct characteristic values then $\|R\| < 1$ means that $|r_j| < 1$ for $j = 1, 2, \ldots, m$, and

$$\lim_{k \to \infty} r_j^k = 0 \quad \text{for} \quad j = 1, 2, \ldots, m.$$

Thus

$$\lim_{k \to \infty} A(k) = \lim_{k \to \infty} (a_1 r_1^k A_1 + a_2 r_2^k A_2 + \ldots + a_m r_m^k A_m) = 0.$$

In the case of multiple roots, the proof is more difficult, but the result is the same.

Since $\|R\| = \sqrt{0.5} < 1$ in Example 6.5, $A(k)$ goes to zero no matter what the initial value $A(0)$. This means that the vector

$$A = \begin{pmatrix} 0 \\ 0 \end{pmatrix}$$

is a stable equilibrium vector for that dynamical system.

In the case that $\|R\| = 1$, many types of behavior may occur. Let's consider the different types of behavior that can occur when R is a 2-by-2 matrix with distinct characteristic values. The behavior for m - by - m matrices is similar, but notationally more difficult to discuss.

The first case is when $r_1 = 1$ and $|r_2| < 1$. In this case the solution is

$$A(k) = ar_1^k A_1 + br_2^k A_2.$$

Since r_2^k goes to zero and $r_1^k = 1$,

$$\lim_{k \to \infty} A(k) = aA_1,$$

the value of a depending on the initial value. This was the case for our study of genetics in the last section. Note that A_1 is **not** a stable equilibrium vector, since the solution may go to any multiple of A_1, that multiple depending on the initial condition $A(0)$.

The second case is when $r_1 = -1$ and $|r_2| < 1$. Again, since r_2^k goes to zero, it follows that, for large values of k,

$$A(k) = a(-1)^k A_1,$$

approximately. Thus, the solution goes to a 2-cycle. The particular 2-cycle again depends on a, which depends on $A(0)$.

The third case is when $r_1 = 1$ and $r_2 = -1$. In this case you have a combination of cases 1 and 2, and you find that the solution is the 2-cycle

$$A(k) = aA_1 + b(-1)^k A_2,$$

the particular 2-cycle depending on $A(0)$.

The fourth case is when $r_1 = a + bi$ and $r_2 = a - bi$, where $a^2 + b^2 = 1$. Much like the second case and the results for second order linear dynamical systems, you will find that $A(k)$ oscillates. Whether it goes to a cycle of some fixed length or becomes *almost periodic* depends on the numbers a and b.

The cases in which 1 or -1 are double roots are discussed later in this chapter.

Let's now discuss what happens when $\|R\| > 1$, and there are no double roots. Suppose that $|r_1| = \|R\| > 1$ and $|r_2| < |r_1|$. We know that $A(k)$ goes to infinity in some sense, since $|r_1|^k$ goes to infinity. We would like to get more information. The trick is that, when $\|R\| > 1$, you should divide $A(k)$ by $\|R\|^k$. We first saw this trick in Section 5.9.

Example 6.8

Let's apply this technique to Example 6.4, in which we studied the dynamical system

$$A(n+1) = RA(n), \quad \text{where} \quad R = \begin{pmatrix} 1 & 2 \\ -1 & 4 \end{pmatrix}.$$

In this example, we found that the general solution was

$$A(k) = a2^k A_1 + b3^k A_2,$$

where

$$A_1 = \begin{pmatrix} 2 \\ 1 \end{pmatrix} \quad \text{and} \quad A_2 = \begin{pmatrix} 1 \\ 1 \end{pmatrix}.$$

Letting

$$B(k) = \frac{A(k)}{3^k},$$

we have

$$B(k) = \frac{A(k)}{3^k} = a \left(\tfrac{2}{3}\right)^k A_1 + b \left(\tfrac{3}{3}\right)^k A_2 \to b A_2 = b \begin{pmatrix} 1 \\ 1 \end{pmatrix}$$

since $(2/3)^k$ goes to zero and $3/3 = 1$. If

$$A(k) = \begin{pmatrix} a(k) \\ b(k) \end{pmatrix}$$

then we have shown that

$$\lim_{k \to \infty} \frac{a(k)}{3^k} = b \quad \text{and} \quad \lim_{k \to \infty} \frac{b(k)}{3^k} = b.$$

This tells us that $A(k)$ grows on the order of 3^k. But it also tells us that

$$\lim_{k \to \infty} \frac{a(k)}{b(k)} = 1.$$

To review, by dividing $A(k)$ by $|r_1|^k$, where $\|R\| = |r_1|$, and then computing the limit, we obtained a limit vector. This tells us that the solution grows exponentially, but that the components go to a fixed ratio, one-to-one in this example.

What happens is that, when we consider

$$B(k) = \frac{A(k)}{\|R\|^k},$$

it's as if $B(k)$ was the solution to a dynamical system where the largest characteristic value had an absolute value of 1. Thus, $B(k)$ behaves as one of the four cases given above for $\|R\| = 1$.

6.4.1 Problems

1. For each part of Problem 1 of Section 6.3, find $\|R\|$.

2. Describe the long term behavior of

$$B(k) = \frac{A(k)}{\|R\|^k}$$

   (a) for Problem 1 part (a) of Section 6.3,
   (b) for Problem 1 part (b) of Section 6.3,
   (c) for Problem 1 part (d) of Section 6.3.

3. For Problem 1 part (c) of Section 6.3, compute $A(1)$, $A(2)$, and so forth, until you can determine the behavior of the solution.

6.5 Regular Markov chains

In this section we continue the discussion of Markov chains started in Section 2.4. Suppose we conduct an experiment that has m possible results or **states** as mathematicians call them. Also suppose we keep repeating this experiment, but that the probability of each of the states occurring on the $(n+1)$th repetition of the experiment depends only on the result of the nth repetition of the experiment. This experiment is called a Markov chain.

One example of a Markov chain is our marble drawing experiment of Section 2.4. Recall that there were two bags, the red bag and the blue bag. The red bag contained 3 red marbles and 2 blue marbles, while the blue bag contained 3 red marbles and 7 blue marbles. A marble is drawn from a bag, its color is recorded, and the marble is returned to the bag from which it was drawn. The next marble is then chosen from the bag that is the same color as the last marble drawn. There are two states or results for each draw, a red marble or a blue marble. The probability of getting a red marble on the $(n+1)$th draw depends only on what marble we got on the nth draw, since that determined which bag we would draw from.

Suppose we have m states, $E_1, E_2, \ldots, E_m$. E_1 is red, E_2 is blue, and $m = 2$ in the marble drawing example. Let $p_1(n)$ be the probability of state E_1 occurring on the nth repetition of our experiment. Likewise let $p_2(n), \ldots, p_m(n)$ be the probabilities of states $E_2, \ldots, E_m$, respectively, occurring on the nth repetition of the experiment. Since one of the m states must occur on the nth repetition, it follows that

$$p_1(n) + p_2(n) + \ldots + p_m(n) = 1. \tag{4}$$

Given that state E_1 was the result of the last repetition of the experiment, we must be given the probabilities that E_1, E_2, ..., and E_m will occur on the next repetition of the experiment. Reading $P(E_2|E_1)$ as the probability of E_2 occurring on the next repetition given that E_1 occurred on the last repetition, we denote these probabilities as

$$P(E_1|E_1) = p_{11}, \quad P(E_2|E_1) = p_{21}, \quad \ldots, \quad P(E_m|E_1) = p_{m1}.$$

Notice that

$$p_{11} + p_{21} + \ldots + p_{m1} = 1,$$

since, given that E_1 has happened on the last repetition, one of E_1, E_2, ..., or E_m must occur on the next repetition.

Remark: The probability that E_2 occurred given that E_1 occurred is denoted p_{21}. Observe that event E_1 occurred **before** event E_2, that is, the number that occurs first in the subscript corresponds to the event that happened last.

In the marble drawing example of Section 2.4,

$$P(E_1|E_1) = p_{11} = 0.6 \quad \text{and} \quad P(E_2|E_1) = p_{21} = 0.4$$

since there are 3 red and 2 blue marbles in the red bag, the bag from which you draw given that the previous draw was E_1 = red. Note that $0.6 + 0.4 = 1$.

Likewise, given that E_2 occurred on the last repetition of the experiment, we must know the probabilities of E_1, ..., E_m occurring on the next repetition, that is, we must know

$$P(E_1|E_2) = p_{12}, \quad P(E_2|E_2) = p_{22}, \quad \ldots, \quad P(E_m|E_2) = p_{m2}.$$

Again in the marble drawing example, we have

$$P(E_1|E_2) = p_{12} = 0.3 \quad \text{and} \quad P(E_2|E_2) = p_{22} = 0.7$$

since there are 3 red and 7 blue marbles in the blue bag, the bag from which you draw given that the previous draw was E_2 = blue. Note that $0.3 + 0.7 = 1$.

Similarly, if $m > 2$, we must know

$$P(E_1|E_3) = p_{13}, \quad \ldots, \quad P(E_m|E_3) = p_{m3},$$
$$\vdots \qquad \ddots \qquad \vdots$$
$$P(E_1|E_m) = p_{1m}, \quad \ldots, \quad P(E_m|E_m) = p_{mm}.$$

Again note that

$$p_{12} + p_{22} + \quad \cdots \quad + p_{m2} = 1,$$
$$\vdots$$
$$p_{1m} + p_{2m} + \quad \cdots \quad + p_{mm} = 1.$$

Example 6.9

Suppose we have three bags of marbles. The red bag contains 2 red, 3 blue, and 5 yellow marbles; the blue bag contains 1 red, 5 blue, and 4 yellow marbles; and the yellow bag contains 3 red, 1 blue, and 6 yellow marbles. A marble is drawn from a bag, its color is noted, and the marble is returned. E_1 is red, E_2 is blue, and E_3 is yellow. The next marble is drawn from the bag that is the same color as the marble just drawn.

Given that a red marble E_1 was just drawn, we know that the next marble will be drawn from the red bag so that the probabilities that the next marble drawn is red, blue, and yellow are 0.2, 0.3, and 0.5, respectively, that is,

$$p_{11} = 0.2, \quad p_{21} = 0.3, \quad p_{31} = 0.5.$$

Note that $0.2 + 0.3 + 0.5 = 1$, since we must get one of the marbles from the red bag. Likewise

$$p_{12} = 0.1, \quad p_{22} = 0.5, \quad p_{32} = 0.4$$
$$p_{13} = 0.3, \quad p_{23} = 0.1, \quad p_{33} = 0.6.$$

Suppose we wish to compute $p_1(n+1)$, that is, the probability that the $(n + 1)$th repetition of the experiment will result in state E_1. There are m ways this can happen. The first case is that we get E_1 on repetition n and $n + 1$, denoted $E_1 E_1$; the second case is that we get E_2 on repetition n and E_1 on repetition $n+1$, denoted $E_2 E_1$; ...; and the mth case is that we get E_m on repetition n and E_1 on repetition $n + 1$, denoted $E_m E_1$.

Case 1 is a two-stage experiment. The probability of the first stage, getting E_1 on the nth repetition, is $p_1(n)$. The probability of the second stage, getting E_1 given that we just got E_1 is p_{11}. By the multiplication principle,

$$p(\text{case } 1) = p_{11} p_1(n).$$

Likewise, the probability of the second, third, ..., and mth cases are

$$p(\text{case } 2) = p_{12} p_2(n), \quad \cdots, \quad p(\text{case m}) = p_{1m} p_m(n).$$

Recall that p_{jm} is the probability of $E_m E_j$, that is, the probability of E_j occurring on the next repetition given that E_m occurred on the last repetition.

Adding up the probabilities of these cases gives us

$$p_1(n+1) = p_{11}p_1(n) + p_{12}p_2(n) + \ldots + p_{1m}p_m(n).$$

Similarly,

$$p_2(n+1) = p_{21}p_1(n) + p_{22}p_2(n) + \ldots + p_{2m}p_m(n)$$
$$\vdots$$
$$p_m(n+1) = p_{m1}p_1(n) + p_{m2}p_2(n) + \ldots + p_{mm}p_m(n).$$

This gives us a dynamical system of m equations.

Let's compute $p_1(n+1)$ for Example 6.9, that is, the probability that we get a red marble on the $(n+1)$th draw. We can get a red marble in three ways or cases: from the red bag, from the blue bag, or from the yellow bag. The probability we are drawing from the red bag on the $(n+1)$th draw is the probability that we got a red marble on our nth draw, $p_1(n)$. The probability that we then draw a red marble (second stage) is p_{11}. Thus, the probability of the first case is

$$p_{11}p_1(n) = 0.2p_1(n).$$

The probability that we get a red marble from the blue bag on the $(n+1)$th draw is the probability that the nth marble was blue $p_2(n)$ and that we then got a red marble from the blue bag $p_{12} = 0.1$. By the multiplication principle, this probability is

$$p_{12}p_2(n) = 0.1p_2(n).$$

Similarly, the probability that we get a red marble from the yellow bag is

$$p_{13}p_3(n) = 0.3p_3(n).$$

Thus,
$$p_1(n+1) = 0.2p_1(n) + 0.1p_2(n) + 0.3p_3(n).$$

Similarly,

$$p_2(n+1) = 0.3p_1(n) + 0.5p_2(n) + 0.1p_3(n)$$
$$p_3(n+1) = 0.5p_1(n) + 0.4p_2(n) + 0.6p_3(n).$$

We can rewrite the m equations as the first order dynamical system

$$P(n+1) = RP(n),$$

by defining the vector $P(n)$ and the matrix R as

$$P(n) = \begin{pmatrix} p_1(n) \\ \vdots \\ p_m(n) \end{pmatrix} \quad \text{and} \quad R = \begin{pmatrix} p_{11} & \cdots & p_{1m} \\ \vdots & \ddots & \vdots \\ p_{m1} & \cdots & p_{mm} \end{pmatrix}.$$

The general solution is

$$P(k) = R^k P(0).$$

The vector $P(k)$ is called the **probability vector** associated with the Markov chain, and the m-by-m matrix R is called the **transition matrix**.

Since each of the components $p_j(k)$ of $P(k)$ is the probability of event E_j occurring on the kth draw, we must have

$$0 \le p_j(k) \le 1,$$

that is, each component of $P(k)$ must be between 0 and 1 (inclusive). Also, since one of the events E_j must occur, **the sum of the components of $P(k)$ must equal 1**.

Since each of the components of R is a probability, every number in the transition matrix R must be between 0 and 1 (inclusive). Also, from the way R was constructed, **the sum of the numbers in each column of R must equal 1**.

In Example 6.9

$$P(n) = \begin{pmatrix} p_1(n) \\ p_2(n) \\ p_m(n) \end{pmatrix} \quad \text{and} \quad R = \begin{pmatrix} 0.2 & 0.1 & 0.3 \\ 0.3 & 0.5 & 0.1 \\ 0.5 & 0.4 & 0.6 \end{pmatrix}.$$

Notice that the numbers in each column of R add up to 1. This is because the numbers in the first column are p_{11}, p_{21}, and p_{31}, and it was given above that they add up to 1 (since they are just the proportions of red, blue, and yellow marbles in the red bag). Likewise, the numbers in the second and third columns add up to 1 since they are just the proportions of red, blue, and yellow marbles in the blue and yellow bags, respectively.

Let's find the general solution to the dynamical system

$$P(n+1) = RP(n)$$

of Example 6.9. Since we have an aversion to computing R^k, we find the characteristic values for R. Thus,

$$|R - rI| = (0.2 - r)(0.5 - r)(0.6 - r) + 0.005 + 0.036$$
$$-0.15(0.5 - r) - 0.03(0.6 - r) - 0.04(0.2 - r).$$

Simplifying this, after a good bit of careful computation, you should get

$$|R - rI| = -r^3 + 1.3r^2 - 0.3r = -r(r - 1)(r - 0.3) = 0.$$

Thus, the three characteristic values are $r = 1$, 0, and 0.3, and the general solution is

$$P(k) = a1^k P_1 + b0^k P_2 + c(0.3)^k P_3 = aP_1 + c(0.3)^k P_3,$$

where P_1, P_2, and P_3 are the characteristic vectors corresponding to $r = 1$, 0, and 0.3, respectively. Since $(0.3)^k$ goes to zero as k goes to infinity,

$$\lim_{k \to \infty} P(k) = aP_1.$$

Let's find the characteristic vector corresponding to $r = 1$. Note that we have saved ourselves some work in that we do not need to know the characteristic vectors corresponding to $r = 0$ and $r = 0.3$ to approximate $P(k)$ for large k. To find P_1, we compute

$$(R - I)P_1 = \begin{pmatrix} -0.8 & 0.1 & 0.3 \\ 0.3 & -0.5 & 0.1 \\ 0.5 & 0.4 & -0.4 \end{pmatrix} \begin{pmatrix} x \\ y \\ z \end{pmatrix} = \begin{pmatrix} 0 \\ 0 \\ 0 \end{pmatrix}.$$

At this point you should be able to find a solution to these equations. One solution (characteristic vector) is

$$P_1 = \begin{pmatrix} 16 \\ 17 \\ 37 \end{pmatrix}.$$

Since $P(k) \to aP_1$ and the components ($p_1(k)$, $p_2(k)$, and $p_3(k)$) must add up to 1, it follows that the components of aP_1 must add up to 1, that is,

$$16a + 17a + 37a = 1, \quad \text{or} \quad a = \tfrac{1}{70}.$$

Thus,

$$\begin{array}{rcll} p_1(k) & = & \text{the probability the } k\text{th draw is red} & \to \quad 16/70, \\ p_2(k) & = & \text{the probability the } k\text{th draw is blue} & \to \quad 17/70, \\ p_3(k) & = & \text{the probability the } k\text{th draw is yellow} & \to \quad 37/70. \end{array}$$

Notice that we did not need $P(0)$ in order to compute the long term probabilities, that is, we did not need to know from which bag we drew our first marble in order to compute the probability that our 100th marble was red.

Remark: Many expositions on Markov chains multiply row vectors by matrices PR instead of matrices by column vectors RP. We did not use that convention, because it does not seem aesthetically pleasing to write the dynamical system as

$$P(n+1) = P(n)R.$$

As a word of caution, when writing the vector on the left, $P(n)R$, the matrix R is not the same matrix that we have been considering but is its transpose.

The general solution to the dynamical system

$$P(n+1) = RP(n)$$

is

$$P(k) = a_1(r_1)^k P_1 + \ldots + a_m(r_m)^k P_m$$

where $r_1, \ldots, r_m$ are the characteristic values (assuming that there are no double roots). Since the components of $P(k)$ are the probabilities of the m states happening on the kth repetition, the components are all positive and add up to 1. Thus, $P(k)$ cannot go to infinity and so $|r_j| \leq 1$ for $j = 1, \ldots, m$.

Likewise, since the sum of the components equals 1, $P(k)$ does not go to zero, so there must be at least one characteristic value, say r_1, whose absolute value equals 1, that is, $|r_1| = 1$. There may be more than one characteristic value whose absolute value equals 1.

The simplest type of Markov chain is one in which exactly one characteristic value of R, say r_1, equals one (and is not a double root), and all other characteristic values satisfy

$$|r_j| < 1 \quad \text{for} \quad j = 2, \ldots, m.$$

In such a case,

$$\lim_{k \to \infty} P(k) = aP_1.$$

The vector P_1 is a characteristic vector corresponding to $r_1 = 1$, and thus it satisfies

$$(R - I)P_1 = 0.$$

The number a is chosen so that the components of $P(k)$ add up to 1, that is, if

$$P_1 = \begin{pmatrix} p_1 \\ \vdots \\ p_m \end{pmatrix},$$

then a is chosen so that $ap_1 + \ldots + ap_m = 1$, so that

$$a = \frac{1}{p_1 + \ldots + p_m}.$$

This was the case for our marble drawing example of Section 2.4 and in Example 6.9. All that was necessary in these examples to find the probabilities $P(k)$ for large k was to find the characteristic vector corresponding to $r_1 = 1$, and solve a simple equation for the number a.

Such matrices as these are easy to work with, but how does one identify them? A **regular Markov chain** is one in which the matrix, R^k, has **no zeros** in any position, for **some** value of k. The 3-by-3 matrix R in Example 6.9, has no zeros in any position, so this example is a regular Markov chain. In the next section, we will see transition matrices R in which R^k has some zeros for every power k. It can be shown that the matrix corresponding to a regular Markov chain has one characteristic value equal to 1 and the rest are less than 1 in absolute value.

Example 6.10

Consider two tennis players, Ace and Spike. We will assume that when someone wins a tennis match, it gives him confidence and the other player loses confidence. Because of this, if a player wins a match, he is more likely to win the next match, and if he loses a match he is more likely to lose the next match. Specifically, suppose if Spike beats Ace in a match, then the likelihood Spike will win the next match is 0.6, while if Spike loses to Ace, the likelihood Spike will win the next match is 0.3.

Let the probability that Spike wins match n be $p(n)$, and the probability that Ace wins match n be $q(n)$. From the above, you should be able to derive

$$p(n + 1) = 0.6p(n) + 0.3q(n)$$

as the equation that gives the probability that Spike will win match $n+1$. From the above, we also know that if Spike wins a match, the probability that Ace wins the next match (Spike loses) is $1 - 0.6 = 0.4$, and if Ace wins a match, the probability that Ace wins the next match is 0.7. Thus,

$$q(n + 1) = 0.4p(n) + 0.7q(n).$$

We now have the Markov chain

$$\begin{pmatrix} p(n+1) \\ q(n+1) \end{pmatrix} = \begin{pmatrix} 0.6 & 0.3 \\ 0.4 & 0.7 \end{pmatrix} \begin{pmatrix} p(n) \\ q(n) \end{pmatrix}.$$

Since the matrix R has no zeros, this is a regular Markov chain. Therefore, we solve

$$(R - I)P_1 = \begin{pmatrix} -0.4 & 0.3 \\ 0.4 & -0.3 \end{pmatrix} \begin{pmatrix} x \\ y \end{pmatrix} = \begin{pmatrix} 0 \\ 0 \end{pmatrix}.$$

One solution is that $y = 4$ and $x = 3$. Thus,

$$\lim_{k \to \infty} P(k) = a \begin{pmatrix} 3 \\ 4 \end{pmatrix} = \begin{pmatrix} 3a \\ 4a \end{pmatrix}.$$

Since $3a + 4a = 1$, we get $a = 1/7$. We then have

$$\lim_{k \to \infty} p(k) = \tfrac{3}{7} \quad \text{and} \quad \lim_{k \to \infty} q(k) = \tfrac{4}{7}.$$

Thus, Spike will win (approximately) 3/7 of the games while Ace will win 4/7.

Note that this system could have been rewritten as a first order affine dynamical system and solved similarly using the techniques developed in Section 2.4.

You may wonder why a regular Markov chain has one root equal to one and all others less than one (in absolute value). While the answer to this requires a bit more mathematics than we presently have at our disposal, we can get some insight into why this it is true by considering the converse. Suppose we have a Markov chain in which the transition matrix R has $r = 1$ as a single root of the characteristic equation and all other roots are less than one in absolute value. Also assume that all the components of P_1, the characteristic vector corresponding to $r = 1$, are nonzero. Then this Markov chain is regular, that is, for some value of k, the matrix R^k has no zeroes.

To see that this is true, let's reconsider the regular Markov chain of Example 6.9. The matrix R and the characteristic vector P_1 corresponding to the characteristic value $r = 1$ are

$$R = \begin{pmatrix} 0.2 & 0.1 & 0.3 \\ 0.3 & 0.5 & 0.1 \\ 0.5 & 0.4 & 0.6 \end{pmatrix} \quad \text{and} \quad P_1 = \begin{pmatrix} 16/70 \\ 17/70 \\ 37/70 \end{pmatrix}.$$

Suppose that you drew the first marble from the red bag, that is,

$$P(0) = \begin{pmatrix} 1 \\ 0 \\ 0 \end{pmatrix}.$$

Thus, for large values of k we have, approximately,

$$P(k) = R^k P(0) = P_1.$$

Denote the matrix R^k as

$$R^k = \begin{pmatrix} a_{11} & a_{12} & a_{13} \\ a_{21} & a_{22} & a_{23} \\ a_{31} & a_{32} & a_{33} \end{pmatrix}.$$

Then

$$R^k P(0) = \begin{pmatrix} a_{11} & a_{12} & a_{13} \\ a_{21} & a_{22} & a_{23} \\ a_{31} & a_{32} & a_{33} \end{pmatrix} \begin{pmatrix} 1 \\ 0 \\ 0 \end{pmatrix} = \begin{pmatrix} a_{11} \\ a_{21} \\ a_{31} \end{pmatrix} = P_1.$$

Thus, $a_{11} = 16/70$, $a_{21} = 17/70$, and $a_{31} = 37/70$.
By letting

$$P(0) = \begin{pmatrix} 0 \\ 1 \\ 0 \end{pmatrix},$$

we also get

$$R^k P(0) = \begin{pmatrix} a_{11} & a_{12} & a_{13} \\ a_{21} & a_{22} & a_{23} \\ a_{31} & a_{32} & a_{33} \end{pmatrix} \begin{pmatrix} 0 \\ 1 \\ 0 \end{pmatrix} = \begin{pmatrix} a_{12} \\ a_{22} \\ a_{32} \end{pmatrix} = P_1,$$

and the second column of the matrix R^k is the same as P_1.
Likewise, the third column of R^k is P_1 also. Thus,

$$\lim_{k \to \infty} R^k = \begin{pmatrix} 16/70 & 16/70 & 16/70 \\ 17/70 & 17/70 & 17/70 \\ 37/70 & 37/70 & 37/70 \end{pmatrix}.$$

Thus, if there are no zeros in the components of P_1, and since each column of R^k is approximately equal to P_1, then R^k has no zeros, for some power of k (and for all powers k greater than some value k_0).

It is more difficult to show that if R is the transition matrix for a regular Markov chain, that is, if R^k has no zeros for some k, then $r = 1$ is the only root whose absolute value equals 1, and its characteristic vector P_1 has no zeros.

6.5.1   Problems

1. Which of the following vectors cannot be a probability vector $P(n)$ and why?

$$\text{(a)} \begin{pmatrix} 0.4 \\ 0.5 \\ 0.2 \end{pmatrix}, \quad \text{(b)} \begin{pmatrix} 0.3 \\ 0.2 \\ 0.5 \end{pmatrix}, \quad \text{(c)} \begin{pmatrix} 0.8 \\ -0.1 \\ 0.3 \end{pmatrix}, \quad \text{(d)} \begin{pmatrix} 0 \\ 0 \\ 1 \end{pmatrix}.$$

2. Which of the following matrices cannot be a transition matrix and why? Which transition matrices are regular?

$$\text{(a)} \begin{pmatrix} 0.2 & 0.3 \\ 0.9 & 0.7 \end{pmatrix}, \quad \text{(b)} \begin{pmatrix} -0.1 & 0.6 \\ 1.1 & 0.4 \end{pmatrix}, \quad \text{(c)} \begin{pmatrix} 0.4 & 1 \\ 0.6 & 0 \end{pmatrix},$$

$$\text{(d)} \begin{pmatrix} 0.2 & 0.3 \\ 0.8 & 0.7 \end{pmatrix}, \quad \text{(e)} \begin{pmatrix} 0 & 1 \\ 1 & 0 \end{pmatrix}, \quad \text{(f)} \begin{pmatrix} 0.4 & 0.6 \\ 0.3 & 0.7 \end{pmatrix}.$$

3. For each of these regular transition matrices, find

$$\lim_{k \to \infty} P(k),$$

that is, find a characteristic vector corresponding to $r = 1$ and then find the value of a such that the components of aP_1 add up to 1.

$$\text{(a)} \begin{pmatrix} 0.2 & 0.6 \\ 0.8 & 0.4 \end{pmatrix}, \quad \text{(b)} \begin{pmatrix} 0.6 & 1 \\ 0.4 & 0 \end{pmatrix}, \quad \text{(c)} \begin{pmatrix} 0.7 & 0.3 & 0.9 \\ 0.3 & 0.6 & 0 \\ 0 & 0.1 & 0.1 \end{pmatrix}.$$

4. Suppose we have three bags: a red bag containing 2 red, 2 blue, and 2 green marbles; a blue bag containing 2 red and 6 green marbles; and a green bag containing 2 red and 6 blue marbles. A marble is drawn at random from one of the bags and its color is recorded. The next marble is drawn from the bag that is the same color as the marble just drawn. What are the probabilities that the 100th marble drawn is red, is blue, and is green? You do not need to know from which bag you drew the first marble.

5. Two hamburger chains (to avoid controversy, call them A and B) are in competition. Suppose that if a person goes to A for a hamburger, the probability of going back to A for the next hamburger is 0.8, while the probability of going to B for the next hamburger is 0.2. Suppose also that if a person goes to B for a hamburger, the probability of going back to B for the next hamburger is 0.7, while the probability of going to A for the next hamburger is 0.3. Compute chain A's percentage of the hamburger market.

6.6 Absorbing Markov chains

Suppose we have a Markov chain in which there is at least one state, say E_j, such that if this state occurs on the nth repetition of the experiment, then it will occur on the $(n+1)$th repetition, also. This state is then called an **absorbing state**. In other words, a state E_j is an absorbing state if p_{jj}, the probability that state E_j will occur on the next repetition of the experiment given that E_j occurred on the last repetition, is 1, and therefore $p_{ij} = 0$ for $i \neq j$, where p_{ij} is the probability that state E_i will occur on the next repetition of the experiment given state E_j just occurred. Thus, the jth column of the transition matrix R will have a 1 in the jth position and 0's in every other position of that column.

Definition 6.11

*Suppose we have a Markov chain in which there is at least one absorbing state. Suppose, for any starting state, it is possible to end at some absorbing state. This process is then called an **absorbing Markov chain**.*

Example 6.12

Suppose we have four bags of marbles. The red bag contains 1 red marble; the blue bag contains 1 blue marble; the green bag contains 3 red, 1 blue, 4 green, and 2 yellow marbles; and the yellow bag contains 1 red, 2 blue, 3 green, and 4 yellow marbles. A marble is drawn from the yellow bag, its color is recorded, and the marble is returned to the yellow bag. The $(n+1)$th marble is drawn from the bag that is the same color as the nth marble drawn.

In this problem, red and blue marbles are absorbing states since once a red marble is drawn, we must get red marbles from that point on, and the same goes for blue marbles. The dynamical system that describes this problem is

$$P(n+1) = RP(n),$$

where

$$R = \begin{pmatrix} 1 & 0 & 0.3 & 0.1 \\ 0 & 1 & 0.1 & 0.2 \\ 0 & 0 & 0.4 & 0.3 \\ 0 & 0 & 0.2 & 0.4 \end{pmatrix}.$$

The above example is an absorbing Markov chain. Notice that we don't have to get red or blue on the first draw. In fact you may have to go through many repetitions before you can possibly reach an absorbing state, such as when an orange bag is added that contains only orange, yellow, and green marbles. This is still an absorbing Markov chain since, eventually, you can get a red or blue marble.

Example 6.13

Suppose we have four bags of marbles. The red bag contains 1 red marble; the blue bag contains 1 blue marble, 1 red marble, and 2 green marbles;

Fig. 58. Man leaving bar must arrive at home to the left or fall into the lake to the right.

the green bag contains 4 green and 2 yellow marbles; and the yellow bag contains 3 green and 4 yellow marbles. A marble is drawn from a bag, its color is recorded, and the marble is returned to that bag. The $(n+1)$th marble is drawn from the bag that is the same color as the nth marble drawn. This is **not** an absorbing Markov chain or a regular Markov chain. The reason it is not an absorbing Markov chain is that if the first marble is drawn from the yellow bag, it is impossible ever to get a red marble, and you will keep getting green and yellow marbles for ever. It is not a regular Markov chain because there is an absorbing state, red, and R^k will always have some zeros.

The problem with absorbing Markov chains with more than one absorbing state is that $r = 1$ is a multiple root of the characteristic equation $|R - rI| = 0$. Thus, to find the probabilities of eventually ending in each of the absorbing states, we need to find all the characteristic values, all the corresponding characteristic vectors, and then the particular solution using the given initial state. This is a long and tedious method for solving the problem.

The goal of the rest of this section is to find a short cut for determining the probabilities of ending in each of the absorbing states. We do this by way of an 'application'.

Let's consider what is called a **random walk**. Suppose a man leaves a bar after having too much to drink. His home is two blocks to the left, while a lake is one block to his right. He will stumble one block to the left with probability 0.2 or one block to the right with probability 0.8. For simplicity, let's assume it takes him 1 minute to walk one block. After walking one block, he will again walk left with probability 0.2 or right with probability 0.8. He continues in this manner until he arrives home or falls into the lake. If he arrives home or falls into the lake, he remains there. See Figure 58.

Let home be corner a and the lake be corner d, as indicated in the figure. Let $a(n)$ be the probability that the man will be at corner a when n minutes have passed. Likewise $b(n)$, $c(n)$, and $d(n)$ are the probabilities that the man will be at corners b, c, and d when n minutes have passed.

To compute $a(n + 1)$, the probability that the man is at corner a when $n + 1$ minutes have passed, we must consider two cases. Case 1 is that the man is at corner a when n minutes have passed, since he then stays at home. The probability of case 1 is $a(n)$. Case 2 is that the man is at corner b when n minutes have passed and he then walks left. Case 2 is a two-stage process. The first stage is that he is at corner b when n minutes have passed and this has probability $b(n)$. The second stage is that he turns left, and the probability of this is 0.2. By the multiplication principle, the probability of case 2 is $0.2b(n)$. Adding the two cases together gives our first equation

$$a(n + 1) = a(n) + 0.2b(n).$$

For the man to be at corner b when $n + 1$ minutes have passed, he must have been at corner c when n minutes had passed and then turned left. Notice that if he had been at corner a when n minutes had passed, he would have stopped. Thus, we only have one case. Using the multiplication principle, we get

$$b(n + 1) = 0.2c(n).$$

Similarly, we get the equations

$$c(n + 1) = 0.8b(n) \quad \text{and} \quad d(n + 1) = 0.8c(n) + d(n)$$

corresponding to corners c and d, respectively.

Combining these four equations, we get the dynamical system

$$P(n + 1) = RP(n),$$

where

$$P(n) = \begin{pmatrix} a(n) \\ b(n) \\ c(n) \\ d(n) \end{pmatrix} \quad \text{and} \quad R = \begin{pmatrix} 1 & 0.2 & 0 & 0 \\ 0 & 0 & 0.2 & 0 \\ 0 & 0.8 & 0 & 0 \\ 0 & 0 & 0.8 & 1 \end{pmatrix}.$$

The first step is to find a simpler method for separating the notation for the absorbing and nonabsorbing states. Let's denote the absorbing states by E_1, E_2, and so forth. Let's denote the nonabsorbing states by F_1, F_2, and so forth. Thus, we will denote corner a by E_1 and corner d by E_2. We will denote corner b by F_1 and corner c by F_2.

Let $p_j(n)$ be the probability of absorbing state E_j occurring on the nth repetition of the experiment, that is, $p_1(n)$ for corner a and $p_2(n)$ for corner d in this case. Also, let $q_j(n)$ be the probability of nonabsorbing state F_j occurring on the nth repetition of the experiment, that is, $q_1(n)$ for corner b and $q_2(n)$ for corner c in this case. Using this notation, we write our dynamical system as

$$
\begin{pmatrix} p_1(n+1) \\ p_2(n+1) \\ q_1(n+1) \\ q_2(n+1) \end{pmatrix} = \begin{pmatrix} 1 & 0 & 0.2 & 0 \\ 0 & 1 & 0 & 0.8 \\ 0 & 0 & 0 & 0.2 \\ 0 & 0 & 0.8 & 0 \end{pmatrix} \begin{pmatrix} p_1(n) \\ p_2(n) \\ q_1(n) \\ q_2(n) \end{pmatrix}. \tag{5}
$$

Notice that this matrix is a rearrangement of the matrix R given above. This is because the states are given in a different order, that is, the corners are listed as a, d, b, and c instead of a, b, c, and d.

The first equation from this system is

$$
p_1(n+1) = p_1(n) + 0.2q_1(n).
$$

This says that the probability of ending at corner a after $n+1$ minutes is the probability of being at corner a after n minutes plus the probability of being at corner b after n minutes $(q_1(n))$ and then turning left (0.2). You should be able to check that the other three equations are also correct.

Let's rewrite dynamical system (5) as

$$
\begin{pmatrix} p_1(n+1) \\ p_2(n+1) \\ - \\ q_1(n+1) \\ q_2(n+1) \end{pmatrix} = \begin{pmatrix} 1 & 0 & | & 0.2 & 0 \\ 0 & 1 & | & 0 & 0.8 \\ - & - & + & - & - \\ 0 & 0 & | & 0 & 0.2 \\ 0 & 0 & | & 0.8 & 0 \end{pmatrix} \begin{pmatrix} p_1(n) \\ p_2(n) \\ - \\ q_1(n) \\ q_2(n) \end{pmatrix}. \tag{6}
$$

Observe from the way this is written that the probability vector can be broken into the two smaller vectors

$$
P(n) = \begin{pmatrix} p_1(n) \\ p_2(n) \end{pmatrix} \quad \text{and} \quad Q(n) = \begin{pmatrix} q_1(n) \\ q_2(n) \end{pmatrix}.
$$

Also, the transition matrix can be broken into the four smaller matrices

$$
I_2 = \begin{pmatrix} 1 & 0 \\ 0 & 1 \end{pmatrix}, \qquad 0_2 = \begin{pmatrix} 0 & 0 \\ 0 & 0 \end{pmatrix},
$$

$$
S = \begin{pmatrix} 0.2 & 0 \\ 0 & 0.8 \end{pmatrix}, \qquad R = \begin{pmatrix} 0 & 0.2 \\ 0.8 & 0 \end{pmatrix}.
$$

Using this notation, we can rewrite our absorbing Markov chain as

$$
\begin{pmatrix} P(n+1) \\ Q(n+1) \end{pmatrix} = \begin{pmatrix} I_2 & S \\ 0_2 & R \end{pmatrix} \begin{pmatrix} P(n) \\ Q(n) \end{pmatrix}.
$$

While $P(n)$ and $Q(n)$ are vectors and I_2, S, 0_2, and R are matrices, let's proceed as if they were all just numbers. Dynamical system (6) can be rewritten as the two equations

$$P(n+1) = P(n) + SQ(n) \qquad (7)$$

and

$$Q(n+1) = RQ(n). \qquad (8)$$

Dynamical system (8) is in reality a first order dynamical system of 2 equations, and its solution is

$$Q(k) = R^k Q(0).$$

We note here that since we can eventually reach some absorbing state from each of the nonabsorbing states, the characteristic values for R will all have absolute value less than one, that is, $\|R\| < 1$. You should find the characteristic values of R to see that this is true. Thus, the probability of being at any one nonabsorbing state after k tries must go to zero. So

$$\lim_{k \to \infty} R^k Q(0) = \begin{pmatrix} 0 \\ 0 \end{pmatrix}.$$

Thus, the probabilities $q_1(k)$ and $q_2(k)$ must decrease to zero.

Substitution of $Q(n)$ into equation (7) gives

$$P(n+1) = P(n) + SR^n Q(0). \qquad (9)$$

This is a first order nonhomogeneous dynamical system.

Recall that the general solution of the first order nonhomogeneous dynamical system

$$a(n+1) = a(n) + r^n b$$

was of the form

$$a(k) = a + r^k c,$$

where the number a depended on the initial value $a(0)$ and the number c depended on the equation. Thus, we might suspect that the general solution to the nonhomogeneous dynamical system (9) is of the form

$$P(k) = A + SR^k C,$$

where the vectors A and C depend on the system and the initial value $P(0)$.

To see if this is true, let's substitute our 'guess' into the dynamical system (9) and see if we can find vectors A and C that satisfy the equation. Since

$$P(n+1) = A + SR^{n+1}C = A + SR^n RC,$$

substitution gives

$$A + SR^n RC = A + SR^n C + SR^n Q(0).$$

Canceling the As, and bringing all the terms to the left gives

$$SR^n RC - SR^n C - SR^n Q(0) = 0,$$

(where 0 is the vector with two zeros). Factoring out SR^n gives

$$SR^n(RC - C - Q(0)) = 0.$$

Thus, the equation is satisfied if

$$RC - C - Q(0) = 0, \quad \text{that is, if} \quad (R - I)C = Q(0).$$

After multiplying both sides by $(R - I)^{-1}$ on the left, we get

$$C = (R - I)^{-1}Q(0).$$

Thus, the general solution to dynamical system (9) is

$$P(k) = A + SR^k(R - I)^{-1}Q(0).$$

Let's now use the initial value $P(0)$ to find the vector A.

$$P(0) = A + S(R - I)^{-1}Q(0),$$

since $R^0 = I$. Thus,

$$A = P(0) - S(R - I)^{-1}Q(0) = P(0) + S(I - R)^{-1}Q(0)$$

(note that we used the rule that $-(R - I)^{-1} = (I - R)^{-1}$) and the particular solution is

$$P(k) = P(0) + S(I - R)^{-1}Q(0) - SR^k(I - R)^{-1}Q(0).$$

Since R^k goes to zero as k goes to infinity, it follows that

$$\lim_{k \to \infty} P(k) = P(0) + S(I - R)^{-1}Q(0).$$

Remember that the components of the vector $P(0)$ give the probabilities that we **start** in the absorbing states E_1 and E_2. But if we start in one of these states, we will always remain there, and the problem is easy. Therefore, in most applications we assume that we do not start in an absorbing state, that is, each component of $P(0)$ is zero. In this case, the probabilities of ending in each absorbing state are given by

$$\lim_{k \to \infty} P(k) = S(I - R)^{-1}Q(0).$$

We have shown the following.

Theorem 6.14

Suppose we have an absorbing Markov chain given by the dynamical system

$$\begin{pmatrix} P(n+1) \\ Q(n+1) \end{pmatrix} = \begin{pmatrix} I_m & S \\ 0_{mk} & R \end{pmatrix} \begin{pmatrix} P(n) \\ Q(n) \end{pmatrix},$$

where $P(n)$ is the m-vector which gives the probabilities of being in each of the m absorbing states after n repetitions, $Q(n)$ is the ℓ-vector which gives the probabilities of being in each of the ℓ nonabsorbing states after n repetitions, S is a m-by-ℓ matrix giving the probabilities of going from the each of the nonabsorbing states to each of the absorbing states, R is the ℓ-by-ℓ matrix giving the probabilities of going from each of the nonabsorbing states to each of the nonabsorbing states, Im is the m-by-m identity matrix, and $0_{\ell m}$ is an ℓ-by-m matrix with all zeros. Then the probabilities of ending in each of the absorbing states is given by the vector

$$P(0) + S(I - R)^{-1}Q(0).$$

Applying this theorem to our bar problem, we note that

$$I - R = \begin{pmatrix} 1 & -0.2 \\ -0.8 & 1 \end{pmatrix}.$$

You should then be able to compute that

$$(I - R)^{-1} = \tfrac{5}{21} \begin{pmatrix} 5 & 1 \\ 4 & 5 \end{pmatrix}.$$

Since you start at corner c which is state F_2, we have that

$$Q(0) = \begin{pmatrix} 0 \\ 1 \end{pmatrix} \quad \text{and} \quad P(0) = \begin{pmatrix} 0 \\ 0 \end{pmatrix}$$

so that

$$S(I - R)^{-1}Q(0) = \tfrac{5}{21} \begin{pmatrix} 0.2 & 0 \\ 0 & 0.8 \end{pmatrix} \begin{pmatrix} 5 & 1 \\ 4 & 5 \end{pmatrix} \begin{pmatrix} 0 \\ 1 \end{pmatrix} = \begin{pmatrix} 1/21 \\ 20/21 \end{pmatrix}.$$

Thus, the probability the man will eventually find his way home is $1/21$ and the probability he will be 'absorbed' in the lake is $20/21$.

Example 6.15

Let's apply Theorem 6.14 to Example 6.12. Suppose we draw our first marble from the yellow bag. What is the probability the 100th marble will be red, that is, what fraction of the cases will end in absorbing state 'red?'

Let E_1 be the state that a red marble is drawn. Likewise, E_2, F_1, and F_2 are the states that a blue, green, and yellow marble are drawn, respectively. Notice that E_1 and E_2 are absorbing states and that F_1 and F_2 are nonabsorbing states. Similarly, we define $p_1(n)$, $p_2(n)$, $q_1(n)$, and $q_2(n)$ as the probabilities that the corresponding colored marbles are drawn on the nth draw. Recall that the dynamical system that modeled this marble drawing situation was

$$
\begin{pmatrix} p_1(n+1) \\ p_2(n+1) \\ q_1(n+1) \\ q_2(n+1) \end{pmatrix} = \begin{pmatrix} 1 & 0 & 0.3 & 0.1 \\ 0 & 1 & 0.1 & 0.2 \\ 0 & 0 & 0.4 & 0.3 \\ 0 & 0 & 0.2 & 0.4 \end{pmatrix} \begin{pmatrix} p_1(n) \\ p_2(n) \\ q_1(n) \\ q_2(n) \end{pmatrix}.
$$

Notice that

$$
P(n) = \begin{pmatrix} p_1(n) \\ p_2(n) \end{pmatrix}, \quad Q(n) = \begin{pmatrix} q_1(n) \\ q_2(n) \end{pmatrix}, \quad Q(0) = \begin{pmatrix} 0 \\ 1 \end{pmatrix},
$$

$$
S = \begin{pmatrix} 0.3 & 0.1 \\ 0.1 & 0.2 \end{pmatrix}, \quad R = \begin{pmatrix} 0.4 & 0.3 \\ 0.2 & 0.4 \end{pmatrix}.
$$

Thus the probabilities of eventually ending in either the red or blue bag are given by

$$
S(I-R)^{-1}Q(0)
$$

since $P(0) = 0$. We compute that

$$
I - R = \begin{pmatrix} 0.6 & -0.3 \\ -0.2 & 0.6 \end{pmatrix}, \quad \text{so} \quad (I-R)^{-1} = \tfrac{1}{3}\begin{pmatrix} 6 & 3 \\ 2 & 6 \end{pmatrix}.
$$

Now

$$
S(I-R)^{-1} = \tfrac{1}{3}\begin{pmatrix} 0.3 & 0.1 \\ 0.1 & 0.2 \end{pmatrix} \begin{pmatrix} 6 & 3 \\ 2 & 6 \end{pmatrix} = \tfrac{1}{6}\begin{pmatrix} 4 & 3 \\ 2 & 3 \end{pmatrix}.
$$

Since the first marble is drawn from the yellow bag, we have

$$
S(I-R)^{-1}Q(0) = \tfrac{1}{6}\begin{pmatrix} 4 & 3 \\ 2 & 3 \end{pmatrix} \begin{pmatrix} 0 \\ 1 \end{pmatrix} = \begin{pmatrix} 0.5 \\ 0.5 \end{pmatrix},
$$

so that the probability we end in state E_1 is 0.5 and the probability that we end in state E_2 is 0.5.

Suppose we draw the first marble from the green bag instead of from the yellow bag. What is the probability of ending in state E_1. This is easy, once we have computed the matrix $S(I - R)^{-1}$. The answer is

$$S(I - R)^{-1}Q(0) = \tfrac{1}{6} \begin{pmatrix} 4 & 3 \\ 2 & 3 \end{pmatrix} \begin{pmatrix} 1 \\ 0 \end{pmatrix} = \begin{pmatrix} 2/3 \\ 1/3 \end{pmatrix},$$

that is, we end with a red marble two-thirds of the time, and with a blue marble one-third of the time.

Suppose we flip a fair coin and if head comes up, we draw our first marble from the yellow bag, while if tails comes up, we draw our first marble from the green bag. What are the probabilities of ending in each of the absorbing states? In this case, since

$$Q(0) = \begin{pmatrix} 0.5 \\ 0.5 \end{pmatrix},$$

the answer is given by

$$S(I - R)^{-1}Q(0) = \tfrac{1}{6} \begin{pmatrix} 4 & 3 \\ 2 & 3 \end{pmatrix} \begin{pmatrix} 0.5 \\ 0.5 \end{pmatrix} = \begin{pmatrix} 7/12 \\ 5/12 \end{pmatrix},$$

that is, we end with a red marble seven-twelfths of the time and with a blue marble five-twelfths of the time.

6.6.1   Problems

1. Suppose we have four bags of marbles. The red bag contains 1 red marble; the blue bag contains 1 blue marble; the green bag contains 2 red, 2 blue, 4 green, and 2 yellow marbles; and the yellow bag contains 2 red, 1 blue, 3 green, and 4 yellow marbles. A marble is drawn from the yellow bag, its color is recorded, and the marble is returned to the yellow bag. The $(n + 1)$th marble is drawn from the bag that is the same color as the nth marble drawn. What is the probability the 100th marble is red, that is, in what fraction of the cases will we end in the absorbing state, red? What is the probability we end in the absorbing state, blue?

2. What is the answer to Problem 1 if the first marble is drawn from the green bag?

3. In Problem 1, suppose there is also a white bag containing 2 green marbles, 3 white marbles, and 1 yellow marble.

(a) If the first marble drawn is from the white bag, what are the probabilities of eventually ending in the red bag and eventually ending in the blue bag?

(b) Suppose it is equally likely that the first marble is drawn from anyone of the five bags. What are the probabilities of eventually ending in the red bag and eventually ending in the blue bag?

4. Consider the drunk staggering home from the bar. Find the probability that the man arrives home given that the bar is at corner b instead of corner c.

5. Consider the drunk staggering home from the bar. Suppose he staggers left one block with probability 0.4 and right with probability 0.6. Suppose home is 2 blocks to the left of the bar and the lake is 2 blocks to the right of the bar. What is the probability that the drunk gets home safely? Hint: There are 5 corners, 2 of them are absorbing and 3 of them are nonabsorbing.

6. Suppose that a man leaves a bar. His home is one block to the left and a wall is one block to the right. When he is at the bar, he goes left with probability 0.72 and right with probability 0.28. When he is at home, he remains there. When he is at the wall, he goes left with probability 0.5 and remains at the wall with probability 0.5. Model this as a Markov chain, that is, find the transition matrix R, then find the particular solution. Use this solution to find $a(10)$, the probability he is at home after 10 minutes.

7. Suppose that a man leaves a bar. His home is one block to the left and a wall is one block to the right. When he is at the bar, he goes left with probability 0.2 and right with probability 0.8. When he is at home, he goes right with probability 0.8 and remains home with probability 0.2. When he is at the wall, he goes left with probability 0.5 and remains at the wall with probability 0.5. Model this as a Markov chain, that is, find the transition matrix R. This is a regular Markov chain, and therefore to find the long term probabilities, all that is necessary is to find the characteristic vector corresponding to the characteristic value, $r = 1$. Find this vector.

6.7 Applications of absorbing Markov chains

In this section, we will use our methods to study two problems. The first problem is a bit contrived. The second is a cost accounting problem.

6.7.1 The good, the bad, and the ugly

In a variation of the movie **The Good, the Bad, and the Ugly**, suppose we have three gunfighters, A, B, and C, who are entering a three-way duel. Gunfighter A is a good shot and hits his target 70 per cent of the time. Gunfighter B is not as good a shot and hits his target 50 per cent of the time. Gunfighter C is wondering how he got into this mess, since he hits his target only 30 per cent of the time.

The rules of the gunfight are that on the count of three, all three gunfighters draw and shoot one shot at one of the others (simultaneously). As their strategy, each will shoot at the strongest opponent still remaining. Thus, on the first shot, A shoots at B, while B and C both shoot at A. If more than one gunfighter survives, the process is repeated. Who will most likely win the gunfight?

Each state will be the possible survivors of a gunfight. We will list the absorbing states first, that is, states in which the gunfight ends. Thus, E_1 is that nobody survives, E_2 is that only A survives, E_3 is that only B survives, and E_4 is that only C survives.

We now list the nonabsorbing states. First we note that when all three gunfighters are alive, nobody shoots at C. Thus, A and/or B must be shot first and, therefore, we cannot have the state in which A and B are the only survivors. Thus, we let F_1 be the state in which A and C are the only survivors. Proceeding, F_2 is the state in which B and C are the only survivors, and F_3 is the state in which all three survive.

Let $p_1(n)$ be the probability that state E_1 (nobody survives) occurs after n rounds of shots have been fired. Likewise for $p_2(n)$, $p_3(n)$, $p_4(n)$, $q_1(n)$, $q_2(n)$, and $q_3(n)$.

Let's compute $p_1(n+1)$. There are three cases (or ways) in which nobody survives round $n+1$. These are that nobody survived round n (probability $p_1(n)$), that only A and C survived round n and then A and C shoot each other, and that only B and C survived round n and then B and C shoot each other. The second case is a three-stage process, the first stage being that only A and C survive round n (probability $q_1(n)$), the second stage being that A shoots C (probability 0.7), and the third stage being that C shoots A (probability 0.3). Thus, the probability of the second case is, using the multiplication principle, $0.21q_1(n)$. Likewise, using three stages, we get that the probability of the third case is $(0.5)(0.3)q_2(n) = 0.15q_2(n)$.

Adding the probabilities of the three cases, we get that

$$p_1(n+1) = p_1(n) + 0.21q_1(n) + 0.15q_2(n).$$

To get $p_2(n+1)$, we consider two cases, that only A survives round n, and that only A and C survive round n and then A shoots C but C

misses A. This second case is a three-stage process. The probability that only A and C survive round n is $q_1(n)$, the probability A shoots C is 0.7, and the probability C misses A is 0.7. Thus

$$p_2(n+1) = p_2(n) + 0.49q_1(n).$$

In a similar manner, you should find that

$$
\begin{aligned}
p_3(n+1) &= p_3(n) + 0.35q_2(n), \\
p_4(n+1) &= p_4(n) + 0.09q_1(n) + 0.15q_2(n) + 0.455q_3(n), \\
q_1(n+1) &= 0.21q_1(n) + 0.245q_3(n), \\
q_2(n+1) &= 0.35q_2(n) + 0.195q_3(n), \\
q_3(n+1) &= 0.105q_3(n).
\end{aligned}
$$

In computing these equations, there is one moderately difficult probability, the probability that B or C or both shoot A. This probability has two cases. The first is that B shoots A (in which case it is irrelevant what C does). The second is that B misses and C hits. The sum of these cases gives the probability that B or (and) C shoots A as $0.5 + (0.5)(0.3) = 0.65$.

We now rewrite our equations as the dynamical system

$$
\begin{pmatrix}
p_1(n+1) \\
p_2(n+1) \\
p_3(n+1) \\
p_4(n+1) \\
- \\
q_1(n+1) \\
q_2(n+1) \\
q_3(n+1)
\end{pmatrix}
=
\left(
\begin{array}{cccc|ccc}
1 & 0 & 0 & 0 & 0.21 & 0.15 & 0 \\
0 & 1 & 0 & 0 & 0.49 & 0 & 0 \\
0 & 0 & 1 & 0 & 0 & 0.35 & 0 \\
0 & 0 & 0 & 1 & 0.09 & 0.15 & 0.455 \\
\hline
0 & 0 & 0 & 0 & 0.21 & 0 & 0.245 \\
0 & 0 & 0 & 0 & 0 & 0.35 & 0.195 \\
0 & 0 & 0 & 0 & 0 & 0 & 0.105
\end{array}
\right)
\begin{pmatrix}
p_1(n) \\
p_2(n) \\
p_3(n) \\
p_4(n) \\
- \\
q_1(n) \\
q_2(n) \\
q_3(n)
\end{pmatrix}
$$

In this case, we have the matrices

$$
S = \begin{pmatrix}
0.21 & 0.15 & 0 \\
0.49 & 0 & 0 \\
0 & 0.35 & 0 \\
0.09 & 0.15 & 0.455
\end{pmatrix}
\quad \text{and} \quad
R = \begin{pmatrix}
0.21 & 0 & 0.245 \\
0 & 0.35 & 0.195 \\
0 & 0 & 0.105
\end{pmatrix}
$$

With a little computation, we then have

$$
(I - R)^{-1} = \begin{pmatrix}
1.266 & 0 & 0.347 \\
0 & 1.538 & 0.335 \\
0 & 0 & 1.117
\end{pmatrix}.
$$

where the components of $(I-R)^{-1}$ have been rounded to 3 decimal places. Now we find that

$$S(I-R)^{-1} = \begin{pmatrix} 0.266 & 0.231 & 0.123 \\ 0.620 & 0 & 0.170 \\ 0 & 0.538 & 0.117 \\ 0.114 & 0.231 & 0.590 \end{pmatrix}.$$

Since we start in state F_3, the answer to our problem is

$$S(I-R)^{-1}Q(0) = \begin{pmatrix} 0.266 & 0.231 & 0.123 \\ 0.620 & 0 & 0.170 \\ 0 & 0.538 & 0.117 \\ 0.114 & 0.231 & 0.590 \end{pmatrix} \begin{pmatrix} 0 \\ 0 \\ 1 \end{pmatrix} = \begin{pmatrix} 0.123 \\ 0.170 \\ 0.117 \\ 0.590 \end{pmatrix}.$$

Therefore, the probability nobody survives the gunfight is 0.123, the probability that A wins is 0.170, the probability that B wins is 0.117, and the probability that C wins is 0.590.

If one of the gunfighters didn't show up for the fight, say B didn't show, then you are starting in state F_1 and the probabilities of the different results are

$$\begin{pmatrix} 0.266 & 0.231 & 0.123 \\ 0.620 & 0 & 0.170 \\ 0 & 0.538 & 0.117 \\ 0.114 & 0.231 & 0.590 \end{pmatrix} \begin{pmatrix} 1 \\ 0 \\ 0 \end{pmatrix} = \begin{pmatrix} 0.266 \\ 0.620 \\ 0 \\ 0.114 \end{pmatrix},$$

that is, the probability that nobody survives is 0.266, the probability that A wins is 0.620, the probability that B wins is 0 since he wasn't in the fight, and the probability that C wins is 0.114. Obviously, C hopes that B shows up.

6.7.2 Cost accounting

The next problem we will consider is a problem in cost accounting. Suppose that a company has four departments, Marketing, Manufacturing, Maintenance, and Accounting. Two of the departments, Marketing and Manufacturing are production departments, and their expenses are kept to themselves. Maintenance and Accounting are service departments and their expenses are distributed to the departments that they serve.

For example, suppose that Marketing's direct expenses are 50 000 dollars, Manufacturing's direct expenses are 70 000 dollars, Maintenance's direct expenses are 40 000 dollars, and Accounting's direct expenses are 20 000 dollars for a total of 180 000 dollars for the company.

Assume that Maintenance spends 20 per cent of its time working for the Marketing department (cleaning and repairing Marketing's facilities), 40 per cent of its time working for Manufacturing, 30 per cent of its time working for itself, and 10 per cent of its time working for Accounting. Similarly Accounting figures it spends 30, 30, 20, and 20 per cent of its time working for Marketing, Manufacturing, Maintenance, and Accounting, respectively.

The idea is that Maintenance will distribute its 40 000 dollars to the four departments according to the proportion of time it spends working for each department, that is, it will distribute 20 per cent of 40 000 or 8000 dollars to Marketing, 16 000 dollars to Manufacturing, 12 000 to Maintenance, and 4000 dollars to Accounting. Likewise, Accounting will distribute its 20 000 dollars in expenses to the other departments in the amounts of 6000 dollars to Marketing, 6000 dollars to Manufacturing, 4000 dollars to Maintenance, and 4000 dollars to Accounting.

After the redistribution, the costs for each department are 64 000 dollars for Marketing, 92 000 dollars for Manufacturing, 16 000 dollars for Maintenance, and 8000 dollars for Accounting for the same total of 180 000 dollars.

The problem is that Maintenance and Accounting still have costs. The solution is to redistribute these new costs according to the same formula as for the previous costs. This redistribution will continue until all of the 180 000 dollars costs are given to Marketing and Manufacturing. What are the total costs for Marketing and Manufacturing?

To solve this problem, we let the costs to Marketing and Manufacturing after the nth redistribution be represented by $p_1(n)$ and $p_2(n)$, respectively. Also, we let the costs to Maintenance and Accounting after the nth redistribution be represented by $q_1(n)$ and $q_2(n)$, respectively.

The costs to Marketing after the $(n+1)$th redistribution are the costs after the nth redistribution plus the new costs from Maintenance and Accounting, that is,

$$p_1(n+1) = p_1(n) + 0.2q_1(n) + 0.3q_2(n).$$

Similarly, we get

$$
\begin{aligned}
p_2(n+1) &= p_2(n) + 0.4q_1(n) + 0.3q_2(n), \\
q_1(n+1) &= 0.3q_1(n) + 0.2q_2(n), \\
q_2(n+1) &= 0.1q_1(n) + 0.2q_2(n).
\end{aligned}
$$

This gives us the dynamical system

$$\begin{pmatrix} p_1(n+1) \\ p_2(n+1) \\ - \\ q_1(n+1) \\ q_2(n+1) \end{pmatrix} = \begin{pmatrix} 1 & 0 & | & 0.2 & 0.3 \\ 0 & 1 & | & 0.4 & 0.3 \\ - & - & + & - & - \\ 0 & 0 & | & 0.3 & 0.2 \\ 0 & 0 & | & 0.1 & 0.2 \end{pmatrix} \begin{pmatrix} p_1(n) \\ p_2(n) \\ - \\ q_1(n) \\ q_2(n) \end{pmatrix}.$$

But this is just an absorbing Markov chain in which

$$S = \begin{pmatrix} 0.2 & 0.3 \\ 0.4 & 0.3 \end{pmatrix}, \quad R = \begin{pmatrix} 0.3 & 0.2 \\ 0.1 & 0.2 \end{pmatrix},$$

$$P(0) = \begin{pmatrix} 50\,000 \\ 70\,000 \end{pmatrix}, \quad Q(0) = \begin{pmatrix} 40\,000 \\ 20\,000 \end{pmatrix}.$$

Although $P(0)$ and $Q(0)$ are not probability vectors, that is irrelevant as far as the math analysis goes. (You could use the fraction of the total costs for each component of $P(0)$ and $Q(0)$.) Therefore, since

$$(I - R)^{-1} = \tfrac{5}{27} \begin{pmatrix} 8 & 2 \\ 1 & 7 \end{pmatrix},$$

the answer to our problem is

$$\begin{aligned} \lim_{k \to \infty} P(k) &= P(0) + S(I - R)^{-1} Q(0) \\ &= \begin{pmatrix} 50\,000 \\ 70\,000 \end{pmatrix} + \tfrac{5}{27} \begin{pmatrix} 0.2 & 0.3 \\ 0.4 & 0.3 \end{pmatrix} \begin{pmatrix} 8 & 2 \\ 1 & 7 \end{pmatrix} \begin{pmatrix} 40\,000 \\ 20\,000 \end{pmatrix} \\ &= \begin{pmatrix} 73\,333 \\ 106\,667 \end{pmatrix} \end{aligned}$$

rounded to the nearest dollar.

Thus, of the 180 000 dollars expenses for the company, 73 333 dollars are attributed to Marketing and 106 667 dollars are attributed to Manufacturing.

6.7.3 Problems

1. Suppose that, in a gunfight, A hits his target with probability 0.4, B hits his target with probability 0.3, and C hits his target with probability 0.2. What are the probabilities that each gunfighter survives and that nobody survives this gunfight?

2. Suppose in Problem 1 that there is a fourth gunfighter D who hits his target with probability 0.1. What are the different nonabsorbing states in a gunfight with four gunfighters, A, B, C, and D?

3. In the cost accounting problem of this section, what are the costs attributed to Marketing and Manufacturing if the initial costs attributed to each department are 80 000 for Marketing, 120 000 dollars for Manufacturing, 70 000 dollars for Maintenance, and 40 000 dollars for Accounting.

4. Suppose a company has five departments, Marketing, Toy Manufacturing, Machine Manufacturing, Maintenance, and Accounting, with initial costs of 40 000, 60 000, 70 000, 60 000, and 30 000 dollars, respectively. Suppose that the amount of time spent servicing Marketing, Toy Manufacturing, Machine Manufacturing, Maintenance, and Accounting by the Maintenance department is 10, 20, 30, 30, and 10 per cent, and by the Accounting department is 10, 30, 30, 10, and 20 per cent, respectively. Of the 260 000 dollars total costs for the company, what amount is attributed to Marketing, Toy Manufacturing, and Machine Manufacturing?

5. Suppose we have a pair of dogs. They mate and produce two offspring. The two offspring mate and produce another pair of offspring, and so forth. The possible states are that both offspring are dominant homozygotes denoted E_1, both offspring are recessive homozygotes denoted E_2, both offspring are heterozygotes denoted F_1, one of the offspring is a dominant and the other a recessive homozygote denoted F_2, one of the offspring is a dominant homozygote and the other is a heterozygote denoted F_3, and one of the offspring is a recessive homozygote and the other is a heterozygote denoted F_4.

   (a) Construct the transition matrix for this problem, and identify the matrices S and R.

   (b) Find $(I - R)^{-1}$ and use this to compute the probabilities of ending in the states E_1 and E_2 given that the original pair of dogs were both heterozygotes.

   (c) Repeat part (b) for the case when one of the original pair of dogs was a dominant homozygote and the other was a heterozygote.

6. Suppose, for our gunfight, we let $e_1(n)$ be the expected number of times we are in state F_1 after n rounds of the gunfight. Likewise for $e_2(n)$ and $e_3(n)$. Also let $E(n)$ be the 3-vector whose components are $e_1(n)$, $e_2(n)$, and $e_3(n)$. Since we start in state F_3, we have $e_1(0) = 0$, $e_2(0) = 0$, and $e_3(0) = 1$, that is, $E(0) = Q(0)$. The expected number of times for being in state F_1 after $n + 1$ rounds

is the expected number of times of being in state F_1 after n rounds plus the probability of being in state F_1 on round $n+1$. This gives the equation

$$e_1(n+1) = e_1(n) + q(n+1).$$

We can derive similar equations for $e_2(n+1)$ and $e_3(n+1)$, giving the dynamical system

$$E(n+1) = E(n) + Q(n+1) = E(n) + R^{n+1}Q(0). \qquad (10)$$

Show that the solution to dynamical system (10) is

$$E(k) = (I-R)^{-1}Q(0) + R^{k+1}(R-I)^{-1}RQ(0).$$

By computing the limit as k goes to infinity, you then find that the expected number of times for being in each nonabsorbing state before the gunfight ends is given by

$$(I-R)^{-1}Q(0)$$

and the total of the numbers in the third column of $(I-R)^{-1}$ is the expected total number rounds of shots it will take for the gunfight to end, (similarly for the first and second columns if either B or A, respectively, do not show up for the fight).

6.8 Long term behavior of systems

Let's review our study of linear dynamical systems. We know that the solution to a first order linear dynamical system of m equations

$$A(n+1) = RA(n), \qquad (11)$$

is

$$A(k) = R^k A(0).$$

For small values of k, this form of the solution is useful, but for studying the **behavior** of the system for large values of k, this form of the solution is almost useless. To get a more useful form for the solution, we found the characteristic values for R, that is, the roots to the equation,

$$|R - rI| = 0.$$

We then found the corresponding characteristic vectors, A_1, A_2, and so forth. The solution to the dynamical system was then given as

$$A(k) = c_1 r_1^k A_1 + \ldots + c_m r_m^k A_m.$$

For systems of three or more equations it is often difficult to find the characteristic values and the corresponding characteristic vectors. Theoretically, we could use Newton's method to find the roots, but we may have difficulty in even computing the determinant of $|R - rI|$.

This was the case for many examples of Markov chains. Thus, we learned additional techniques that simplified computations in certain special cases. For regular Markov chains we only needed to find the characteristic vector corresponding to the characteristic value $r = 1$ in order to determine the long term behavior (probabilities). In the case of absorbing Markov chains, $r = 1$ is a multiple root, so this method is too difficult. We then learned a clever technique to determine long term behavior in the last section. The result of solving a simple dynamical system gave the long term behavior as

$$\lim_{k \to \infty} P(k) = P(0) + S(I - R)^{-1} Q(0).$$

But these were special cases. What can we do when we are given a dynamical system in which (i) we cannot find the roots of the characteristic equation, and (ii) the largest characteristic value (which we defined as $\|R\|$) is not $r = 1$ so that we cannot use the techniques that we applied to Markov chains? Our goal in this section is to find a relatively easy computational method for studying these types of dynamical systems. Let's make a moderately restrictive assumption.

Assumption: Suppose that there is one characteristic value, say r_1, such that $|r_1|$ is **larger** than the absolute value of each of the other characteristic values, that is,

$$|r_1| > |r_j|, \quad \text{for} \quad j = 2, \ldots, m.$$

This assumption implies that r_1 is not a double root, and that r_1 is a real number, since complex characteristic values occur in conjugate pairs which have the same absolute value.

Recall that the solution to a dynamical system of m equations is

$$A(k) = c_1 r_1^k A_1 + c_2 r_2^k A_2 + \ldots + c_m r_m^k A_m.$$

The trick to this section is the following: instead of studying the solution $A(k)$ to the dynamical system $A(n+1) = RA(n)$, we will study the solution $B(k)$ to the dynamical system

$$B(n+1) = \frac{1}{r_1} RB(n). \tag{12}$$

The solution to dynamical system (12) is

$$B(k) = r_1^{-k} A(n).$$

Notice that by dividing the solution $A(k)$ by r_1^k, we have

$$B(k) = c_1 \left(\frac{r_1}{r_1}\right)^k A_1 + c_2 \left(\frac{r_2}{r_1}\right)^k A_2 + \ldots + c_m \left(\frac{r_m}{r_1}\right)^k A_m. \tag{13}$$

Notice that
$$\frac{r_1}{r_1} = 1, \quad \text{so that} \quad \left(\frac{r_1}{r_1}\right)^n = 1.$$

Letting
$$s_2 = \frac{r_2}{r_1}, \ldots, s_m = \frac{r_m}{r_1},$$

we can rewrite the solution (13) as

$$B(k) = c_1 A_1 + c_2 s_2^k A_2 + \ldots + c_m s_m^k A_m.$$

From our assumption, we know that $|r_j| < |r_1|$, so $|s_j| < 1$ for $j = 2, \ldots, m$, so that s_j^k goes to zero as k goes to infinity. We now have that

$$\lim_{k \to \infty} B(k) = \frac{A(k)}{r_1^k} = c_1 A_1,$$

where A_1 is the characteristic vector corresponding to r_1.

Note that if we know the characteristic vector r_1, we can then approximate a characteristic vector corresponding to r_1 with the vector

$$\frac{A(k)}{r_1^k}$$

where k is a large integer. Note that this characteristic vector is a multiple of the original characteristic vector, but that is no problem.

The question remains, how do we find r_1? Let's denote the first component of the vector $A(k)$ by $a_1(k)$ and the first component of the vector

A_j by a_{1j} for $j = 1, \ldots, k$. Then the first component of the solution to the original dynamical system (11) is given by

$$a_1(k) = c_1 r_1^k a_{11} + c_2 r_2^k a_{12} + \ldots + c_m r_m^k a_{1m}.$$

(The notation is a little messy, so try not to let it confuse you.) Now the trick to answering our question is to study

$$\frac{a_1(n+1)}{a_1(n)}.$$

First, we observe that

$$r_1^{-k} a_1(k) = c_1 a_{11} + c_2 s_2^k a_{12} + \ldots + c_m s_m^k a_{1m} \to c_1 a_{11}$$

and

$$r_1^{-k} a_1(k+1) = c_1 r_1 a_{11} + c_2 r_2 s_2^k a_{12} + \ldots + c_m r_m s_m^k a_{1m} \to c_1 r_1 a_{11}$$

as k goes to infinity. Now we see that

$$\lim_{k \to \infty} \frac{a_1(k+1)}{a_1(k)} = \lim_{k \to \infty} \frac{r_1^{-k} a_1(k+1)}{r_1^{-k} a_1(k)} = \frac{c_1 r_1 a_{11}}{c_1 a_{11}} = r_1.$$

To summarize, consider the dynamical system (11)

$$A(n+1) = RA(n).$$

If you are not given an $A(0)$ value, make one up. Then compute $A(1)$, $A(2)$, and so forth (preferably with the aid of a computer). Let $a_1(k)$ be the first component of $A(k)$. Then approximate r_1 as

$$r_1 = \frac{a_1(k+1)}{a_1(k)}$$

where k is a 'large' integer. We then approximate the characteristic vector A_1 with

$$A_1 = \frac{A(k)}{r_1^k},$$

where k is again a 'large' integer.

Let's use this technique on a simple example in which we know r_1 and A_1, so that we can compare results.

Example 6.16

In Section 6.7, we discussed the growth of a population that was broken into equal age groups. To review, we assumed the population was broken into three age groups, a_1, a_2, and a_3, which corresponded to the ages 0–1, 1–2, and 2–3 years, respectively. We let $a_1(n)$, $a_2(n)$, and $a_3(n)$ represent the number in each age group at the beginning of year n. Since $a_1(n+1)$ is the number born during year n, we assumed that

$$a_1(n+1) = 0.5a_1(n) + 5a_2(n) + 3a_3(n),$$

where 0.5, 5, and 3 are the birth rates for the age groups a_1, a_2, and a_3, respectively.

We know that $a_2(n+1)$ is proportional to $a_1(n)$, since those in the 1–2 age group in year $n+1$ are the survivors of the 0–1 age group of year n. Thus,

$$a_2(n+1) = 0.5a_1(n),$$

where 0.5 is the survival rate for age group a_1. Likewise, we let 2/3 be the survival rate for age group a_2, giving

$$a_3(n+1) = \tfrac{2}{3}a_2(n).$$

Combining these three equations, we get dynamical system (11), where

$$A(n) = \begin{pmatrix} a_1(n) \\ a_2(n) \\ a_3(n) \end{pmatrix} \quad \text{and} \quad R = \begin{pmatrix} 0.5 & 5 & 3 \\ 0.5 & 0 & 0 \\ 0 & \tfrac{2}{3} & 0 \end{pmatrix}.$$

Recall that the characteristic equation is

$$|R - rI| = r^3 - 0.5r^2 - 2.5r - 1 = (r + 0.5)(r + 1)(r - 2)$$

and the largest characteristic value is $r_1 = 2$. We also computed the characteristic vector

$$A_1 = \begin{pmatrix} 12 \\ 3 \\ 1 \end{pmatrix}$$

corresponding to $r_1 = 2$, or any multiple of this vector. Thus, we had

$$A(k) = c_1 2^k A_1 + c_2(-0.5)^k A_2 + c_3(-1)^k A_3,$$

and

$$\lim_{k \to \infty} \frac{A(k)}{2^k} = c_1 A_1,$$

and the population grows exponentially like 2^k, but the age groups stabilize in the proportions of $(12 : 3 : 1)$.

Suppose we couldn't find the roots of the characteristic equation. Let's use the techniques of this section to approximate r_1 and A_1. First, we need to make up an initial vector, say

$$A(0) = \begin{pmatrix} 4 \\ 4 \\ 4 \end{pmatrix}.$$

Then using a computer, we compute $A(1)$, $A(2)$, and so forth. The vectors $A(0)$, $A(1)$, $A(2)$, and $A(3)$ are

$$\begin{pmatrix} 4 \\ 4 \\ 4 \end{pmatrix}, \quad \begin{pmatrix} 34 \\ 2 \\ 2.67 \end{pmatrix}, \quad \begin{pmatrix} 35 \\ 17 \\ 1.33 \end{pmatrix}, \quad \begin{pmatrix} 106.5 \\ 17.5 \\ 11.33 \end{pmatrix},$$

respectively. Omitting the intermediate calculations, we get

$$A(9) = \begin{pmatrix} 6020.79 \\ 1495.21 \\ 505.06 \end{pmatrix} \quad \text{and} \quad A(10) = \begin{pmatrix} 12\,001.61 \\ 3010.40 \\ 996.81 \end{pmatrix}.$$

Our first three approximations for r_1 are

$$\frac{a_1(1)}{a_1(0)} = \frac{34}{4} = 8.5, \quad \frac{a_1(2)}{a_1(1)} = 1.03, \quad \frac{a_1(3)}{a_1(2)} = 3.04.$$

Continuing, but omitting the computations, we get the approximation

$$\frac{a_1(10)}{a_1(9)} = \frac{12\,001.61}{6020.79} = 1.99.$$

As you can see, if we approximated r_1 with 1.99, we would only be off by 0.01. If we continued our computations, we would see that

$$\frac{a_1(20)}{a_1(19)} = 1.999\,994,$$

the moral being that the larger the value of k that you use in the approximation $a_1(k+1)/a_1(k)$, the better the approximation. The study of how large k needs to be to have a predetermined degree of accuracy is studied in the mathematical field of numerical analysis.

We now approximate a characteristic vector for $r = 2$ with

$$\frac{A(10)}{2^{10}} = \begin{pmatrix} 11.72 \\ 2.94 \\ 0.97 \end{pmatrix}.$$

Our approximations predict that the long term behavior of this system is

$$\lim_{k \to \infty} \frac{A(k)}{r_1^k} \approx c_1 \begin{pmatrix} 11.72 \\ 2.94 \\ 0.97 \end{pmatrix}$$

for some value of c_1, and, after dividing each component of this vector by $0.97c_1$, we find that the three components are in the ratios of $(12.08 : 3.03 : 1)$. This is a fairly good approximation of the exact answer.

Technically, we should use our approximation of $r_1 = 1.99$ instead of $r_1 = 2$ in the above calculation of A_1. In this case we would get

$$\frac{A(10)}{(1.99)^{10}} = \begin{pmatrix} 12.32 \\ 3.09 \\ 1.02 \end{pmatrix}.$$

but the ratios would still be $(12.08 : 3.03 : 1)$. The reason the ratios are the same is that $A(10)/(1.99)^{10}$ is a constant multiple of $A(10)/2^{10}$. Thus, either one can be used.

If you use $(1.99)^{-20}A(20)$ for the approximation, the ratios are $(11.99992 : 2.99996 : 1)$.

There are a few problems with this approach. First, if the first component of A_1 is zero, then the ratio $a_1(k+1)/a_1(k)$ may not go to r_1. One solution would be to approximate r_1 with $a_2(k+1)/a_2(k)$ if it appears that $\lim_{k \to \infty} a_1(k) = 0$. A better approach would be to approximate r_1 with

$$\frac{a_1(k+1) + \ldots + a_m(k+1)}{a_1(k) + \ldots + a_m(k)}.$$

In the above example, we would have

$$\frac{a_1(3) + a_2(3) + a_3(3)}{a_1(2) + a_2(2) + a_3(2)} = \frac{106.5 + 17.5 + 11.33}{35 + 17 + 1.33} = 2.54,$$

and

$$\frac{a_1(10) + a_2(10) + a_3(10)}{a_1(9) + a_2(9) + a_3(9)} = 1.9958.$$

A second problem is if the initial vector $A(0)$ is a multiple of one of the other characteristic vectors, say A_2, then $a_1(k+1)/a_1(k)$ will approximate r_2, the characteristic value corresponding to A_2. There are ways to avoid this problem, such as doing the approximation using several different initial vectors and using the largest approximation you get. One good choice would be to use m initial vectors. The nth of these vectors has a 1 in the nth position and 0's in each of the other positions. For the above example, you could use each of the vectors

$$\begin{pmatrix} 1 \\ 0 \\ 0 \end{pmatrix}, \quad \begin{pmatrix} 0 \\ 1 \\ 0 \end{pmatrix}, \quad \begin{pmatrix} 0 \\ 0 \\ 1 \end{pmatrix}$$

as $A(0)$ in Example 6.16.

Sometimes there is a multiple root r_j, and, as will be discussed later in this chapter, $r_1^{-k}A(k)$ contains a term of the form $ks_j^k A_j$. This term also goes to zero as k goes to infinity and so it poses no problem.

If r_1 is a multiple root, then the solution to dynamical system (11) will be of the form

$$A(k) = r_1^k \left(A_1 + kA_2 \right) + r_3^k A_3 + \ldots + r_m^k A_m.$$

In this case,

$$\lim_{k \to \infty} \frac{A(k+1)}{A(k)} = \lim_{k \to \infty} \frac{r_1(a_1 + ka_2 + a_2)}{a_1 + ka_2} = r_1,$$

so this also does not pose a problem in finding r_1. But, in this case, $A(k)/r_1^k$ goes to infinity. If you compute $A(k)/kr_1^k$ you will get an estimate for A_2, which will also give the long term ratios for the components of the solution.

There is a real problem if there are other characteristic values, say r_2, such that $|r_2| = |r_1|$, but $r_2 \neq r_1$. For example, suppose we have a population with m equal age groups which is modeled by a dynamical system of m equations (11). If the largest characteristic value (in absolute value) for this dynamical system is positive, then we can estimate that value by computer computations, and then we can estimate the characteristic vector A_1. This vector will give the **stable** age distribution for this population. But sometimes there are complex characteristic values $a \pm ib$ for this dynamical system whose absolute value equals that of the largest positive characteristic value, that is,

$$|a + ib| = \sqrt{a^2 + b^2} = r_1.$$

In this case, the numbers
$$\frac{a_1(k+1)}{a_1(k)}.$$
will oscillate instead of converging to a fixed number. This tells us that the size of the population of each age group $a_j(k)$ will oscillate, that is, increase, decrease, and then increase again. This is an example of **population waves**, and is thought to explain population behavior for many species. In particular, population waves have been observed among humans.

This should indicate that, although we can now successfully analyze a large number of linear dynamical systems, there are still many problems that could be considered, such as cases in which several characteristic values have the same absolute value as r_1 or cases in which r_1 is a multiple root. Hopefully, the reader will further these studies on his or her own.

6.8.1 Problems

1. Compute $a(4)/a(3)$ in Example 6.16.

2. Consider the dynamical system (11), $A(n+1) = RA(n)$, where

$$A(n) = \begin{pmatrix} a(n) \\ b(n) \end{pmatrix}, \quad R = \begin{pmatrix} 4 & -2 \\ 1 & 1 \end{pmatrix}, \quad A(0) = \begin{pmatrix} 1 \\ -1 \end{pmatrix}.$$

   (a) Find the characteristic values for this dynamical system. Also find a characteristic vector

$$A_1 = \begin{pmatrix} a \\ b \end{pmatrix},$$

   corresponding to the characteristic value $r_1 = \|R\|$.

   (b) Using the given value for $A(0)$, compute $A(1)$ through $A(6)$. Using these vectors, compute

$$\frac{a(1)}{a(0)}, \quad \ldots, \quad \frac{a(6)}{a(5)}$$

   and let the last number be your estimate of r_1. Compare your results with part (a).

   (c) Estimate A_1 with the vector $A(6)/r_1^6$ where you use your estimate from part (b) for r_1.

   (d) Find the ratio of the two components of A_1 and compare that to the ratio of the two components of your estimate for A_1.

3. Repeat Problem 2 with

$$R = \begin{pmatrix} 1 & 0.5 \\ 3 & 0.5 \end{pmatrix} \quad \text{and} \quad A(0) = \begin{pmatrix} 1 \\ 1 \end{pmatrix}.$$

4. Consider a population with three equal age groups, a_1, a_2, and a_3. Suppose all of age group a_1 survives to age group a_2 in one time period, while half of age group a_2 survives to age group a_3. Suppose the birth rates for the three age groups are 1, 10, and 16, respectively.

   (a) Find a characteristic vector A_1 corresponding to the characteristic value $r_1 = \|R\|$. This vector gives the stable age distribution of the age groups. Compute the actual vector, not an estimate.

   (b) Estimate r_1 and A_1 by using

$$A(0) = \begin{pmatrix} 1 \\ 0 \\ 0 \end{pmatrix}$$

   and computing $A(1)$ through $A(5)$.

5. For some species, the reproductive rate and survival rate for the young of the species, say 0–1 year and 1–2 years, differ from the rates for the adults, but the reproductive rate and survival rate for the adults is approximately the same for every year, 2–3, 3–4, ... Instead of developing a dynamical system with a large number of equations, one for each possible age, the population can be approximated with three equations, one for those that are under 1 year old (called calves), one for those that are between 1 and 2 years old (called yearlings), and one for those that are over 2 years old (called adults). Let $a_1(n)$, $a_2(n)$, and $a_3(n)$ be the number of calves, yearlings, and adults, respectively, at the beginning of year n. Let s_1, s_2, and s_3 be the survival rates and b_1, b_2, and b_3 be the reproductive rates for the calves, yearlings, and adults, respectively.

   (a) Write a dynamical system to model this population growth.

   (b) For American bison, it is estimated that $b_1 = b_2 = 0$, $b_3 = 0.42$, $s_1 = 0.6$, $s_2 = 0.75$, and $s_3 = 0.95$. Estimate $\|R\|$ with $a_1(5)/a_1(4)$. Let $A(0)$ be such that each age group has the same number of the species.

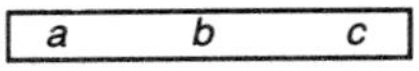

Fig. 59. A study of the temperature of a bar at three points at time n.

(c) Estimate $\|R\|$ by computing $|R - r|$ and then using Newton's method for finding roots.

(d) Estimate the characteristic vector A_1 for the characteristic value $r_1 = \|R\|$ by computing $r_1^{-5}A(5)$. Then give the long term population distribution.

6.9 The heat equation

We now apply our techniques to another type of problem, the distribution of heat through a long rod or bar. We will approximate the movement of heat through a bar by picking several points on our bar and approximating the temperature at those points. We assume that points close to each other will have about the same temperature. For this discussion, let's pick three points on a bar, say a, b, and c. See Figure 59.

We let $a(n)$, $b(n)$, and $c(n)$ be the temperature at time n at the points a, b, and c, respectively. Let's assume the bar is in a vacuum, so that the only thing that affects the temperature at each point is the temperature of the points next to it, that is, b affects a, b affects c, and a and c both affect b.

Let's consider how b is affected by a. At time n, if the temperature at point a is higher than at point b $(a(n) > b(n))$ then point a will cause the temperature at point b to increase $(b(n + 1) > b(n))$. The amount of increase, $b(n + 1) - b(n)$, will be proportional to the amount that a is hotter than b, $p[a(n) - b(n)]$, where p is the constant of proportionality. Similarly if a is cooler than b, the change in temperature, $b(n + 1) - b(n)$, is negative since $p[a(n) - b(n)]$ is negative. Thus, the net effect of point a on point b is summarized by the equation

$$b(n + 1) - b(n) = p[a(n) - b(n)].$$

This is known as **Newton's law of cooling**.

The number p depends on the following: the particular properties of the material from which the bar is made; the length of one unit of time (the smaller the unit of time, the less effect a has on b in that unit of time, and thus the number p is smaller); and the distance between the points a and b (the closer the points are together, the more effect a has on b, and thus p will be larger).

The point c has a similar effect on point b, that is, the effect of c on b is given by

$$b(n+1) - b(n) = p[c(n) - b(n)],$$

where the number p is the same as before. Thus, the **net** change in temperature at point b is the **sum of the effects of points** a **and** c, and the temperature at point b is completely described by the equation

$$b(n+1) - b(n) = p[a(n) - b(n)] + p[c(n) - b(n)],$$

or, after simplification,

$$b(n+1) = p[a(n) + c(n)] + (1 - 2p)b(n).$$

Similarly, after simplification, the equations that describe the temperature at points a and c are

$$a(n+1) = (1 - p)a(n) + pb(n)$$

and

$$c(n+1) = (1 - p)c(n) + pb(n).$$

Combining these equations, we have the dynamical system

$$A(n+1) = RA(n)$$

where

$$A(n) = \begin{pmatrix} a(n) \\ b(n) \\ c(n) \end{pmatrix} \quad \text{and} \quad R = \begin{pmatrix} 1-p & p & 0 \\ p & 1-2p & p \\ 0 & p & 1-p \end{pmatrix}.$$

The characteristic equation is

$$\begin{aligned} |R - rI| &= (1-p-r)^2(1-2p-r) - 2p^2(1-p-r) \\ &= (1-p-r)(1-r)(1-3p-r), \end{aligned}$$

and the three characteristic values are $r = 1$, $r = 1 - p$, and $r = 1 - 3p$. Assuming that p is reasonably small, $(1-p)^k$ and $(1-3p)^k$ go to zero and the eventual temperature in the bar is given by

$$\lim_{k \to \infty} A(k) = \lim_{k \to \infty} [c_1 A_1 + (1-p)^k c_2 A_2 + (1-3p)^k c_3 A_3] = c_1 A_1,$$

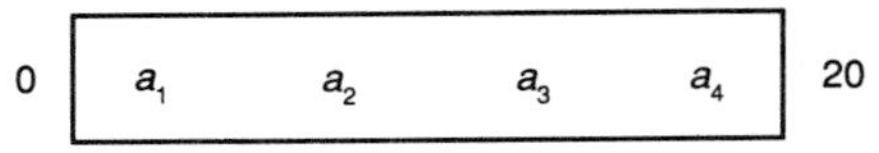

Fig. 60. A study of the temperature of a bar at four points at time n. The left and right ends of the bar are kept at 0 and 20 degrees, respectively.

where A_1 is a characteristic vector corresponding to the characteristic value $r_1 = 1$. An easy computation gives

$$A_1 = \begin{pmatrix} 1 \\ 1 \\ 1 \end{pmatrix}$$

or some multiple of this vector. Thus, eventually all points on the bar are the same temperature.

This was not very illuminating, so we will add a new component to our problem. We now assume that we have a bar with several (equidistant) points on it, say four. Let's assume that the left end of the bar is being chilled, that is, the point to the left of the bar is kept at constant temperature of 0 degrees centigrade. Let's also assume that the point to the right of the bar is kept at a constant temperature of 20 degrees centigrade. See Figure 60.

Here we have a total of six points, counting the ends which are kept at constant temperatures. For the four points of the bar, let $a_j(n)$ be the temperature at point a_j at time n, for $j = 1, 2, 3$, and 4, counting the points from left to right. For simplicity of exposition, denote the temperature at time n of the left and right end points by $a_0(n)$ and $a_5(n)$, respectively. Note that $a_0(n) = 0$ and $a_5(n) = 20$ for all n.

We assume that the temperature at each point a_j, with $j = 1, 2, 3$, and 4, satisfies an equation similar to the one for point b in the discussion above, that is,

$$a_j(n+1) = p[a_{j-1}(n) + a_{j+1}(n)] + (1 - 2p)a_j(n).$$

For points a_1 and a_4, this becomes

$$\begin{aligned} a_1(n+1) &= p[0 + a_2(n)] + (1 - 2p)a_1(n), \\ a_4(n+1) &= p[a_3(n) + 20] + (1 - 2p)a_4(n). \end{aligned}$$

For simplicity, let's assume that $p = 0.5$, so that the four equations become

$$a_1(n+1) = 0.5a_2(n), \qquad a_2(n+1) = 0.5a_1(n) + 0.5a_3(n),$$
$$a_3(n+1) = 0.5a_2(n) + 0.5a_4(n), \quad a_4(n+1) = 0.5a_3(n) + 10.$$

This becomes the first order affine dynamical system

$$A(n+1) = RA(n) + B, \tag{14}$$

where

$$A(n) = \begin{pmatrix} a_1(n) \\ a_2(n) \\ a_3(n) \\ a_4(n) \end{pmatrix}, \quad R = \begin{pmatrix} 0 & 0.5 & 0 & 0 \\ 0.5 & 0 & 0.5 & 0 \\ 0 & 0.5 & 0 & 0.5 \\ 0 & 0 & 0.5 & 0 \end{pmatrix}, \quad B = \begin{pmatrix} 0 \\ 0 \\ 0 \\ 10 \end{pmatrix}.$$

We know that the solution to this dynamical system is of the form

$$A(k) = R^k C + A,$$

where A and C are two yet to be determined vectors. The vector C depends on the initial value, that is, the initial temperature distribution of the 4 points of the bar. The vector A is the **equilibrium vector** for the dynamical system, that is, the (unknown) vector A that satisfies

$$A = RA + B, \quad \text{or} \quad A = (I - R)^{-1}B.$$

This is a system of four equations and four unknowns (the four unknown components of A). The solution is then

$$A = (I - R)^{-1}B = \tfrac{1}{5} \begin{pmatrix} 8 & 6 & 4 & 2 \\ 6 & 12 & 8 & 4 \\ 4 & 8 & 12 & 6 \\ 2 & 4 & 6 & 8 \end{pmatrix} \begin{pmatrix} 0 \\ 0 \\ 0 \\ 10 \end{pmatrix} = \begin{pmatrix} 4 \\ 8 \\ 12 \\ 16 \end{pmatrix}.$$

(In practice, it is easier to solve the four equations directly than it is to compute $(I-R)^{-1}$. The direct approach is recommended for the problems at the end of this section.)

We now have the solution

$$A(k) = R^k C + A,$$

and if $\|R\| < 1$, then $R^k C$ goes to zero and the temperature of the bar goes to its (stable) equilibrium A.

In order to avoid finding and factoring the characteristic equation, we will estimate $\|R\|$ using the techniques of the previous section. To do this, we first make up an initial vector, say

$$A(0) = \begin{pmatrix} 1 \\ 1 \\ 1 \\ 1 \end{pmatrix}.$$

We then compute $A(1)$, $A(2)$, and so forth, for the **linear dynamical system**

$$A(n+1) = RA(n),$$

(not the first order affine dynamical system (14) we have been studying). The vectors $A(1)$ through $A(5)$ are

$$\begin{pmatrix} 0.5 \\ 1 \\ 1 \\ 0.5 \end{pmatrix}, \quad \begin{pmatrix} 0.5 \\ 0.75 \\ 0.75 \\ 0.5 \end{pmatrix}, \quad \begin{pmatrix} 0.375 \\ 0.625 \\ 0.625 \\ 0.375 \end{pmatrix}, \quad \begin{pmatrix} 0.312 \\ 0.5 \\ 0.5 \\ 0.312 \end{pmatrix}, \quad \begin{pmatrix} 0.25 \\ 0.406 \\ 0.406 \\ 0.25 \end{pmatrix},$$

respectively. Our estimates, $a_1(n+1)/a_1(n)$, for r_1 are 0.5, 1, 0.75, 0.832, and 0.801 for $n = 0$, 1, 2, 3, and 4, respectively. If you continued, you would find that

$$\frac{a_1(n+1)}{a_1(n)} = 0.8090, \quad \text{for } n = 11, 12, \ldots,$$

to 4 decimal place accuracy. Therefore, $\|R\| = 0.8090$, approximately, so

$$\|R\| < 1.$$

Hence, $A(k)$ gets closer to A.

For your information, below are the temperature distributions at times $n = 0$, 1, 5, 10, and 30, respectively.

$$\begin{pmatrix} 1 \\ 1 \\ 1 \\ 1 \end{pmatrix}, \quad \begin{pmatrix} 0.5 \\ 1 \\ 1 \\ 14 \end{pmatrix}, \quad \begin{pmatrix} 1.5 \\ 4.78 \\ 7.91 \\ 15.13 \end{pmatrix}, \quad \begin{pmatrix} 3.31 \\ 6.59 \\ 10.88 \\ 15.99 \end{pmatrix}, \quad \begin{pmatrix} 3.99 \\ 7.98 \\ 11.98 \\ 16.00 \end{pmatrix}.$$

Remark: Using calculus and differential equations, it is possible to model the continuous change in temperature throughout a bar. In fact, the continuous version of our dynamical system can be derived by first constructing a dynamical system (much like the one we derived) and then letting the time interval and the distance between the points both go to zero. This shows the close relationship that often exists between discrete and continuous models, that is, between dynamical systems and calculus.

In many applications, a dynamical system is derived, much like

$$A(n + 1) = RA(n) + B,$$

in which there is an equilibrium vector A. The goal is to show that the equilibrium vector is stable by showing that the matrix, R, satisfies $\|R\| < 1$. If this is true, then the equilibrium vector is stable and the solution $A(k)$ goes to the equilibrium vector A as k goes to infinity. We have seen this time and again in our discussions. In such cases, mathematicians call the matrix R a **contraction mapping**. Because of this, one major area of mathematical research is the study of *mappings* such as the matrix R, to determine which mappings are contractions, that is, which mappings satisfy

$$\|R\| < 1.$$

6.9.1 Problems

1. Consider the dynamical system

$$
\begin{aligned}
a_1(n + 1) &= p[c_1 + a_2(n)] + (1 - 2p)a_1(n), \\
a_2(n + 1) &= p[a_1(n) + a_3(n)] + (1 - 2p)a_2(n), \\
a_3(n + 1) &= p[a_2(n) + a_4(n)] + (1 - 2p)a_3(n), \\
a_4(n + 1) &= p[a_3(n) + c_2] + (1 - 2p)a_4(n),
\end{aligned}
$$

which describes the transfer of heat between the four points of the bar, where c_1 is the constant temperature to the left of the bar and c_2 is the constant temperature to the right of the bar.

(a) Rewrite these as a system of equations, that is, give the matrix R and the vector B, when $p = 0.25$, $c_1 = 0$, and $c_2 = 20$.

(b) Find the equilibrium vector for this system of equations.

(c) Compute $A(1)$, $A(2)$, $A(3)$, and $A(4)$, where $A(n+1) = RA(n)$, and

$$
A(0) = \begin{pmatrix} 16 \\ 16 \\ 16 \\ 16 \end{pmatrix}.
$$

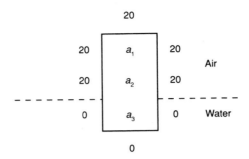

Fig. 61. A study of the temperature of a bar at three points at time n. One-third of the bar is immersed in water at 0 degrees and the remainder is in air at 20 degrees.

(d) Find $a_1(4)/a_1(3)$. Does $\|R\|$ appear to be less than 1? (Note that, to 4 decimal place accuracy, $\|R\| = 0.9045$. This would be found if you computed $a_1(10)/a_1(9)$.)

2. Repeat Problem 1 with $p = 0.75$, $c_1 = 10$, and $c_2 = 14$. It must be pointed out that $a_1(4)/a_1(3)$ is not a good estimate for $\|R\|$. To 4 decimal place accuracy, the largest characteristic value (in absolute value) is $r_1 = -0.9635$, which is not found until $a_1(41)/a_1(40)$. Thus, $\|R\| = |r_1| = 0.9635$.

3. Consider a bar, such that part of the bar is in air that is kept at a constant temperature of 20 degrees, and part of the bar is submersed in water that is kept at a constant temperature of 0 degrees. See Figure 61. We will assume that the temperature at each point on the bar, a_1, a_2, and a_3, depends on the temperature of the four nearest points, that is, the points above, below, to the left, and to the right. The points that affect the temperature of the point a_1 are the point above which is 20 degrees, the points to the left and to the right which are both 20 degrees, and the point below which is $a_2(n)$ degrees. Thus, the change in temperature is given by the equation

$$
\begin{aligned}
a_1(n+1) &= a_1(n) + 3p[20 - a_1(n)] + p[a_2(n) - a_1(n)] \\
&= (1 - 4p)a_1(n) + pa_2(n) + 60p.
\end{aligned}
$$

(a) Derive the equations for the temperature at points a_2 and a_3.

(b) Give the first order affine dynamical system describing the transfer of heat at the three points a_1, a_2, and a_3, that is, find the matrix R and the vector B in terms of p.

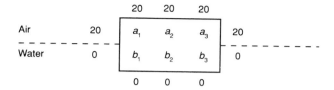

Fig. 62. A study of the temperature of a bar at six points at time n. One-half of the bar is immersed in water at 0 degrees and the remainder is in air at 20 degrees.

(c) Give the system when $p = 0.25$.

(d) Solve for the equilibrium vector.

(e) Approximate $\|R\|$.

4. Suppose we have a grid of six points on our bar as shown in Figure 62.

(a) Write a dynamical system of six equations that describes the flow of heat in this bar, using the same assumptions as in Problem 3.

(b) Rewrite these equations as a first order affine dynamical system and find the equilibrium vector for this system.

6.10 Multiple roots

Suppose we wish to solve the dynamical system of m equations

$$A(n + 1) = RA(n), \tag{15}$$

given $A(0)$. If the characteristic equation $|R - r| = 0$ has m distinct roots, $r_1, \ldots, r_m$, then we find the corresponding m characteristic vectors $A_1, \ldots, A_m$ and write the general solution as

$$A(k) = c_1 r_1^k A_1 + \ldots + c_m r_m^k A_m.$$

To find the particular solution we then solve the system of m equations

$$c_1 A_1 + \ldots + c_m A_m = A(0)$$

for the m unknowns $c_1, \ldots, c_m$.

In this section, we will see what happens when we get a multiple root of $|R - rI| = 0$.

**Example
6.17**

Find the solution to the dynamical system (15) when

$$R = \begin{pmatrix} 2 & 0 \\ 0 & 2 \end{pmatrix} \quad \text{and} \quad A(0) = \begin{pmatrix} 3 \\ -2 \end{pmatrix}.$$

The characteristic equation is easily found to be

$$|R - rI| = (2 - r)^2,$$

and $r = 2$ is the only characteristic value for the matrix R. Normally, we expect to have two distinct characteristic values for a 2-by-2 matrix, but let's proceed, anyway.

The next step is to compute a characteristic vector corresponding to $r = 2$, that is, find a vector A so that

$$(R - 2I)A = \begin{pmatrix} 2-2 & 0 \\ 0 & 2-2 \end{pmatrix} \begin{pmatrix} x \\ y \end{pmatrix} = \begin{pmatrix} 0 \\ 0 \end{pmatrix}.$$

But this is just $0 = 0$. Thus x can be anything, say a, and y can be anything, say b. Therefore the vector A is

$$A = \begin{pmatrix} a \\ b \end{pmatrix} = a \begin{pmatrix} 1 \\ 0 \end{pmatrix} + b \begin{pmatrix} 0 \\ 1 \end{pmatrix}.$$

We now see that we have two entirely different characteristic vectors,

$$A_1 = \begin{pmatrix} 1 \\ 0 \end{pmatrix} \quad \text{and} \quad A_2 = \begin{pmatrix} 0 \\ 1 \end{pmatrix}.$$

So while we have only one characteristic value, we have two characteristic vectors and all appears to be well with the world.

Mathematicians say that the vectors A_1 and A_2 are **linearly independent**. For two vectors this means that neither vector is a nonzero multiple of the other. In the case of three vectors being linearly independent, it means that no one of them can be written as a sum of the other two (or as a sum of multiples of the other two).

The general solution to our dynamical system is then

$$A(k) = 2^k (c_1 A_1 + c_2 A_2).$$

A simple calculation shows that the particular solution is

$$A(k) = 2^k (3A_1 - 2A_2) = 2^k \begin{pmatrix} 3 \\ -2 \end{pmatrix}.$$

As we can see from this example, we may have no problems when there is a multiple root. What is important is that, when R is an m-by-m matrix, we must have m linearly independent characteristic vectors corresponding to the characteristic values, even though there may not be m distinct characteristic values. Sometimes trouble may occur, that is, we may not be able to find enough characteristic vectors. To see this, we consider an example similar to the last one, but with quite different results.

Example 6.18

Find the solution to the dynamical system (15) when

$$R = \begin{pmatrix} 2 & 1 \\ 0 & 2 \end{pmatrix} \quad \text{and} \quad A(0) = \begin{pmatrix} 3 \\ -2 \end{pmatrix}.$$

The characteristic equation is easily found to be

$$|R - rI| = (2 - r)^2,$$

and $r = 2$ is again the only characteristic value.

We now compute a characteristic vector (or vectors) corresponding to $r = 2$. To do this we solve the equations

$$(R - 2I)A = \begin{pmatrix} 2 - 2 & 1 \\ 0 & 2 - 2 \end{pmatrix} \begin{pmatrix} x \\ y \end{pmatrix} = \begin{pmatrix} 0 \\ 0 \end{pmatrix},$$

which reduces to the two equations $y = 0$ and $0 = 0$. Thus, x can be anything. Letting $x = 1$, we get

$$A_1 = \begin{pmatrix} 1 \\ 0 \end{pmatrix},$$

or any multiple of this. Thus, we only have one characteristic value and one corresponding characteristic vector (within multiplication by a constant). Thus, if we attempted to give the general solution, it would be

$$A(k) = c_1 2^k A_1,$$

but the equations

$$c_1 A_1 = A(0)$$

have no solution, so we would be unable to find the particular solution.

The vector A_2 from Example 6.17 was a characteristic vector corresponding to the characteristic value $r = 2$ for the matrix in that example but not for the matrix in this example. Maybe we can find out what went wrong by computing

$$(R - 2I)A_2$$

and finding out why it does not equal the zero vector.

$$(R - 2I)A_2 = \begin{pmatrix} 0 & 1 \\ 0 & 0 \end{pmatrix} \begin{pmatrix} 0 \\ 1 \end{pmatrix} = \begin{pmatrix} 1 \\ 0 \end{pmatrix}.$$

Notice that $(R - 2I)A_2 = A_1$, or

$$RA_2 = 2A_2 + A_1.$$

Let's compute $R^k A_2$. To do this, let $B(k) = R^k A_2$. Then

$$
\begin{aligned}
B(n + 1) &= R^{n+1} A_2 = R^n (RA_2) = R^n (2A_2 + A_1) \\
&= 2R^n A_2 + R^n A_1 = 2B(n) + 2^n A_1.
\end{aligned}
$$

We thus have the first order nonhomogeneous dynamical system

$$B(n + 1) = 2B(n) + 2^n A_1. \tag{16}$$

As we remember from Theorem 2.42, since the coefficient of $B(n)$ equals the base of the exponential which equals 2, the general solution is of the form

$$B(k) = 2^k (A + kB),$$

where A depends on the initial value $B(0) = R^0 A_2 = A_2$. To compute B, we substitute $B(n + 1) = (n + 1)2^{n+1}B$ and $B(n) = n2^n B$ into the dynamical system to get

$$(n + 1)2^{n+1}B = 2n2^n B + 2^n A_1.$$

Simplification gives

$$2n2^n B + 2(2)^n B = 2n2^n B + 2^n A_1.$$

Subtracting $2n2^n B$ from both sides and then dividing by 2^n gives

$$2B = A_1, \quad \text{or} \quad B = 2^{-1}A_1.$$

The general solution is therefore

$$B(k) = 2^k A + k2^{k-1}A_1.$$

Since

$$B(0) = 2^0 A + (0)2^{-1} A_1 = A = A_2,$$

it follows that the particular solution is

$$R^k A_2 = B(k) = 2^k A_2 + k2^{k-1} A_1.$$

We can now give the particular solution to our dynamical system. Since

$$A(0) = 3A_1 - 2A_2,$$

it follows that

$$A(k) = R^k A(0) = R^k (3A_1 - 2A_2) = 3R^k A_1 - 2R^k A_2.$$

Since

$$R^k A_1 = 2^k A_1 \quad \text{and} \quad R^k A_2 = 2^k A_2 + k2^{k-1} A_1,$$

it follows by substitution that

$$
\begin{aligned}
A(k) &= 3(2^k)A_1 - 2(2^k A_2 + k2^{k-1} A_1) \\
&= 2^k (3A_1 - 2A_2 - kA_1).
\end{aligned}
$$

If you simplify this, you will get that

$$A(k) = 2^k \begin{pmatrix} 3-k \\ -2 \end{pmatrix}.$$

Let's review these steps for solving a dynamical system in which r_1 is a double root of the equation $|R - rI| = 0$, but where (multiples of) the vector A_1 is the only characteristic vector corresponding to the characteristic value r_1. This means that the only solutions to the system of equations

$$(R - r_1)A = 0$$

are multiples of A_1. (Recall that this means $RA_1 = r_1 A_1$ and $R^k A_1 = r_1^k A_1$.)

We then look for another vector A_2 which satisfies the system of equations

$$(R - r_1)A_2 = A_1.$$

In this case, we have

$$RA_2 = r_1 A_2 + A_1.$$

We then define $B(k) = R^k A_2$ and get the nonhomogeneous dynamical system

$$B(n+1) = R^n(RA_2) = R^n(r_1 A_2 + A_1) = r_1 R^n A_2 + R^n A_1,$$

or

$$B(n+1) = r_1 B(n) + r_1^n A_1.$$

Since the general solution of this system of equations is of the form

$$B(k) = r_1^k (A + kB),$$

we substitute into the dynamical system and solve. If you do this, you will get

$$B = r_1^{-1} A_1.$$

Using the initial value $B(0) = A_2$ gives

$$A = A_2,$$

and therefore the particular solution to the nonhomogeneous dynamical system is

$$B(k) = r_1^k A_2 + k r_1^{k-1} A_1, \quad \text{that is,} \quad R^k A_2 = r_1^k A_2 + k r_1^{k-1} A_1.$$

We summarize this discussion as a theorem.

Theorem 6.19

Suppose we have dynamical system (15),

$$A(n+1) = RA(n),$$

and we are given $A(0)$. Suppose that the roots of the characteristic equation are r_1, r_2, ..., r_{m-1}, with r_1 being a double root. Suppose that A_1, ..., A_{m-1} are characteristic vectors corresponding to the characteristic values, so that there is only one characteristic vector corresponding to r_1. Find a vector A_m satisfying the equation

$$(R - r_1)A_m = A_1.$$

Then the general solution of the dynamical system is

$$A(k) = c_1 r_1^k A_1 + \ldots + c_{k-1} r_{m-1}^k A_{m-1} + c_m \left(r_1^k A_m + k r_1^{k-1} A_1 \right).$$

To find the particular solution, solve the equations

$$c_1 A_1 + \ldots + c_m A_m = A(0)$$

for the unknowns c_1, ..., c_m.

Example 6.20

Find the particular solution to the dynamical system (15), where

$$R = \begin{pmatrix} 4 & 1 \\ -1 & 2 \end{pmatrix} \quad \text{and} \quad A(0) = \begin{pmatrix} 3 \\ 2 \end{pmatrix}.$$

To do this, we first find the roots of the characteristic equation

$$|R - rI| = (4 - r)(2 - r) - 1(-1) = (r - 3)^2 = 0.$$

The only root is $r = 3$. We find a characteristic vector corresponding to $r = 3$ by solving

$$(R - 3I)A = \begin{pmatrix} 1 & 1 \\ -1 & -1 \end{pmatrix} \begin{pmatrix} x \\ y \end{pmatrix} = \begin{pmatrix} 0 \\ 0 \end{pmatrix}.$$

Since this is only the equation $x + y = 0$, letting $y = 1$, we get $x = -1$ and

$$A_1 = \begin{pmatrix} -1 \\ 1 \end{pmatrix}.$$

We now know that

$$R^k A_1 = 3^k A_1.$$

Now we look for a vector A_2 such that

$$(R - 3I)A_2 = A_1,$$

that is, we solve the equations

$$(R - 3I)A_2 = \begin{pmatrix} 1 & 1 \\ -1 & -1 \end{pmatrix} \begin{pmatrix} x \\ y \end{pmatrix} = \begin{pmatrix} -1 \\ 1 \end{pmatrix} = A_1.$$

This is just the equation $x + y = -1$. Letting $y = 0$, we get $x = -1$ and one solution is

$$A_2 = \begin{pmatrix} -1 \\ 0 \end{pmatrix}.$$

(There are many solutions. Any one will work.) From Theorem 6.19, we know that

$$R^k A_2 = 3^k A_2 + k3^{k-1} A_1.$$

The general solution to the above dynamical system is therefore

$$\begin{aligned} A(k) &= R^k(c_1 A_1 + c_2 A_2) \\ &= c_1 R^k A_1 + c_2 R^k A_2 \\ &= 3^k(c_1 A_1 + c_2 A_2) + c_2 k 3^{k-1} A_1. \end{aligned}$$

To find the particular solution, we need to solve

$$c_1 A_1 + c_2 A_2 = A(0).$$

This is just the two equations

$$-c_1 - c_2 = 3 \quad \text{and} \quad c_1 = 2.$$

The solution is easily found to be $c_1 = 2$ and $c_2 = -5$, so the particular solution is

$$A(k) = 3^k(2A_1 - 5A_2) - 5k3^{k-1}A_1 = 3^{k-1}\left(\begin{array}{c} 21 - 5k \\ -6 + 5k \end{array} \right).$$

Example 6.21

We will now do an algebraically messy problem. Find the general solution to the dynamical system (15), where

$$R = \left(\begin{array}{ccc} -15 & -28 & -62 \\ -5 & -11 & -23 \\ 6 & 12 & 26 \end{array} \right).$$

Let's find the characteristic values and the corresponding characteristic vectors. After a bit of algebra you should get

$$|R - rI| = r^3 - 3r + 2 = (r - 2)(r + 1)^2 = 0.$$

Therefore the characteristic values are $r = -1$ and $r = 2$, with $r = -1$ being a double root.

You should be able to find that characteristic vectors associated with $r = -1$ and $r = 2$ are

$$A_1 = \left(\begin{array}{c} -2 \\ 1 \\ 0 \end{array} \right) \quad \text{and} \quad A_2 = \left(\begin{array}{c} -2 \\ -1 \\ 1 \end{array} \right),$$

respectively (or any multiple of these vectors).

Since we are short one vector, we need to find a vector A_3 such that

$$(R + I)A_3 = A_1,$$

that is, we need to solve the system of equations

$$\begin{array}{rcl} -14x - 28y - 62z & = & -2, \\ -5x - 10y - 23z & = & 1, \\ 6x + 12y + 27z & = & 0. \end{array}$$

Multiplying the second equation by 6/5 and adding to the third equation gives, after simplification, $z = -2$. Substituting -2 for z in the first two equations and simplifying gives

$$-14x - 28y = -126 \quad \text{and} \quad -5x - 10y = -45,$$

both of which become

$$x + 2y = 9.$$

We can let y be any number we wish, say $y = 1$. This makes $x = 7$ and

$$A_3 = \begin{pmatrix} 7 \\ 1 \\ -2 \end{pmatrix}.$$

It now follows from Theorem 6.19, that the general solution is

$$\begin{aligned}
A(k) &= R^k(c_1 A_1 + c_2 A_2 + c_3 A_3) \\
&= c_1(-1)^k A_1 + c_2 2^k A_2 + c_3((-1)^k A_3 + k(-1)^{k-1} A_1) \\
&= (-1)^k(c_1 A_1 + c_3 A_3) + 2^k c_2 A_2 + k(-1)^{k-1} c_3 A_1.
\end{aligned}$$

If we are given any vector $A(0)$, we can rewrite $A(0)$ in terms of A_1, A_2, and A_3 to get the particular solution.

In computing A_3, we had the equations $x + 2y = 9$ and $z = -2$, and then let $y = 1$. We could have let $y = 0$ to get the vector

$$A_3' = \begin{pmatrix} 9 \\ 0 \\ -2 \end{pmatrix}.$$

Notice that

$$A_3 - A_3' = \begin{pmatrix} -2 \\ 1 \\ 0 \end{pmatrix} = A_1.$$

In fact A_3 can always be replaced by $A_3 + aA_1$, where a is any fixed constant. The reason is that

$$(R + I)A_3 = A_1,$$

but, since $(R + I)A_1 = 0$, it follows that

$$(R + I)(A_3 + aA_1) = (R + I)A_3 + a(R + I)A_1 = A_1 + 0 = A_1.$$

On the other hand, you cannot replace A_3 with a multiple of A_3 because

$$(R + I)(aA_3) = a(R + I)A_3 = aA_1 \neq A_1.$$

You may feel that things are somewhat confusing and that you might be asked a question you cannot answer. This is true. We are only dealing with dynamical systems of two or three equations, and have only considered the case of a double root. In systems of four or more equations, the determination of $|R - rI|$ is much more complex. It may be difficult actually to compute the roots of the polynomial $|R - rI|$. There may be problems of complex multiple roots, triple roots, and so forth. These are all dealt with in a similar manner to that which we have discussed, although the algebra will be more complex. (Linear algebra courses deal with many of these problems.) Hopefully, you have an appreciation of how these problems can be solved algebraically, so that mathematics does not seem magical.

Example 6.21 also shows that problems may be algebraically long and tedious, while the ideas are relatively simple. Many people get bogged down in the algebra and miss the ideas. They then feel they do not understand what is happening. People that are good at mathematics are those that can look at the computations and say to themselves: 'I can do these calculations, so I won't worry about them. Instead, I want to know the purpose of these calculations.'

6.10.1 Problems

1. Consider dynamical system (15) where

$$R = \begin{pmatrix} -5 & 4 \\ -9 & 7 \end{pmatrix} \quad \text{and} \quad A(0) = \begin{pmatrix} 1 \\ 3 \end{pmatrix}.$$

(a) Find the general solution.

(b) Find the particular solution.

2. Repeat Problem 1 when

$$R = \begin{pmatrix} 13 & 25 \\ -9 & -17 \end{pmatrix} \quad \text{and} \quad A(0) = \begin{pmatrix} -1 \\ 1 \end{pmatrix}.$$

3. Repeat Problem 1 when

$$R = \tfrac{1}{3}\begin{pmatrix} 4 & 1 \\ -1 & 2 \end{pmatrix} \quad \text{and} \quad A(0) = \begin{pmatrix} 3 \\ 0 \end{pmatrix}.$$

This is an example in which $\|R\| = 1$, but the solution goes to infinity.

4. Repeat Problem 1 when

$$R = \begin{pmatrix} -4 & 8 & -4 \\ -3 & 4 & -4 \\ 2 & -4 & 2 \end{pmatrix} \quad \text{and} \quad A(0) = \begin{pmatrix} 1 \\ 3 \\ 1 \end{pmatrix}.$$

5. Consider the affine dynamical system

$$A(n+1) = RA(n) + B,$$

where

$$R = \begin{pmatrix} 13 & 25 \\ -9 & -17 \end{pmatrix}, \quad B = \begin{pmatrix} 1 \\ 0 \end{pmatrix}, \quad A(0) = \begin{pmatrix} -1 \\ 1 \end{pmatrix}.$$

(a) Find the equilibrium vector for this system.

(b) Find the general solution to this equation.

(c) Find the particular solution to this equation.

6. Repeat Problem 5 when

$$R = \begin{pmatrix} -3 & -2 \\ 2 & 1 \end{pmatrix}, \quad B = \begin{pmatrix} 0 \\ -2 \end{pmatrix}, \quad A(0) = \begin{pmatrix} -2 \\ 1 \end{pmatrix}.$$

7. Repeat Problem 5 when

$$R = \begin{pmatrix} -11 & 12 & -10 \\ -5 & 3 & -11 \\ 2 & -6 & 2 \end{pmatrix}, \quad B = \begin{pmatrix} -2 \\ 12 \\ 9 \end{pmatrix}, \quad A(0) = \begin{pmatrix} 3 \\ 1 \\ -1 \end{pmatrix}.$$

Nonlinear systems of several equations

7

7.1 An introduction to nonlinear dynamical systems of several equations

We have seen before that nonlinear equations are often more accurate models of the real world than linear equations. In fact, many linear models (such as Malthus's population model) are linearizations of nonlinear equations. Unfortunately, it is usually impossible to find a solution for nonlinear dynamical systems in the sense that simple algebraic expressions for $A(k)$ are usually unknown. In this section, we will combine our techniques for studying linear dynamical systems with our concept of linearization in order to determine the qualitative behavior of the solutions to nonlinear systems of equations.

For simplicity, we will identify a general first order nonlinear dynamical system as

$$A(n + 1) = F(A(n)),$$

where $A(n)$ is an m-vector, and F is a vector valued function, that is, for each m-vector A, $F(A)$ is a new m-vector. For example, let $A(n)$ be the 2-vector

$$A(n) = \left(\begin{array}{c} a(n) \\ b(n) \end{array} \right),$$

and let F be the function

$$F(a, b) = \left(\begin{array}{c} f(a, b) \\ g(a, b) \end{array} \right) = \left(\begin{array}{c} a^2 - 2b + 3 \\ ab - 7b \end{array} \right).$$

Then the nonlinear dynamical system

$$A(n + 1) = F(A(n))$$

becomes

$$
\begin{aligned}
a(n + 1) &= f(a(n), b(n)) = a^2(n) - 2b(n) + 3 & (1) \\
b(n + 1) &= g(a(n), b(n)) = a(n)b(n) - 7b(n). & (2)
\end{aligned}
$$

Normally, we cannot find solutions to nonlinear dynamical systems. In such cases, an approach that often works is to find the equilibrium vectors (or fixed points) for the system and then determine which equilibrium vectors are stable (or attracting). We will then know that if an initial vector $A(0)$ is close to a stable equilibrium vector A, then the long term behavior of the system is that the solution $A(k)$ goes to that equilibrium vector, that is,

$$\lim_{k \to \infty} A(k) = A.$$

For first order nonlinear dynamical systems of a single equation

$$a(n+1) = f(a(n)),$$

we found that the equilibrium value a was stable if

$$|f'(a)| < 1.$$

There is a corresponding result for nonlinear systems of several equations involving the partial derivatives of f and g. Before discussing this result, we need some notation. Let

$$f_1(x,y) = \frac{\partial f(x,y)}{\partial x} \quad \text{and} \quad f_2(x,y) = \frac{\partial f(x,y)}{\partial y}.$$

For equation (1) we have

$$f_1(a,b) = 2a \quad \text{and} \quad f_2(a,b) = -2,$$

and for equation (2) we have

$$g_1(a,b) = b \quad \text{and} \quad g_2(a,b) = a - 7.$$

The key to studying stability of nonlinear dynamical systems is the following theorem.

Theorem 7.1 *Consider the nonlinear dynamical system*

$$\left(\begin{array}{c} a(n+1) \\ b(n+1) \end{array} \right) = \left(\begin{array}{c} f(a(n), b(n)) \\ g(a(n), b(n)) \end{array} \right)$$

where f and g are continuously differentiable functions of two variables. Suppose that the vector

$$A = \left(\begin{array}{c} a \\ b \end{array} \right)$$

is an equilibrium vector for the dynamical system, that is,

$$a = f(a,b) \quad \text{and} \quad b = g(a,b).$$

Construct the matrix

$$R = \left(\begin{array}{cc} f_1(a,b) & f_2(a,b) \\ g_1(a,b) & g_2(a,b) \end{array} \right).$$

If

$$\|R\| < 1,$$

then A is a **stable equilibrium vector** *and*

$$\lim_{k \to \infty} A(k) = A$$

if A(0) is close enough to A. If $\|R\| > 1$, *then A is unstable.*

This theorem can be extended to nonlinear dynamical systems of m equations in a natural way. A sketch of the proof of this theorem will be given at the end of this section. First, we will use this theorem to analyze the nonlinear dynamical system

$$
\begin{aligned}
a(n+1) &= 1.3a(n) - 0.3a^2(n) - 0.15a(n)b(n) \\
b(n+1) &= 1.3b(n) - 0.3b^2(n) - 0.15a(n)b(n).
\end{aligned}
$$

Here we have

$$
\begin{aligned}
f(x,y) &= 1.3x - 0.3x^2 - 0.15xy, & g(x,y) &= 1.3y - 0.3y^2 - 0.15xy, \\
f_1(x,y) &= 1.3 - 0.6x - 0.15y, & f_2(x,y) &= -0.15x, \\
g_1(x,y) &= -0.15y, & g_2(x,y) &= 1.3 - 0.6y - 0.15x.
\end{aligned}
$$

In the next section, we will show that this system models the population growth of two species that are competing for the same food and space.

We first need to find the equilibrium vectors. To do this, we substitute a for $a(n)$ and $a(n+1)$, and b for $b(n)$ and $b(n+1)$ in the nonlinear system, giving us

$$a = 1.3a - 0.3a^2 - 0.15ab \quad \text{and} \quad b = 1.3b - 0.3b^2 - 0.15ab.$$

We then solve for the unknowns a and b.

Bringing all terms to the left in both equations, and factoring gives

$$a(-0.3 + 0.3a + 0.15b) = 0$$

and

$$b(-0.3 + 0.3b + 0.15a) = 0.$$

If $a = 0$, the second equation states that $b = 0$ or $b = 1$. If $b = 0$, the first equation states that $a = 0$ or $a = 1$. Thus, three equilibrium vectors are

$$\begin{pmatrix} a \\ b \end{pmatrix} = \begin{pmatrix} 0 \\ 0 \end{pmatrix}, \quad \begin{pmatrix} 1 \\ 0 \end{pmatrix}, \quad \begin{pmatrix} 0 \\ 1 \end{pmatrix}.$$

If neither a nor b is 0, then we can divide the first equation by a, and the second by b, giving the two equations

$$-0.3 + 0.3a + 0.15b = 0 \quad \text{and} \quad -0.3 + 0.3b + 0.15a = 0.$$

Solving these two linear equations gives $a = b = 2/3$, and the fourth (and last) equilibrium vector is

$$\begin{pmatrix} a \\ b \end{pmatrix} = \frac{2}{3} \begin{pmatrix} 1 \\ 1 \end{pmatrix}.$$

We will now study the behavior of the first equilibrium vector,

$$\begin{pmatrix} a \\ b \end{pmatrix} = \begin{pmatrix} 0 \\ 0 \end{pmatrix}.$$

We have

$$f_1(0,0) = 1.3 - 0.6(0) - 0.15(0) = 1.3.$$

Similarly,

$$f_2(0,0) = -0.15(0) = 0, \quad g_1(0,0) = 0, \quad g_2(0,0) = 1.3.$$

Thus we have

$$R = \begin{pmatrix} 1.3 & 0 \\ 0 & 1.3 \end{pmatrix}.$$

It is easy to compute that

$$|R - rI| = (1.3 - r)^2,$$

so $r = 1.3$ is a double root of the characteristic equation and $\|R\| = 1.3 > 1$. Thus, by Theorem 7.1, this equilibrium vector is unstable, that is, if both species start with populations close to zero, then they will not both die out.

We will now study the behavior of the second equilibrium vector,

$$\begin{pmatrix} a \\ b \end{pmatrix} = \begin{pmatrix} 1 \\ 0 \end{pmatrix}.$$

We have

$$R = \begin{pmatrix} f_1(1,0) & f_2(1,0) \\ g_1(1,0) & g_2(1,0) \end{pmatrix} = \begin{pmatrix} 0.7 & -0.15 \\ 0 & 1.15 \end{pmatrix}.$$

Thus,

$$|R - rI| = (0.7 - r)(1.15 - r)$$

and $\|R\| = 1.15 > 1$. Thus, by Theorem 7.1, this equilibrium vector is unstable also. Similarly, the equilibrium vector

$$\begin{pmatrix} a \\ b \end{pmatrix} = \begin{pmatrix} 0 \\ 1 \end{pmatrix}$$

is unstable.

Finally, for the equilibrium vector

$$\begin{pmatrix} a \\ b \end{pmatrix} = \begin{pmatrix} 2/3 \\ 2/3 \end{pmatrix},$$

we have

$$f_1\left(\tfrac{2}{3}, \tfrac{2}{3}\right) = 0.8, \qquad f_2\left(\tfrac{2}{3}, \tfrac{2}{3}\right) = -0.1,$$
$$g_1\left(\tfrac{2}{3}, \tfrac{2}{3}\right) = -0.1, \qquad g_2\left(\tfrac{2}{3}, \tfrac{2}{3}\right) = 0.8.$$

In this case,

$$R = \begin{pmatrix} 0.8 & -0.1 \\ -0.1 & 0.8 \end{pmatrix}$$

and $|R - rI| = (0.8 - r)^2 - 0.1$. Since

$$(0.8 - r)^2 - 0.1 = r^2 - 1.6r + 0.63 = (r - 0.9)(r - 0.7),$$

it follows that the characteristic values are $r = 0.9$ and $r = 0.7$, and so

$$\|R\| = 0.9 < 1.$$

Therefore, this equilibrium vector is stable, and if each population starts near 2/3 (of a unit), then both populations will get closer to 2/3 and the two species will live in relative harmony.

Let's now see a sketch of the proof of Theorem 7.1. The proof of the corresponding result in Chapter 3 used the mean value theorem in one variable. Similarly, this proof uses a several-variable version of the mean value theorem.

Theorem 7.2

Mean value theorem in two variables: *If $f(x, y)$ is differentiable, then there exists a point (x_0, y_0) on the line connecting the points (x_1, y_1) and (x_2, y_2) such that*

$$f(x_2, y_2) - f(x_1, y_1) = f_1(x_0, y_0)(x_2 - x_1) + f_2(x_0, y_0)(y_2 - y_1).$$

Proof of Theorem 7.1: Suppose we have the dynamical system

$$a(n + 1) = f(a(n), b(n)) \tag{3}$$
$$b(n + 1) = g(a(n), b(n)), \tag{4}$$

and the equilibrium vector

$$A = \begin{pmatrix} a \\ b \end{pmatrix},$$

that is, $a = f(a, b)$ and $b = g(a, b)$. Let's study how $a(k)$ changes from equilibrium, that is,

$$a(k) - a.$$

Subtraction of a from both sides of equation (3) combined with the substitution $a = f(a, b)$ gives

$$a(n + 1) - a = f(a(n), b(n)) - f(a, b).$$

Now we use the mean value theorem in two variables, where

$$x_2 = a(n), \quad y_2 = b(n), \quad x_1 = a, \quad y_1 = b.$$

This gives

$$
\begin{aligned}
a(n + 1) - a &= f(a(n), b(n)) - f(a, b) \\
&= f_1(x_0, y_0)[a(n) - a] + f_2(x_0, y_0)[b(n) - b].
\end{aligned}
$$

Similarly,

$$
\begin{aligned}
b(n + 1) - b &= g(a(n), b(n)) - g(a, b) \\
&= g_1(x_0', y_0')[a(n) - a] + g_2(x_0', y_0')[b(n) - b].
\end{aligned}
$$

Note that we get different points for f and g. What is important is that, if $a(n)$ is close to a and $b(n)$ is close to b, then (x_0, y_0) and (x_0', y_0') are both close to (a, b) and thus $f_1(x_0, y_0)$ is close to $f_1(a, b)$, and so forth. Thus, the linear system given by

$$
\begin{pmatrix} a(n + 1) - a \\ b(n + 1) - b \end{pmatrix} = \begin{pmatrix} f_1(a, b) & f_2(a, b) \\ g_1(a, b) & g_2(a, b) \end{pmatrix} \begin{pmatrix} a(n) - a \\ b(n) - b \end{pmatrix}
$$

gives a good approximation for our nonlinear system (3) and (4) when $(a(0), b(0))$ is close to (a, b) (at least for the first few values of k). But the solution to this system is

$$
\begin{pmatrix} a(k) - a \\ b(k) - b \end{pmatrix} = \begin{pmatrix} f_1(a, b) & f_2(a, b) \\ g_1(a, b) & g_2(a, b) \end{pmatrix}^k \begin{pmatrix} a(0) - a \\ b(0) - b \end{pmatrix}.
$$

We know that if $\|R\| < 1$, where

$$
R = \begin{pmatrix} f_1(a, b) & f_2(a, b) \\ g_1(a, b) & g_2(a, b) \end{pmatrix},
$$

then

$$\lim_{k \to \infty} \begin{pmatrix} a(k) - a \\ b(k) - b \end{pmatrix} = \begin{pmatrix} 0 \\ 0 \end{pmatrix}$$

or

$$\lim_{k \to \infty} \begin{pmatrix} a(k) \\ b(k) \end{pmatrix} = \begin{pmatrix} a \\ b \end{pmatrix}.$$

Remark 1: The one problem with this proof is we approximated the matrix R evaluated at the points (x_0, y_0) and (x_0', y_0'), with a matrix R_e evaluated at the equilibrium vector (a, b). Suppose that $\|R_e\| < 1$. In a formal proof, we would need to argue that if $(a(0), b(0))$ starts close enough to (a, b), then $\|R\|$ is close to $\|R_e\|$, and therefore $\|R\| < 1$ also.

Remark 2: In the proof of Theorem 7.1, we developed the linearized system

$$\begin{pmatrix} a(n+1) - a \\ b(n+1) - b \end{pmatrix} = \begin{pmatrix} f_1(a, b) & f_2(a, b) \\ g_1(a, b) & g_2(a, b) \end{pmatrix} \begin{pmatrix} a(n) - a \\ b(n) - b \end{pmatrix}$$

to approximate our nonlinear dynamical system. By letting

$$A(n) = \begin{pmatrix} a(n) \\ b(n) \end{pmatrix}, \quad A = \begin{pmatrix} a \\ b \end{pmatrix}, \quad R = \begin{pmatrix} f_1(a, b) & f_2(a, b) \\ g_1(a, b) & g_2(a, b) \end{pmatrix},$$

this system of equations can be rewritten as

$$A(n+1) - A = R[A(n) - A]$$

which is the affine dynamical system

$$A(n+1) = RA(n) + (I - R)A.$$

This will play a major part in the rest of this chapter.

7.1.1 Problems

1. Consider the nonlinear dynamical system

$$\begin{aligned} a(n+1) &= [1.8 - 0.8a(n) - 0.2b(n)]a(n) \\ b(n+1) &= [1.8 - 0.8b(n) - 0.2a(n)]b(n). \end{aligned}$$

   (a) Find the equilibrium vectors (or points) for this system, and, for each equilibrium vector, determine if it is stable or unstable.

   (b) Pick a point $(a(0), b(0))$ close to each equilibrium vector and compute $A(1)$, $A(2)$, and $A(3)$ using this nonlinear system to see if $A(k)$ seems to agree with your results in part (a).

2. Repeat Problem 1 for the nonlinear dynamical system

$$a(n+1) = [1.4 - 0.4a(n) - 1.2b(n)]a(n)$$
$$b(n+1) = [1.4 - 0.4b(n) - 1.2a(n)]b(n).$$

7.2 Interacting species

In this section we will study two species that interact in an environment. We will study two particular types of interaction, a predator–prey relationship and competition between two species for the same resources.

Let us first review the model for the population growth of one species a. Let $a(n)$ represent the size of the population at time n. Remember that we may choose the size of our units, that is, if we choose 1000 of the species as one unit, then $a(0) = 2.34$ would mean that initially we have 2340 of this species.

Without outside influences, the dynamical system that modeled the growth of this species was

$$a(n+1) - a(n) = r[1 - c_a a(n)]a(n).$$

The constant r was the growth rate of the population given unlimited food and space. The constant c_a determines how the population limits its own growth due to a lack of sufficient food and space. Thus, when $a(n)$ is small and therefore food is plentiful, the growth rate $r[1 - c_a a(n)]$ is approximately equal to r. When $a(n)$ is large and therefore the amount of food per animal is small, the growth rate $r[1 - c_a a(n)]$ is close to zero or negative.

7.2.1 Predator–prey relationship

Let's add a species b of predators, which uses species a as its main food source. How does this affect the growth equation for species a? One possible assumption is that the number of species a that is eaten by species b during time period n depends on both $a(n)$ and $b(n)$, where $b(n)$ is the number of predators in time period n. Specifically, since each individual animal of species b is hunting for prey, the larger $b(n)$, the more of species a that is eaten. Also, the larger $a(n)$, the easier it is to find animals of species a, and thus each predator will eat more prey. In short, the number of species a that is eaten is proportional to both $a(n)$ and $b(n)$. We shall then designate the number eaten as $c\,b(n)a(n)$. The number of species a eaten during time period n is the number that will not be alive in time period $n + 1$, so one possible equation is

$$a(n+1) - a(n) = r[1 - c_a a(n)]a(n) - cb(n)a(n),$$

which can be simplified to

$$a(n+1) - a(n) = r[1 - c_a a(n) - c_b b(n)]a(n),$$

for some positive constants c_a and c_b. (Note that $rc_b = c$.)

Our second assumption, which is partly to simplify matters, is that the predators keep the size of the prey population small, so that the prey do not inhibit their own growth, that is, $c_a = 0$. Therefore, the prey satisfy the growth equation

$$a(n+1) - a(n) = r[1 - c_b b(n)]a(n).$$

We now need to develop an equation to model the growth of the predator population. We first assume that the growth equation for the predators, without a prey species, is

$$b(n+1) - b(n) = s[1 - m_b b(n)]b(n).$$

Again, s is the unrestricted growth rate, while m_b represents how the predators inhibit their own growth. We now assume that the more prey (which is food for the predators) available, the larger the growth rate for the predators. Thus, we assume that the growth rate for the predators is $s[1 - m_b b(n) + m_a a(n)]$. Notice that the growth rate for the predators has been increased by an amount which is proportional to $a(n)$, that is, by an amount that is proportional to the food available. The equation for the predators thus becomes

$$b(n+1) - b(n) = s[1 - m_b b(n) + m_a a(n)]b(n).$$

We now have a dynamical system of two equations which depend on the unknown constants r, c_b, s, m_a, and m_b. In order to simplify matters, we will change the units for the prey species by substituting $a(n)/m_a$ for $a(n)$ in the two equations, and we will change the units for the predators by substituting $b(n)/c_b$ for $b(n)$ in the two equations. The equation for the prey becomes

$$\frac{a(n+1)}{m_a} - \frac{a(n)}{m_a} = r\left(1 - c_b \frac{b(n)}{c_b}\right)\frac{a(n)}{m_a}.$$

After canceling the c_b's and multiplying by m_a, we get

$$a(n+1) - a(n) = r[1 - b(n)]a(n).$$

The equation for the predators becomes

$$\frac{b(n+1)}{c_b} - \frac{b(n)}{c_b} = s\left(1 - m_b\frac{b(n)}{c_b} + m_a\frac{a(n)}{m_a}\right)\frac{b(n)}{c_b}.$$

After canceling the m_a's and multiplying by c_b, we get

$$b(n+1) - b(n) = s[1 - cb(n) + a(n)]b(n),$$

where $c = m_b/c_b$.

To review, if the size of the units is chosen appropriately, the dynamical system that models the population growth for a species of prey a and a species of predators b is

$$
\begin{aligned}
a(n+1) - a(n) &= r[1 - b(n)]a(n) \\
b(n+1) - b(n) &= s[1 - cb(n) + a(n)]b(n).
\end{aligned}
$$

The growth of the species depends only on three constants r, s, and c.

There are many alternative assumptions that might be made about these populations which would lead to quite different equations. One assumption could be that there are a number of places for the prey to hide and so some of the prey would be immune from capture by the predators. Another assumption could be that each predator eats a fixed number of prey, irrespective of the amount of prey available. For the sake of this exposition, we will be happy with the two equations above.

Example 7.3

Suppose we have populations of prey and predators for which $r = 1.2$, $c = 5$, and $s = 0.5$. The dynamical system is thus

$$
\begin{aligned}
a(n+1) - a(n) &= 1.2[1 - b(n)]a(n) \\
b(n+1) - b(n) &= 0.5[1 - 5b(n) + a(n)]b(n).
\end{aligned}
$$

The first step is to find the equilibrium value for the prey population and the equilibrium value for the predator population, that is, the equilibrium vector for this nonlinear dynamical system. We are thus looking for numbers a and b such that if $a(n) = a$ and $b(n) = b$, then $a(n+1) = a$ and $b(n+1) = b$. Making these substitutions into the above equations gives

$$a - a = 1.2(1 - b)a \quad \text{and} \quad b - b = 0.5(1 - 5b + a)b.$$

The three equilibrium vectors

$$\begin{pmatrix} a \\ b \end{pmatrix} = \begin{pmatrix} 0 \\ 0 \end{pmatrix}, \quad \begin{pmatrix} 0 \\ 0.2 \end{pmatrix}, \quad \begin{pmatrix} 4 \\ 2 \end{pmatrix}$$

are easy to find. The first two are not of interest to us since then we would not have two species. The question we now have is, if $a(0)$ is close to 4 and $b(0)$ is close to 1, what happens to $a(k)$ and $b(k)$?

The second step is to use Theorem 7.1. We have, from our dynamical system

$$f(a, b) = 2.2a - 1.2ab \quad \text{and} \quad g(a, b) = 1.5b - 2.5b^2 + 0.5ab,$$

and therefore

$$\begin{aligned} f_1(a, b) &= 2.2 - 1.2b, & f_2(a, b) &= -1.2a, \\ g_1(a, b) &= 0.5b, & g_2(a, b) &= 1.5 - 5b + 0.5a. \end{aligned}$$

Letting $a = 4$ and $b = 1$ gives the matrix

$$R = \begin{pmatrix} 1 & -4.8 \\ 0.5 & -1.5 \end{pmatrix}.$$

We then compute that

$$|R - rI| = r^2 + 0.5r + 0.9.$$

The roots are
$$r = -0.25 \pm \sqrt{0.8375}\, i.$$

Since $|r| = 0.0625 + 0.8375 = 0.9 < 1$, it follows that this equilibrium vector is stable and the two species will coexist at the level of $a = 4$ and $b = 1$.

Because the roots of the characteristic equation are complex, the solution oscillates. If you compute $A(k)$ for reasonable values of $A(0)$, you will see that each population oscillates to its equilibrium value, $a = 4$ for the prey and $b = 1$ for the predators.

The previous type of analysis could be used on the dynamical system

$$\begin{aligned} a(n + 1) - a(n) &= r[1 - b(n)]a(n) \\ b(n + 1) - b(n) &= s[1 - cb(n) + a(n)]b(n) \end{aligned}$$

to derive conditions on r, s, and c that imply the equilibrium vector

$$A = \begin{pmatrix} c - 1 \\ 1 \end{pmatrix}$$

is stable. The inquisitive student might try to find conditions that imply stability of the equilibrium vector. By computing the determinant of the matrix R, setting the most positive root less than one, and solving, you should find that one condition is that $c > 1$. But we must have $c > 1$, so that the equilibrium vector for species a is positive. If you solve for the roots being greater than -1 you will get conditions that require the growth rates r and s to be reasonably small and that $s < r$.

The condition that $c > 1$ means that the predators must restrict their own growth more than they restrict the growth of the prey. The requirement that r be small is reasonable, since we have seen in earlier studies that large growth rates cause instability. The requirement that s be smaller than r means that the food supply (the prey) must increase faster than the population of predators.

7.2.2 Competition between species

We will use the techniques of the last section to study two populations that have overlapping food and space requirements. Again, the equation for the first species would be

$$a(n + 1) - a(n) = r[1 - ca(n)]a(n),$$

in the absence of the second species b. Again, r is the unrestricted growth rate and $1/c$ is the carrying capacity (or equilibrium value) for a in the absence of species b. For simplicity, let's pick the units for a such that $a = 1$ is the carrying capacity for a. Thus, we will use the equation

$$a(n + 1) - a(n) = r[1 - a(n)]a(n)$$

to describe the growth of a in the absence of species b.

Since species b uses some of the same resources as species a, it will then lower the **growth rate** for species a by an amount that is proportional to the size of the population of species b, that is, by $c_b b(n)$. Thus, the growth equation for species a becomes

$$a(n + 1) - a(n) = r[1 - a(n) - c_b b(n)]a(n).$$

If $c_b > 1$, then species b inhibits the growth of species a by more than species a inhibits its own growth. This could happen if species b were a more effective hunter than species a. If $c_b < 1$, then species a inhibits its own growth by more than species b inhibits species a's growth. This could happen if species b were to eat some, but not all, of the same things as species a, that is, their food supplies overlap, but are not the same.

Similarly, the growth equation for species b is

$$b(n + 1) - b(n) = s[1 - c_a a(n) - b(n)]b(n),$$

where s and c_a are given constants, and the size of the units for b is chosen so that $b = 1$ is the carrying capacity for species b in the absence of species a.

To find the equilibrium vectors for this system, we again make the substitution $a = a(n) = a(n + 1)$, and $b = b(n) = b(n + 1)$. After simplifying the left side of both equations, and then dividing by r and s, respectively, we get

$$0 = (1 - a - c_b b)a \quad \text{and} \quad 0 = (1 - c_a a - b)b.$$

Assuming that a and b are both nonzero, the solution to this system of equations is

$$a = \frac{c_b - 1}{c_a c_b - 1} \quad \text{and} \quad b = \frac{c_a - 1}{c_a c_b - 1}.$$

Example 7.4

For simplicity, let's assume that the unrestricted growth rate for each of the two species is one, that is, $r = s = 1$. Let's assume that $c_a = c_b = 2/3$, so that each species restricts its own growth more than does the other species. In this case, the two equations simplify to the dynamical system

$$\begin{aligned} a(n + 1) &= 2a(n) - a^2(n) - \tfrac{2}{3}a(n)b(n) \\ b(n + 1) &= 2b(n) - \tfrac{2}{3}a(n)b(n) - b^2(n). \end{aligned}$$

The equilibrium values are

$$a = b = \frac{2/3 - 1}{4/9 - 1} = 0.6.$$

We have

$$f(a, b) = 2a - a^2 - \tfrac{2}{3}ab \quad \text{and} \quad g(a, b) = 2b - \tfrac{2}{3}ab - b^2,$$

and so

$$\begin{aligned} f_1(a, b) &= 2 - 2a - \tfrac{2}{3}b, & f_2(a, b) &= -\tfrac{2}{3}a, \\ g_1(a, b) &= -\tfrac{2}{3}b, & g_2(a, b) &= 2 - 2b - \tfrac{2}{3}a. \end{aligned}$$

Substituting $2/3$ for a and b gives the matrix

$$R = \begin{pmatrix} f_1(a, b) & f_2(a, b) \\ g_1(a, b) & g_2(a, b) \end{pmatrix} = \begin{pmatrix} 0.4 & -0.4 \\ -0.4 & 0.4 \end{pmatrix}.$$

The characteristic equation is then

$$|R - rI| = (0.4 - r)^2 - 0.16 = r^2 - 0.8r,$$

and the two characteristic values are $r = 0$ and $r = 0.8$ which are both less than one. Thus, the equilibrium vector is stable and the two species will coexist, each at a level of 2/3 of their own carrying capacity.

Example 7.5

Again we assume that the unrestricted growth rate for each of the two species is one. Let's now assume that $c_a = c_b = 3$, so that each species restricts the other's growth more than that species restricts itself. In this case, the two equations simplify to the dynamical system

$$\begin{aligned} a(n+1) &= 2a(n) - a^2(n) - 3a(n)b(n) \\ b(n+1) &= 2b(n) - 3a(n)b(n) - b^2(n). \end{aligned}$$

The equilibrium values are

$$a = b = \frac{3-1}{9-1} = 0.25.$$

Substituting $a = b = 0.25$ gives the matrix

$$R = \begin{pmatrix} f_1(a,b) & f_2(a,b) \\ g_1(a,b) & g_2(a,b) \end{pmatrix} = \begin{pmatrix} 0.75 & -0.75 \\ -0.75 & 0.75 \end{pmatrix}.$$

The characteristic equation is then

$$|R - rI| = (0.75 - r)^2 - 0.5625 = r^2 - 1.5r,$$

and the two characteristic values are $r = 0$ and $r = 1.5$. Since $1.5 > 1$, this equilibrium vector is unstable, and one of the species will eventually die out. Which species dies out depends on the initial populations.

To show that one species actually dies out requires an additional technique which will be discussed in the next section.

Example 7.6

Now we assume that the unrestricted growth rate for each of the two species is one, and that $c_a = 2$ and $c_b = 0.25$. This might be the case when species a eats all the same foods as species b plus some additional foods, and a is a better hunter than b. Thus, a hurts b more than b hurts itself, but b does not hurt a more than a hurts itself. In this case, we get the dynamical system

$$\begin{aligned} a(n+1) &= 2a(n) - a^2(n) - 0.25a(n)b(n) \\ b(n+1) &= 2b(n) - 2a(n)b(n) - b^2(n). \end{aligned}$$

An equilibrium vector is

$$\begin{pmatrix} a \\ b \end{pmatrix} = \begin{pmatrix} 1.5 \\ -2 \end{pmatrix}.$$

In this case there is no equilibrium vector in which both species are positive, so the two species cannot coexist at a stable equilibrium. In fact, species b will die out, which can be shown using the techniques of the next section.

To review, we have (after simplification) the dynamical system

$$
\begin{aligned}
a(n+1) &= (1+r)a(n) - ra^2(n) - rc_b a(n)b(n) \\
b(n+1) &= (1+s)b(n) - sb^2(n) - c_a a(n)b(n),
\end{aligned}
$$

which models two species competing for the same resources. We have

$$
\begin{pmatrix} a \\ b \end{pmatrix} = \frac{1}{c_a c_b - 1} \begin{pmatrix} c_b - 1 \\ c_a - 1 \end{pmatrix}
$$

as the only equilibrium vector in which both species are nonzero.

At this point, we get four cases: case 1 is that $c_a > 1$ and $c_b > 1$; case 2 is that $c_a < 1$ and $c_b < 1$; case 3 is that $c_a > 1$ and $c_b < 1$; and case 4 is that $c_a < 1$ and $c_b > 1$. In case 3, $c_a - 1$ is negative and $c_b - 1$ is positive. If $c_a c_b - 1$ is positive then the equilibrium value for species a is negative, while if $c_a c_b - 1$ is negative then the equilibrium value for species b is negative. Thus, in case 3, we cannot have both species with a positive equilibrium value and the two species cannot coexist at a stable equilibrium. Case 4 is the same as case 3, and will thus be skipped.

In cases 1 and 2, it is easy to see that both a and b are positive. We will therefore study the equilibrium vector

$$
\begin{pmatrix} a \\ b \end{pmatrix} = \frac{1}{c_a c_b - 1} \begin{pmatrix} c_b - 1 \\ c_a - 1 \end{pmatrix}
$$

under the conditions of cases 1 and 2.

We have, from the dynamical system,

$$
\begin{aligned}
f(a,b) &= (1+r)a - ra^2 - rc_b ab \\
g(a,b) &= (1+s)b - sb^2 - sc_a ab.
\end{aligned}
$$

We can then construct the matrix

$$
\begin{aligned}
R &= \begin{pmatrix} f_1(a,b) & f_2(a,b) \\ g_1(a,b) & g_2(a,b) \end{pmatrix} \\
&= \begin{pmatrix} 1 + r - 2ra - rc_b b & -rc_b a \\ -sc_a b & 1 + s - 2sb - sc_a a \end{pmatrix}.
\end{aligned}
$$

Things may look bad now, but remember that $a = f(a, b)$, that is, a satisfies

$$a = (1 + r)a - ra^2 - rc_bab,$$

or, after dividing both sides by a,

$$1 = 1 + r - ra - rc_bb.$$

Thus,

$$f_1(a, b) = 1 + r - 2ra - rc_bb = 1 - ra.$$

Similarly, since $b = g(a, b)$, we get $g_2(a, b) = 1 - sb$. Substitution into the matrix gives

$$R = \begin{pmatrix} 1 - ra & -rc_ba \\ -sc_ab & 1 - sb \end{pmatrix}.$$

We need to substitute in the equilibrium values a and b and find the characteristic equation $|R - xI| = 0$. Because r is being used as a constant, we will use x as the unknown in the characteristic equation. In this problem, we will find the characteristic equation first and, as you will see, we won't have to substitute a and b.

The characteristic equation is

$$\begin{aligned} |R - xI| &= (1 - ra - x)(1 - sb - x) - rsc_bc_aab \\ &= x^2 + (sb + ra - 2)x + 1 - sb - ra + rasb - rsc_ac_bab. \end{aligned}$$

We must find the roots of this equation by using the quadratic formula. The trick here is not to panic. The discriminant D of the quadratic formula is

$$\begin{aligned} D &= (sb + ra - 2)^2 - 4(1 - sb - ra + rasb - rsc_ac_bab) \\ &= (sb)^2 + (ra)^2 - 2sbra + 4rsc_ac_bab \\ &= (sb - ra)^2 + 4rsc_ac_bab, \end{aligned}$$

which is clearly positive, since each of the constants is positive. Therefore, the roots of the characteristic equation are

$$x = \tfrac{1}{2}\left[2 - sb - ra \pm \sqrt{(ra - sb)^2 + 4src_ac_bab}\right].$$

We remember that for the equilibrium value to be stable, we must have that the roots are less than one. Therefore, we must have that

$$\tfrac{1}{2}\left[2 - sb - ra + \sqrt{(ra - sb)^2 + 4src_ac_bab}\right] < 1.$$

Multiplying both sides by 2 and canceling the 2's, gives

$$-sb - ra + \sqrt{(ra - sb)^2 + 4src_ac_bab} < 0.$$

Adding $sb + ra$ to both sides and then squaring gives

$$(ra - sb)^2 + 4src_ac_bab < (sb + ra)^2,$$

or, after multiplying the terms out, canceling, and adding $2rasb$ to both sides,

$$4src_ac_bab < 4srab.$$

Dividing both sides by $4srab$ gives

$$c_ac_b < 1.$$

From the beginning of this discussion, we remember that we only had two cases: c_a and c_b both greater than one, and c_a and c_b both less than one. For the equilibrium vector to be stable, we must have c_ac_b less than one, which is the case only when c_a and c_b are both less than one. Also, when both constants are greater than one, then their product is greater than one and the equilibrium vector is unstable. (It is amazing how often we have problems which seem complex algebraically, as in the above calculation, but in the end most of the terms cancel to give a simple condition, such as $c_ac_b < 1$.)

Remark: We have ignored the condition that the roots of the characteristic equation must be greater than -1. This condition will be true if the growth rates r and s are reasonably small.

Suppose rabbits (species a) and squirrels (species b) inhabit an area. The rabbits eat lettuce and carrots, while the squirrels eat lettuce and nuts. The size of the units are chosen so that the constant which represents the amount that rabbits inhibit their own growth rate is 1. The same goes for squirrels.

Since the lettuce that the rabbits eat is part of the food supply of the squirrels, the rabbits inhibit the growth rate for the squirrels, which is signified by the constant c_a in the equation for species b. Since the squirrels also have nuts available that are not eaten by the rabbits, the rabbits do not harm the growth rate for the squirrels as much as the squirrels harm their own growth rate, that is, $c_a < 1$. From the above, we see that these two species can coexist. (A similar argument shows that $c_b < 1$.)

Suppose that in the area above, there are no nuts, so that the squirrels only have lettuce to eat. Now, when a rabbit eats some lettuce and some carrots, there is more food left for the other rabbits (lettuce and carrots) than there is for the squirrels (only lettuce). Thus, the rabbits hurt the growth rate for the squirrels more than they hurt their own growth rate, that is, $c_a > 1$. Thus these two species cannot coexist, and, consequently, one of them (the squirrels) must die out.

This result is known as **Gause's principle of competitive exclusion**. Specifically, it states that no two species can have identical niche requirements (food, shelter, and so on) and coexist. For more study of population models, see Smith (1968) and Malkevitch and Meyer (1974).

7.2.3 Problems

1. Find the characteristic values for the matrix

$$R = \begin{pmatrix} f_1(a,b) & f_2(a,b) \\ g_1(a,b) & g_2(a,b) \end{pmatrix}$$

associated with the predator–prey equations

$$\begin{aligned} a(n+1) &= [1 + r - rb(n)]a(n) \\ b(n+1) &= [1 + s - csb(n) + sa(n)]b(n) \end{aligned}$$

at the equilibrium $a = c - 1$ and $b = 1$. Assuming that these characteristic values are complex, find a condition between r and c that implies this equilibrium vector is stable.

2. Consider a predator–prey model using the following assumptions. First, assume the birth rate for the prey is constant, but the death rate is proportional to the size of the predator population. Second, assume the birth rate for the predators is proportional to the size of the prey population, but the death rate is constant.

   (a) Develop a nonlinear dynamical system of two equations that model these assumptions.

   (b) Find the equilibrium vector with both populations nonzero.

   (c) Find the two characteristic values of the linearized matrix R and show that $\|R\| > 1$, so that this predator–prey relationship is unstable.

7.3 Phase plane analysis

The dynamical system

$$a(n+1) = 1.3a(n) - 0.3a^2(n) - 0.15a(n)b(n) \tag{5}$$
$$b(n+1) = 1.3b(n) - 0.3b^2(n) - 0.15a(n)b(n) \tag{6}$$

was studied in some detail in Section 7.1. In particular, we found that this system had four equilibrium vectors,

$$A_1 = \begin{pmatrix} 0 \\ 0 \end{pmatrix}, \quad A_2 = \begin{pmatrix} 1 \\ 0 \end{pmatrix}, \quad A_3 = \begin{pmatrix} 0 \\ 1 \end{pmatrix}, \quad A_4 = \tfrac{2}{3}\begin{pmatrix} 1 \\ 1 \end{pmatrix}.$$

We then constructed the matrix

$$R = \begin{pmatrix} f_1(a,b) & f_2(a,b) \\ g_1(a,b) & g_2(a,b) \end{pmatrix},$$

where

$$f(a,b) = 1.3a - 0.3a^2 - 0.15ab,$$
$$g(a,b) = 1.3b - 0.3b^2 - 0.15ab, \tag{7}$$

and a and b are the coordinates of an equilibrium vector. From Theorem 7.1, if any of the characteristic values (solutions to the equation $|R - rI| = 0$) satisfy $|r| > 1$, then the corresponding equilibrium vector is unstable, and if all characteristic values satisfy $|r| < 1$, then the vector is stable.

To prove this result, we first constructed the linear dynamical system

$$A(n+1) = RA(n) + (I - R)A$$

which approximates the solution of the nonlinear system near the equilibrium vector A. From our knowledge of linear systems, we know that the equilibrium vector is stable if $\|R\| < 1$.

Applied to the nonlinear system given above, we find that the characteristic values for the equilibrium vectors are $r = 1.3$ (a double root) for A_1, $r = 0.7$ and $r = 1.15$ for both A_2 and A_3, and $r = 0.9$ and $r = 0.7$ for A_4. Since $\|R\| = 1.3$ for A_1 and $\|R\| = 1.15$ for A_2 and A_3, these equilibrium vectors are unstable. Since $\|R\| = 0.9$ for A_4, this vector is stable. Thus, if the initial vector $A(0)$ is near one of these vectors, we know the behavior of the solution $A(k)$, that is, $A(k)$ goes away from A_1, A_2, and A_3, and towards A_4.

In this section we are going to determine **how** the solution moves towards or away from an equilibrium vector. We will do this by actually constructing the solution to the linear system near an equilibrium value and then analyzing that solution. In particular, we know that the equilibrium vector for the system

$$A(n + 1) = RA(n) + (I - R)A$$

is A, so that the general solution is

$$A(k) = R^k C + A,$$

where the vector C depends on the initial vector and A is the equilibrium vector that we are studying. We also know that

$$R^k C = r_1^k c_1 B_1 + r_2^k c_2 B_2,$$

where r_1 and r_2 are the characteristic values for R, B_1 and B_2 are the corresponding characteristic vectors, and c_1 and c_2 are unknown constants which can be determined once $A(0)$ is given.

Let's find out what is happening by studying the dynamical system given by equations (5) and (6) in detail.

First let's consider the equilibrium vector

$$A = A_2 = \begin{pmatrix} 1 \\ 0 \end{pmatrix}$$

given above. In Section 7.1, we found that

$$R = \begin{pmatrix} 0.7 & -0.15 \\ 0 & 1.15 \end{pmatrix}$$

for this vector. The characteristic values for this matrix are $r_1 = 1.15$ and $r_2 = 0.7$. A little work gives the corresponding characteristic vectors as

$$B_1 = \begin{pmatrix} -1 \\ 3 \end{pmatrix} \quad \text{and} \quad B_2 = \begin{pmatrix} 1 \\ 0 \end{pmatrix},$$

or any multiples of these vectors.

We then find that the solution of the linear system, which approximates the solution of the nonlinear system, is

$$A(k) = (1.15)^k c_1 B_1 + (0.7)^k c_2 B_2 + A_2.$$

Since 1.15 > 1, solutions move away from A_2 in the direction of B_1. To be more specific about this statement, let's represent the solution $A(k)$ as points $(a(k), b(k))$ in a plane. We will let a be the horizontal axis and b be the vertical axis. To move from the point $(a(n), b(n))$ to the point $(a(n+1), b(n+1))$, you add $A(n+1) - A(n)$ to the point $A(n)$. But, after simplification,

$$A(n+1) - A(n) = (1.15)^n(0.15)c_1 B_1 + (0.7)^n(-0.3)c_2 B_2.$$

Since $(0.7)^n$ will be small when n is large, to get from $A(n)$ to $A(n+1)$, you add

$$(1.15)^n(0.15)c_1 B_1,$$

approximately. But this is just a multiple of B_1. To summarize, to move from $(a(n), b(n))$ to $(a(n+1), b(n+1))$, you add a multiple of B_1. Since the vector B_1 is -1 unit in the a direction for every 3 units in the b direction, the points of the solution will move along lines of slope -3, that is, the slope of the line connecting $(a(n), b(n))$ to $(a(n+1), b(n+1))$ is (about) -3.

Note that the multiple of B_1 that you are adding contains the term $(1.15)^n$. This means that you are moving away from A_2 exponentially.

Suppose c_1 is relatively small in the solution. Then for small values of n, the solution is approximately

$$A(k) = (0.7)^k c_2 B_2 + A_2.$$

The points initially move towards A_2 in the direction of B_2, that is, along lines that have zero slope. As $(0.7)^k$ gets small and $(1.15)^k$ gets large, the influence changes and the solution moves away from A_2 in the direction of B_1. The result of these two movements can be seen graphically in Figure 63. On this graph, the points $(a(0), b(0))$, $(a(1), b(1))$, $\ldots$, $(a(n), b(n))$ are plotted and then connected by lines. Arrows are drawn in the direction of the movement of the points. The several sets of curves correspond to solutions for several different initial values. Observe that these solutions start moving towards A_2 in a horizontal direction, then start moving away with a slope of about -3.

Notice also that there are two solutions that actually go to A_2 along the a axis, even though A_2 is unstable. These solutions correspond to solutions in which $c_1 = 0$ and c_2 is either positive or negative.

The solutions plotted in Figure 63 are the solutions to the original nonlinear system and not the linear approximation, although they behave as the linear approximation predicted. Only the first few values of the actual solutions have been plotted. Once these solutions move away from the equilibrium vector A_2, they no longer behave the same way as the

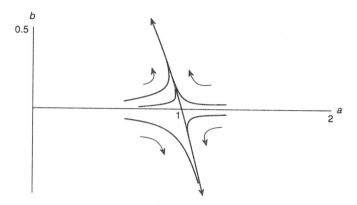

Fig. 63. Movement towards A_2 in direction of B_2 (horizontally), and then away in direction of B_1 (slope of -3).

linear approximations. Put another way, our results are only local, the locale being a neighborhood of A_2.

Now let's consider the stable equilibrium vector

$$A = A_4 = \tfrac{2}{3} \begin{pmatrix} 1 \\ 1 \end{pmatrix}.$$

In Section 7.1, we found that

$$R = \begin{pmatrix} 0.8 & -0.1 \\ -0.1 & 0.8 \end{pmatrix}$$

for this vector. The characteristic values for this matrix are $r_1 = 0.9$ and $r_2 = 0.7$, and the corresponding characteristic vectors are

$$B_1 = \begin{pmatrix} -1 \\ 1 \end{pmatrix} \quad \text{and} \quad B_2 = \begin{pmatrix} 1 \\ 1 \end{pmatrix},$$

or any multiples of these vectors.

We then find that the solution of this linear dynamical system, which approximates the solution of the nonlinear system near the equilibrium vector A_4, is

$$A(k) = (0.9)^k c_1 B_1 + (0.7)^k c_2 B_2 + A_4.$$

Since $0.7 < 1$ and $0.9 < 1$, the vector A_4 is stable, that is, all solutions that start near A_4 move towards A_4. Since $0.7 < 0.9$, we have, after subtracting A_4 from both sides and dividing by $(0.9)^k$,

$$(0.9)^{-k} [A(k) - A_4] = c_1 B_1 + \left(\tfrac{7}{9}\right)^k c_2 B_2.$$

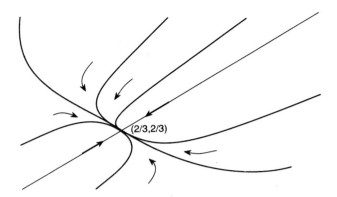

Fig. 64. Most solutions go to equilibrium in the direction of B_1 (slope of -1) which corresponds to largest characteristic value.

Since $(7/9)^k c_2 B_2$ goes to zero, we see that $A(k)$ goes towards A_4 in the direction of B_1. The exceptions to this are those solutions with $c_1 = 0$. See Figure 64 for a graphical display of these results.

Notice in Figure 64 that there are two solutions that go to A_4 in the direction of B_2, one from the left and one from the right. These two solutions correspond to solutions in which $c_1 = 0$. There are two solutions since c_2 can be positive or negative. Again, the solutions plotted are the actual solutions to the original nonlinear dynamical system.

Let's summarize this graphical approach to studying nonlinear dynamical systems. First, find the equilibrium vectors, and then find the characteristic values for one of these equilibrium vectors. Suppose there is one characteristic value that is larger than all the rest (in absolute value) and that it is positive. Then solutions that start near this equilibrium vector eventually move in the direction of the characteristic vector corresponding to the largest characteristic value. The movement is towards or away from the equilibrium vector depending on whether the equilibrium vector is stable or unstable. The one exception to this rule are solutions that do not involve the largest characteristic value, that is, solutions like those in the above discussion where $c_1 = 0$.

There are problems when two characteristic values are the same, and when the largest value is not positive. If the largest value is negative then oscillations will occur in the direction of the corresponding characteristic vector. If the largest positive value is a multiple root, several different types of behavior may occur, one of them being discussed in Problem 1 at

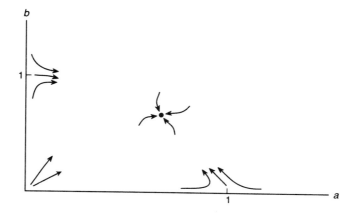

Fig. 65. Behavior near each equilibrium vector is displayed.

the end of this section. If the largest roots are complex, then the solution will cycle about the equilibrium vector, as seen in Problem 5 at the end of this section.

In Problem 1 you will determine the direction of movement of solutions near the equilibrium vectors A_1 and A_3 for the dynamical system given by equations (5) and (6). Figure 65 contains a graphical display of the movement near each of the equilibrium vectors. The analysis is only local, that is, it only describes the behavior of solutions that are near one of the equilibrium vectors, and so we plotted only the first few points of solutions that are moving away from an equilibrium vector.

In Figure 66, we have plotted solutions for several different initial values. Using this figure, you should be able to predict the global behavior of any solution, as long as the initial values are reasonably small. By global behavior, we mean the entire behavior of a solution, not just the behavior near an equilibrium vector.

A similar method for predicting the global behavior is to draw an arrow from the point $A(0)$ in the direction of $A(1)$ for a large collection of initial values $A(0)$. See Figure 67. Given any initial value $A(0)$, we can again 'guess' at the direction of movement of the solution $A(k)$. This method is called **phase plane analysis**.

For our nonlinear dynamical system, we have

$$A(1) - A(0) = \begin{pmatrix} a(1) - a(0) \\ b(1) - b(0) \end{pmatrix} = \begin{pmatrix} 0.3a(0)[1 - a(0) - 0.5b(0)] \\ 0.3b(0)[1 - b(0) - 0.5a(0)] \end{pmatrix}.$$

Thus, phase plane analysis consists of drawing an arrow starting at the

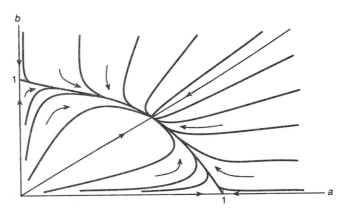

Fig. 66. Behavior in first quadrant is pieced together from local behavior of solutions.

point $(a(0), b(0))$ in the direction given by the vector

$$\left(\begin{array}{c} 0.3a(0)[1 - a(0) - 0.5b(0)] \\ 0.3b(0)[1 - b(0) - 0.5a(0)] \end{array} \right) = \left(\begin{array}{c} f(a(0), b(0)) - a(0) \\ g(a(0), b(0)) - b(0) \end{array} \right),$$

and then repeating this process for a large collection of initial values.

Note that the arrows move $f(a(0), b(0)) - a(0)$ units in the a or horizontal direction. Thus, arrows starting at $(a(0), b(0))$ point towards the right if

$$f(a(0), b(0)) - a(0) > 0$$

and point to the left if $f(a(0), b(0)) - a(0)$ is negative. Similarly, arrows move $g(a(0), b(0)) - b(0)$ units in the b or vertical direction. Thus, arrows starting at $(a(0), b(0))$ point upwards if

$$g(a(0), b(0)) - b(0) > 0$$

and point downwards if $g(a(0), b(0)) - b(0)$ is negative. By combining these two results, you can determine the direction of the arrows in the plane.

Example 7.7

Let's use phase plane analysis to determine the global behavior of solutions to the nonlinear dynamical system

$$\begin{array}{rcll} a(n+1) & = & 0.1[2 - a(n) - 0.25b(n)]a(n) & \quad (8) \\ b(n+1) & = & 0.1[2 - 2a(n) - b(n)]b(n), & \quad (9) \end{array}$$

a variation of which was discussed in Section 7.2 as a model for two species competing for the same resources.

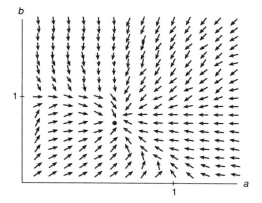

Fig. 67. Direction of movement of solution $[A(1) - A(0)]$ is given at several possible $A(0)$ values in first quadrant.

We must construct arrows in the direction

$$\left(\begin{array}{c} f(a(0), b(0)) - a(0) \\ g(a(0), b(0)) - b(0) \end{array} \right) = \left(\begin{array}{c} 0.1a(0)[1 - a(0) - 0.25b(0)] \\ 0.1b(0)[1 - 2a(0) - b(0)] \end{array} \right).$$

The trick is to realize that arrows point to the left if $0.1a(0)[1 - a(0) - 0.25b(0)] < 0$ and arrows point to the right if $0.1a(0)[1 - a(0) - 0.25b(0)] > 0$. Thus, the graph of the solution to

$$0.1a(1 - a - 0.25b) = 0$$

divides the plane into regions which are solutions to the above inequalities. The solutions are $a = 0$ and $1 - a - 0.25b = 0$. These two lines divide the first quadrant into two regions. Only the first quadrant is given because $a(0)$ and $b(0)$ must be nonnegative, since $a(k)$ and $b(k)$ represent the size of populations. See Figure 68. The arrows go right or left in each region depending on whether $a(1 - a - 0.25b)$ is positive or negative, respectively, for points (a, b) in that region. Arrows are also drawn on the a axis.

Similarly, arrows point up or down in a region if $0.1b(1 - 2a - b)$ is positive or negative, respectively, for points (a, b) in that region. This is given in Figure 69 where the lines $b = 0$ and $1 - 2a - b = 0$ also divide the first quadrant into two regions.

We put all this information together in Figure 70. In essence, Figure 69 is laid on Figure 68 giving three regions. An arrow in one of the regions of Figure 70 goes in a direction that is the composite of the arrows from Figures 68 and 69 that are in that region. For example, suppose we are at a point in which the arrow points to the right in Figure 68 and up

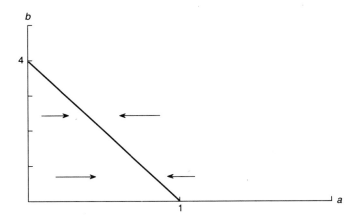

Fig. 68. The values $a(k)$ increase when to the left of the line $1-a-b/4 = 0$, and decrease when to the right of it.

in Figure 69. Then, in Figure 70, the composite arrow would make a 45 degree angle with the a axis.

Notice in Figure 70 that we have arrows drawn in the correct direction. We have also plotted several solutions so that you can see that they move in the correct direction.

A point of intersection between a line from Figure 68 and a line from Figure 69 is an equilibrium vector or fixed point. There are three of these, $(0,0)$, $(1,0)$, and $(0,1)$. It is easy to discern from this figure that solutions move towards the point $(1,0)$ and so species b will die out. One exception to this is a solution that starts on the b axis, that is, with initial values in which species a is extinct at the beginning.

One problem with phase plane analysis for dynamical systems is that the arrows give the direction of movement, but not the distance of the movement. For some discrete dynamical systems, the arrows might appear to move all solutions towards an equilibrium vector making it appear to be stable, but in reality the points are oscillating about the equilibrium vector with increasing amplitude so the equilibrium vector is unstable.

Example 7.8

As a one dimensional example, consider the dynamical system

$$a(n + 1) = -2a(n) - a^2(n).$$

One equilibrium value is $a = 0$. For small initial values $a(0)$ to the left of $a = 0$, the change $a(1) - a(0) = -3a(0) - a^2a(0)$ is positive, so arrows point to the right. For small initial values to the right of $a = 0$, the change $-3a(0) - a^2(0)$ is negative, and arrows point to the left. Thus, the arrows

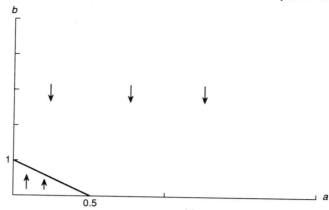

Fig. 69. The values $b(k)$ increase when below the line $1 - 2a - b = 0$, and decrease when above it.

point towards $a = 0$ on both sides making it appear to be stable. But in reality, $a = 0$ is unstable. It is unstable because

$$|f'(0)| = |-2 - 2(0)| = |-2| > 1.$$

From this we see that the solution $a(k)$ is actually oscillating about $a = 0$ with increasing amplitude and the arrows are misleading.

In practice, populations tend to have reasonably small growth rates, resulting in phase plane analysis giving an accurate picture of behavior. In differential equations, phase plane analysis does not have this problem. This is because differential equations model continuous phenomena, and continuous phenomena cannot 'jump' past an equilibrium value as a discrete model can.

7.3.1 Problems

1. Consider the dynamical system (5) and (6),

$$
\begin{aligned}
a(n+1) &= 1.3a(n) - 0.3a^2(n) - 0.15a(n)b(n) \\
b(n+1) &= 1.3b(n) - 0.3b^2(n) - 0.15a(n)b(n).
\end{aligned}
$$

(a) Find the solution to the linear system that approximates the solution to this nonlinear system near the equilibrium vector

$$A_3 = \begin{pmatrix} 0 \\ 1 \end{pmatrix}.$$

Use this solution to describe the direction of movement of solutions that start close to this equilibrium vector.

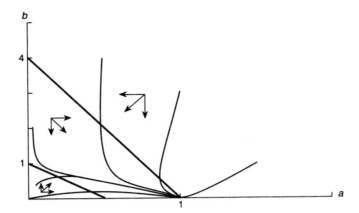

Fig. 70. Composite figure showing movement of points $(a(k), b(k))$ for points in each region determined by the two diagonal lines.

(b) The solution to the linear dynamical system that approximates the solution to this nonlinear system near the equilibrium vector

$$A_1 = \begin{pmatrix} 0 \\ 0 \end{pmatrix}$$

is

$$A(k) = (1.3)^k \begin{pmatrix} a(0) \\ b(0) \end{pmatrix}.$$

This predicts that initial data starting close to zero will continue along the line that connects the initial point to the origin. Pick several points $(a(0), b(0))$ close to the origin and note that the slope of the line connecting $(0,0)$ to $(a(0), b(0))$ is approximately the same as the slope of the line connecting $(a(0), b(0))$ to $(a(1), b(1))$.

2. Consider the nonlinear dynamical system

$$\begin{aligned} a(n+1) &= [1.8 - 0.8a(n) - 0.2b(n)]a(n) \\ b(n+1) &= [1.8 - 0.8b(n) - 0.2a(n)]b(n). \end{aligned}$$

(a) Find the solution to the linear dynamical system that approximates the solution to this system near the equilibrium vector

$$A = \begin{pmatrix} 1 \\ 0 \end{pmatrix}.$$

Use this solution to describe the direction of movement of solutions that start close to this equilibrium vector.

(b) Find the solution to the linear dynamical system that approximates the solution to this system near the equilibrium vector

$$A = \begin{pmatrix} 0.8 \\ 0.8 \end{pmatrix}.$$

Use this solution to describe the direction of movement of solutions that start close to this equilibrium vector.

3. Consider the dynamical system

$$\begin{aligned} a(n+1) &= [1.4 - 0.4a(n) - 1.2b(n)]a(n) \\ b(n+1) &= [1.4 - 0.4b(n) - 1.2a(n)]b(n). \end{aligned}$$

Use phase plane analysis in the first quadrant to analyze the solutions to this system. Do this by constructing the lines

$$a = 0 \quad \text{and} \quad 0.4 - 0.4a - 1.2b = 0$$

and drawing arrows to the left or right according to the solution to an appropriate inequality, and then constructing the lines

$$b = 0 \quad \text{and} \quad 0.4 - 0.4b - 1.2a = 0$$

and drawing arrows up or down. Finally, combine the two constructions to get a phase plane analysis of the behavior of solutions.

4. Use phase plane analysis to analyze the solutions to the dynamical system

$$\begin{aligned} a(n+1) &= \left[2 - a(n) - \tfrac{2}{3}b(n)\right]a(n) \\ b(n+1) &= \left[2 - b(n) - \tfrac{2}{3}a(n)\right]b(n) \end{aligned}$$

in the first quadrant.

5. Use phase plane analysis to analyze the solutions to the dynamical system

$$\begin{aligned} a(n+1) - a(n) &= 1.2[1 - b(n)]a(n) \\ b(n+1) - b(n) &= 0.5[1 - 5b(n) + a(n)]b(n) \end{aligned}$$

for the predator–prey model from Section 7.2. Notice that the solutions oscillate about the equilibrium vector

$$A = \begin{pmatrix} 4 \\ 1 \end{pmatrix}.$$

This happens when the largest characteristic values are complex. It is often difficult to determine the stability of the equilibrium vector from the phase plane analysis in these situations.

7.4 The Hopf bifurcation

In Section 4.3, we introduced bifurcation theory. As a review, let's discuss the pitchfork bifurcation. In this case, we had a nonlinear dynamical system, such as

$$a(n+1) = (1+x)a(n) - a^3(n).$$

This dynamical system involved a parameter x. We found that for $-2 < x \leq 0$ there is one stable equilibrium value, $a = 0$; and for $0 < x < 1$, there are three equilibrium values, $a = \sqrt{x}$, $-\sqrt{x}$, and 0, the first two being stable and the third being unstable.

The moral was that **as the value of x moved past zero, the qualitative behavior of the solutions changed**.

For dynamical systems of several equations, we can have **pitchfork bifurcations, saddle node bifurcations**, and **transcritical bifurcations**, just as we did for nonlinear dynamical systems of a single equation. The analysis of these bifurcations is the same for nonlinear systems of several equations as it was for nonlinear systems of a single equation, so we will not discuss them further.

For a nonlinear dynamical system involving only one dependent variable $a(k)$, the solutions can only go in two directions, left or right. This limits the behavior of the solutions. But for a dynamical system involving at least two dependent variables, say $a(k)$ and $b(k)$, the solutions can go in an infinite number of directions in the ab plane. Hence, the behavior of the solutions can be much more interesting and complicated than in the one dimensional case.

For example, consider the dynamical system

$$\begin{aligned}
a(n+1) &= [3 - a^2(n) - b^2(n)][0.3a(n) - 0.4b(n)] \\
b(n+1) &= [3 - a^2(n) - b^2(n)][0.4a(n) + 0.3b(n)].
\end{aligned} \quad (10)$$

Define the vector $A(n)$ as

$$A(n) = \begin{pmatrix} a(n) \\ b(n) \end{pmatrix}.$$

With the Pythagorean theorem in mind, we define the **magnitude** of a vector as

$$|A(n)| = \sqrt{a^2(n) + b^2(n)}.$$

Using this notation, we can simplify the above dynamical system to

$$a(n+1) = [3 - |A(n)|^2][0.3a(n) - 0.4b(n)]$$
$$b(n+1) = [3 - |A(n)|^2][0.4a(n) + 0.3b(n)].$$

It is easy to see that

$$A = \begin{pmatrix} 0 \\ 0 \end{pmatrix}$$

is an equilibrium vector for this system. With

$$f(a, b) = (3 - a^2 - b^2)(0.3a - 0.4b),$$

the product rule gives

$$f_1(a, b) = -2a(0.3a - 0.4b) + 0.3(3 - a^2 - b^2)$$
$$f_2(a, b) = -2b(0.3a - 0.4b) - 0.4(3 - a^2 - b^2).$$

Thus, $f_1(0,0) = 0.9$ and $f_2(0,0) = -1.2$. Similarly, $g_1(0,0) = 1.2$ and $g_2(0,0) = 0.9$. This gives the linearized matrix as

$$R = \begin{pmatrix} 0.9 & -1.2 \\ 1.2 & 0.9 \end{pmatrix},$$

so that the characteristic equation is

$$|R - rI| = (0.9 - r)^2 + (1.2)^2 = r^2 - 1.8r + 2.25.$$

The roots of this equation are

$$r = 0.9 \pm 1.2i.$$

Since $|r| = 1.5 > 1$, the equilibrium vector A is unstable. This is seen graphically in Figure 71 in which we plotted the points $A(0)$ through $A(17)$ and connected them with straight lines, with $a(0) = b(0) = 0.01$. Notice that the solution $A(k)$ spirals away from the fixed point, the origin. You can also see that $A(k)$ spirals towards the circle of radius one centered at the origin, which is also drawn on the figure. This circle is called the **unit circle** and it is the graph of the equation

$$a^2 + b^2 = 1.$$

The points $A(0)$ through $A(100)$, with the same $A(0)$ as before, are plotted on Figure 72. In this figure, the points are not connected by

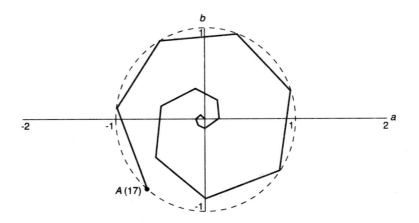

Fig. 71. Solution spiraling away from the unstable fixed point $(0,0)$. Consecutive values of $A(k)$ are connected by lines.

straight lines. Notice that all of the points (after the first few) appear to be 'on' the unit circle. (The solution has actually gone around the circle several times.) In fact, if you kept plotting points $A(101)$, $A(102)$, ..., you would keep going around this circle, but you would never repeat the same point. Using Definition 4.24, we say that the unit circle is an **attractor**.

Since this circle is an attractor, we **know** something, in that we know $A(k)$ is near the unit circle when k is large. We also **do not know** something, in that we don't know where $A(k)$ will be on the circle for any particular value of n.

Remark: Discrete dynamical systems and differential equations involving terms of the form $|A(n)|$ are quite common. They refer to forces that are only related to the distance from a certain point (which is usually the origin). Such forces might be gravity or sound. The force of gravity depends on the distance from the object. Likewise, the intensity of sound depends on the distance from the object (assuming there are no barriers). You should be able to think of many other forces of this type.

We now rephrase Definition 4.24 as follows.

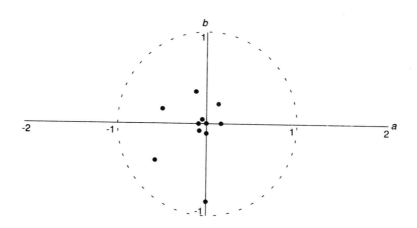

Fig. 72. Solution spiraling away from the unstable fixed point $(0,0)$. The points $A(0)$ through $A(100)$ are plotted, but not connected.

**Definition
7.9**

Let S represent a set of points in the plane. Let $P = (s_1, s_2)$ be a point in the set S. Let $A = (a, b)$ be a point not in the set S. Then we define the **distance between the point** *A* **and the set** *S denoted by $|A - S|$ to be the distance from the point A to the point in S that is closest to A, that is,*

$$|A - S| = \min_{P \in S} \sqrt{(a - s_1)^2 + (b - s_2)^2}.$$

Remark: This definition is not precise in that there may not be a point in S that is closest to A. We could overcome this by requiring that S be a **closed set** or by defining $|A - S|$ as the largest number that is less than or equal to

$$\sqrt{(a - s_1)^2 + (b - s_2)^2}$$

for every point P in S.

**Definition
7.10**

A set S is an **attractor** *for a nonlinear dynamical system if there is a number ϵ such that if $|A(0) - S| < \epsilon$ then $\lim_{k \to \infty} |A(k) - S| = 0$.*

This definition means that if you start near some point in the set S, then the solution goes to the set S, that is, for large values of k, you know that $A(k)$ is near some point of S. Examples of attractors are stable fixed points, stable m-cycles, and the unit circle for the dynamical system (10).

Let's now prove algebraically that the unit circle is an attractor for the dynamical system (10). It is clear that if

$$\lim_{k \to \infty} |A(k)| = 1$$

then $|A(k) - S|$ goes to zero where S is the unit circle. Thus, the trick is to study $|A(k)|$, not $A(k)$.

We have

$$|A(n+1)|^2 = a^2(n+1) + b^2(n+1).$$

From the dynamical system (10), we have

$$
\begin{aligned}
a^2(n+1) &= (3 - |A(n)|^2)^2[0.3a(n) - 0.4b(n)]^2 \\
&= (3 - |A(n)|^2)^2[0.09a^2(n) - 0.24a(n)b(n) + 0.16b^2(n)]
\end{aligned}
$$

and

$$b^2(n+1) = (3 - |A(n)|^2)^2[0.16a^2(n) + 0.24a(n)b(n) + 0.09b^2(n)].$$

Noting that $(3 - |A(n)|^2)^2$ is a common term in $a^2(n+1)$ and $b^2(n+1)$, we can factor it out when we add. Addition of the terms gives

$$a^2(n+1) + b^2(n+1) = (3 - |A(n)|^2)^2[0.25a^2(n) + 0.25b^2(n)]$$

after simplification. This can be rewritten as

$$|A(n+1)| = 0.5(3 - |A(n)|^2)|A(n)|$$

after factoring and taking square roots.

Since we are taking positive square roots, we should have the term $|3 - |A(n)|^2|$ instead of $3 - |A(n)|^2$. We will assume that $|A(n)| < \sqrt{3}$, so that both terms are the same. This avoids unnecessary confusion in the algebra.

By letting $|A(n)| = c(n)$, to simplify notation, we have the first order nonlinear dynamical system

$$c(n+1) = 1.5c(n) - 0.5c^3(n).$$

Let's find the fixed points for this system, that is, let's solve

$$c = 1.5c - 0.5c^3.$$

Bringing the terms to the left and factoring gives

$$0.5c(-1 + c^2) = 0.5c(-1 + c)(1 + c) = 0,$$

so the fixed points are $c = 0$, 1, and -1. Remembering that $c = |A| \geq 0$, we can discard $c = -1$.

To study the stability of a fixed point, we use the derivative of the function $f(c) = 1.5c - 0.5c^3$, that is,

$$f'(c) = 1.5 - 1.5c^2.$$

Since $f'(0) = 1.5$, we see that $c = 0$ is a repelling fixed point for this system. Since $c^2 = |A|^2 = a^2 + b^2 = 0$, this means that the point $(a, b) = (0, 0)$ is repelling or unstable.

Since $f'(1) = 0 < 1$, we see that $c = 1$ is an attracting fixed point. Thus, $c(k)$ goes to 1, and so the points $A(k)$ go to the unit circle.

In summary, if $c(k) = |A(k)|$ has a **positive** attracting fixed point c, then we know that the circle of radius c centered at the origin is an attractor for the corresponding nonlinear dynamical system.

In the previous discussion, the trick was to avoid studying the system of two equations. The way this was accomplished was to study

$$c(n) = |A(n)| = \sqrt{a^2(n) + b^2(n)}.$$

Often, this reduces our system of equations to a dynamical system involving only a single equation (which we know how to study). Our analysis of this equation gives us results about our system. Again, we use the mathematical principle of reducing a difficult problem (studying systems of two equations) to an easier problem (studying one equation).

We will now study the **Hopf bifurcation**, a bifurcation that occurs frequently in the study of nonlinear dynamical systems of several equations. Briefly, what occurs is that we have a nonlinear dynamical system involving a parameter x. There is a constant c such that for $x \leq c$ the system has an attracting fixed point, but for $x > c$ the fixed point is repelling and an attractor S (often a circle) bifurcates from the fixed point. Specifically, there is a circle centered at the fixed point, such that the solutions $A(k)$ go to the circle. The closer x is to c, the smaller the radius of the circle. In fact, as x decreases to c, the radius goes to zero.

The Hopf bifurcation is similar to the pitchfork bifurcation, in which there are two attracting fixed points, one on each side of the repelling fixed point, and as x goes to c, the two attracting values go to the repelling value. Figure 73 displays the pitchfork bifurcation for the dynamical system

$$c(n + 1) = (1 + x)c(n) - c^3(n).$$

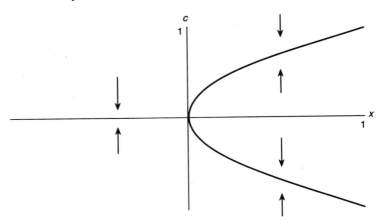

Fig. 73. Pitchfork for dynamical system $c(n+1) = (1+x)c(n) - c^3(n)$. Stable fixed points are given by the curve $x = c^2$.

To get the bifurcation diagram for a Hopf bifurcation, revolve the parabola in Figure 73 about the x axis, giving you a **parabolic cone** instead of a parabola. For each x value greater than 0, you get an attracting circle.

Let's be specific. Consider the nonlinear dynamical system

$$
\begin{aligned}
a(n+1) &= [2 + x - a^2(n) - b^2(n)][0.3a(n) - 0.4b(n)] \\
b(n+1) &= [2 + x - a^2(n) - b^2(n)][0.4a(n) + 0.3b(n)],
\end{aligned}
\quad (11)
$$

where x is an unknown parameter. Note that, when $x = 1$, this is dynamical system (10).

Our goal is to prove two facts: first that if $-2 < x < 0$, then the point $A = (0,0)$ is an attracting fixed point; and second that if $0 < x < 2$, then the origin is a repelling fixed point and the circle $a^2 + b^2 = x$ is an attractor.

To do this, we define the new dependent variable $c(n)$ as before, that is,

$$
c(n) = \sqrt{a^2(n) + b^2(n)}.
$$

Then we have

$$
\begin{aligned}
a^2(n+1) &= [2 + x - c^2(n)]^2[0.3a(n) - 0.4b(n)]^2 \\
b^2(n+1) &= [2 + x - c^2(n)]^2[0.4a(n) + 0.3b(n)]^2.
\end{aligned}
$$

Therefore, adding the two equations and then factoring out the common term gives

$$
c^2(n+1) = [2 + x - c^2(n)]^2[(0.3a(n) - 0.4b(n))^2 + (0.4a(n) + 0.3b(n))^2].
$$

Simplifying the last expression gives

$$c^2(n+1) = [2 + x - c^2(n)]^2[0.25c^2(n)],$$

or, after taking square roots,

$$c(n+1) = 0.5[2 + x - c^2(n)]c(n). \tag{12}$$

This again shows that quite often problems become algebraically complex, but if we are careful then most terms cancel and a relatively simple dynamical system results.

Technically, we should have $|2+x-c^2(n)|$, but we will only be studying values of x and $c(n)$ for which this expression is positive. Hence, to avoid confusion, we omit the absolute value sign, as things are difficult enough without it.

For dynamical system (12), $f(c) = 0.5(2+x)c - 0.5c^3$, so

$$f'(c) = 0.5(2+x) - 1.5c^2 = 1 + 0.5x - 1.5c^2.$$

The fixed points are the solutions to $c = f(c)$, which reduces to the equation $0 = 0.5c(x - c^2)$. The solutions are thus

$$c = 0, \quad \sqrt{x}, \quad -\sqrt{x}.$$

Since $c \geq 0$, we can omit the last value.

To study the stability of $c = 0$, we compute that $f'(0) = 1 + 0.5x$. Solving

$$-1 < 1 + 0.5x < 1,$$

we find that $c = 0$ is attracting if $-4 < x < 0$. But since we also need $2 + x - c^2(n) > 0$, we will restrict x to the interval

$$-2 < x < 0.$$

To study the stability of $\sqrt{x}$ for $x > 0$, we compute

$$f'(\sqrt{x}) = 1 + 0.5x - 1.5x = 1 - x.$$

Solving for $-1 < 1 - x < 1$, we find that $c = \sqrt{x}$ is attracting if $0 < x < 2$. (Note that if $c(n)$ is close to $\sqrt{x}$, then $2 + x - c^2(n)$ is close to 2 and is therefore positive.) Thus, for $0 < x < 2$, the solution $A(k)$ for large k is near the circle of radius $\sqrt{x}$, centered at the origin.

This can be seen in Figure 74. For any x value in the interval $0 < x < 2$, the attractor is the circle obtained by intersecting the parabolic

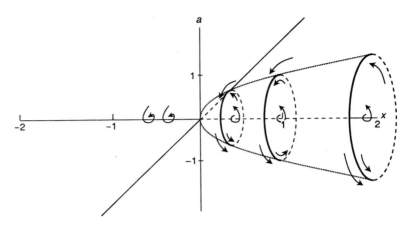

Fig. 74. The Hopf bifurcation is seen here. Solutions spiral towards the parabolic cone given by $x = a^2 + b^2$.

cone $a^2 + b^2 = x$ with a plane that is perpendicular to the x axis at that x value. A solution $A(k)$ to the dynamical system will cycle about that particular circle. This is the unit circle when $x = 1$ (giving dynamical system (10)).

Also, if $-2 < x \le 0$, then solutions will cycle into the origin. To see that solutions actually cycle to the point $(0, 0)$, you need to compute the matrix

$$R = \begin{pmatrix} f_1(0,0) & f_2(0,0) \\ g_1(0,0) & g_2(0,0) \end{pmatrix}$$

and find that the characteristic values are complex.

Attractors are not all the same. The dynamical system

$$a(n+1) = 1.5a(n) - 0.5a^3(n)$$

has $a = 1$ and $a = -1$ as attracting fixed points. Thus, the set

$$S = \{-1, 1\}$$

is an attractor for this system. It was shown in Section 4.2 that the dynamical system

$$b(n+1) = 3.2b(n) - 2.2b^2(n)$$

has a stable 2-cycle consisting of the two values

$$T = \left\{ \frac{21 + \sqrt{21}}{22}, \frac{21 - \sqrt{21}}{22} \right\}.$$

Thus T is also an attractor.

Using Definition 4.29, we say that attractor T is **transitive**, in that, for any $b(0)$ near T, $b(k)$ gets near both points in T. In particular $b(k)$ is near one value of T for even k and is near the other value for odd k. This was seen in Section 4.4.

For the first equation, $a(k)$ is close to the same number for all large values of k. Thus, the attractor S can be broken into two smaller attractors, $S' = \{-1\}$ and $S'' = \{+1\}$. There are two intervals of initial values, N' and N'', such that if $a(0) \in N'$ then $a(k)$ goes to -1, but if $a(0) \in N''$ then $a(k)$ goes to S''. Attractor S is **not transitive**.

When the attractor is a circle, the same can be true. In Problem 1, the attractor is a circle. But the solution $A(k)$ goes to a 4-cycle on that circle. The particular 4-cycle depends on the initial vector. Thus, the attractor is not transitive. In fact this circle can be decomposed into an infinite number of stable 4-cycles.

In Problem 2 and for dynamical system (11), the attractor is transitive. This means that for any point P on the circle (attractor), there is a k such that $A(k)$ is near P. To be more precise, for any small positive ϵ, there is a k such that $|A(k) - P| < \epsilon$. This is true for any solution that goes to the circle, although the value of k is different for different initial values.

7.4.1 Problems

1. Consider the nonlinear dynamical system

$$
\begin{aligned}
a(n+1) &= (1.6 - 0.15|A(n)|^2)b(n) \\
b(n+1) &= -(1.6 - 0.15|A(n)|^2)a(n),
\end{aligned}
$$

where

$$|A(n)|^2 = a^2(n) + b^2(n).$$

(a) Find a nonlinear dynamical system for $c(n) = |A(n)|$.

(b) Show that $A = (0,0)$ is a repelling fixed point for the system of two equations by showing that $c = 0$ is a repelling fixed point for the dynamical system derived in part (a).

(c) Show that the circle $a^2 + b^2 = 4$ is an attractor by showing that $c = 2$ is an attracting fixed point for the system derived in part (a).

(d) Compute $A(1)$ through $A(8)$ when $A(0) = (2,0)$.

(e) Compute $A(1)$ through $A(8)$ when $A(0) = (1.4, 1.4)$.

2. Consider the nonlinear dynamical system

$$a(n+1) = (x - |A(n)|)[0.8a(n) + 0.6b(n)]$$
$$b(n+1) = (x - |A(n)|)[-0.6a(n) + 0.8b(n)].$$

(a) Find a nonlinear dynamical system for $c(n) = |A(n)|$. You should find that the nonnegative equilibrium values for this system are $c = 0$ and (when $x > 1$) $c = x - 1$.

(b) Show that $A = (0,0)$ is an attracting fixed point for $0 < x < 1$ by showing that $c = 0$ is an attracting fixed point for the system derived in part (a). (Why do we omit the interval $-1 < x < 0$?)

(c) Show that if $1 < x < 3$, then $c = x - 1$ is an attracting fixed point for the system derived in part (a) and, consequently, the circle $a^2 + b^2 = (x-1)^2$ is an attractor for the nonlinear system of two equations.

3. Consider the nonlinear dynamical system

$$a(n+1) = \frac{(1 + x - |A(n)|^2)[a(n) - b(n)]}{\sqrt{2}}$$

$$b(n+1) = \frac{(1 + x - |A(n)|^2)[a(n) + b(n)]}{\sqrt{2}}.$$

(a) Find a nonlinear dynamical system for $c(n) = |A(n)|$ and show that $c = 0$ and (when $x > 0$) $c = \sqrt{x}$ are nonnegative fixed points for this system.

(b) Show that the origin is an attracting fixed point for $-1 < x < 0$ by showing that $c = 0$ is an attracting fixed point for the system derived in part (a). (Note that this also shows that A is repelling for $x > 0$.)

(c) Show that if $0 < x < 1$, then $c = \sqrt{x}$ is an attracting fixed point for the system derived in part (a) and, consequently, the circle $a^2 + b^2 = x$ is an attractor for the nonlinear system of two equations.

(d) (To be done on a computer or programmable calculator.) For $x = 0.16$, pick initial values $a(0)$ and $b(0)$ such that $a^2(0) + b^2(0)$ is near, but less than, 0.16. Compute $A(1) = (a(1), b(1))$, $A(2), \ldots, A(50)$. Did you observe that, for large k, the points $(a(k), b(k))$ satisfy

$$a^2(k) + b^2(k) = x?$$

Did you also observe that the points formed an 8-cycle? If you take different values for $A(0)$, you will get a different 8-cycle, but it will still be on the circle $a^2 + b^2 = x$ (if the new initial vector is not a multiple of any of the eight points on the first 8-cycle). Thus, this attractor is not transitive.

7.5 Chaos revisited

As in our study of nonlinear dynamical systems in Chapter 4, when studying a nonlinear dynamical system involving a parameter, x we want to discover the qualitative behavior of the solutions for each value x, at least for x in some reasonable range. Normally the qualitative behavior of the solutions remains the same for x in certain intervals.

Specifically, we might discover that for $-2 < x < 0$ there are no fixed points and all solutions tend to infinity, but that for $0 \leq x < 1$ there is an attracting and a repelling fixed point, such that solutions starting close enough to the attracting fixed point will go towards that value as k goes to infinity. The x values at which these intervals meet, $x = 0$ in this case, are called **bifurcation values**.

In the case of a single nonlinear dynamical system, we learned to classify our bifurcation values as saddle node, pitchfork, or transcritical. In the case of dynamical systems of several equations, classification is much more difficult, as there are more types of possible behavior, the Hopf bifurcation of the previous section being one.

Remember that the value x corresponds to some real world phenomenon. If x is in an interval for which the qualitative behavior of solutions is the same (but not an end point of the interval), the dynamical system is said to be **structurally stable**. This means that our predictions will be accurate, even if our measurement of x is slightly inaccurate.

As an example, suppose we estimate that $x = 0.7$ in our discussion above. Since there is an attracting fixed point for $0 \leq x < 1$, we predict that solutions will go to this fixed point. Suppose that our estimate is off slightly (or the world changes a little) and, in reality, $x = 0.71$. Since that is also in the interval $0 \leq x < 1$, solutions will still go to an attracting fixed point (which is slightly different from our predicted fixed point). We say that this system is **structurally stable** because small errors will not affect the qualitative outcome.

Suppose we estimate that $x = 0$. Then we again predict that solutions go to an attracting fixed point, since $0 \leq x < 1$. But if our measurements are slightly off and $x = -0.1$, then solutions go to infinity. Thus, we are not able to make predictions since a slight change in x may result in a dramatic change in the behavior of solutions. This system is **not structurally stable**.

Our goal for any nonlinear dynamical system involving a parameter x is to discover the qualitative behavior of the solutions for **all** values of the parameter, possibly within some realistic range. In our discussion of the Hopf bifurcation in Section 7.4, we found the qualitative behavior of solutions for $-2 < x < 2$.

Let's try to analyze the relatively harmless looking system

$$
\begin{aligned}
a(n+1) &= 1 + b(n) - xa^2(n) \\
b(n+1) &= 0.3a(n).
\end{aligned}
\tag{13}
$$

This system is one of the simplest nonlinear dynamical systems possible, since there is only one squared term. Suppose we want to analyze this system for $0 < x < 2$.

As a first step, we find the fixed points by solving the equations

$$
a = 1 + b - xa^2 \quad \text{and} \quad b = 0.3a
$$

for a and b. Substitution of $0.3a$ for b into the first equation and then using the quadratic formula gives

$$
a = \frac{-0.7 \pm \sqrt{0.49 + 4x}}{2x}.
$$

To find b, remember that $b = 0.3a$. This gives us two fixed points.

For what x values is the point

$$
(a, b) = \left(\frac{-0.7 + \sqrt{0.49 + 4x}}{2x}, \frac{0.3(-0.7 + \sqrt{0.49 + 4x})}{2x} \right)
$$

stable? To find this, we compute the linearized matrix

$$
R = \begin{pmatrix} -2xa & 1 \\ 0.3 & 0 \end{pmatrix},
$$

substitute a into the matrix, and find the characteristic values r_1 and r_2. We then solve the equations

$$
-1 < r_1 < 1 \quad \text{and} \quad -1 < r_2 < 1.
$$

If you solve these inequalities, which are a bit tricky, you will find that this fixed point is attracting if

$$
0 < x < 0.3675.
$$

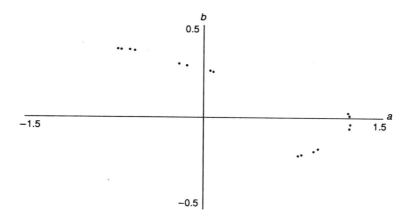

Fig. 75. Attracting 16-cycle when $x = 1.054$.

If you continued your analysis, you would find that as x increased past 0.3675, this fixed point becomes repelling and an attracting 2-cycle emerges. As x keeps increasing, the 2-cycle becomes repelling and an attracting 4-cycle appears. As x increases, the 2^m-cycle becomes repelling and an attracting 2^{m+1}-cycle appears. Finally, chaos develops and all solutions appear to be in a certain number of intervals, the number of intervals decreasing as x increases. These intervals form an attractor for those values of x.

To sketch the above graphically, we pick $A(0) = (0.1, 0.1)$, and compute $A(1)$, $A(2)$, ..., $A(2000)$. Since the first few values of a solution may not be on the attractor, we only plot $A(1001)$ through $A(2000)$. We let $x = 1.054$ in Figure 75. Since there are only 16 points on this figure, we predict that there is an attracting 16-cycle for this value of x. We let $x = 1.1$ in Figure 76. Note that we have two curves of points. We predict that these two curves, taken together, form an attractor for this value of x.

In these figures, we have conducted mathematical experimentation. By plotting figures for different values of x, we can make predictions of the x-intervals on which solutions go to attracting 2-cycles, 4-cycles, and so forth. We could make further calculations to approximate x-intervals

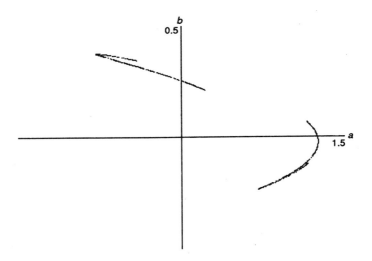

Fig. 76. Attractor when $x = 1.1$.

for which this system is structurally stable. Note that these are only predictions and that further analysis is necessary to prove that our predictions are correct.

We used mathematical experimentation in the last section. We computed Figures 71 and 72, which gave us the idea that a circle formed the attractor. This gave us the idea to make the substitution $a^2(n) + b^2(n) = c^2(n)$. This substitution helped us prove that the figures were correct.

Let's continue our experimentation. Let $x \doteq 1.3$, and study the system

$$\begin{aligned} a(n+1) &= 1 + b(n) - 1.3a^2(n) \\ b(n+1) &= 0.3a(n). \end{aligned}$$

In Figure 77, the points $(a(0), b(0))$ through $(a(1000), b(1000))$ have been plotted with the initial point being $(a(0), b(0)) = (0.1, 0.1)$. We notice that the points take on a somewhat strange crescent shape. Remember that $A(k)$ may not be near the attractor until k is large. To see if that is true in this case, we plot the points $(a(1001), b(1001))$ through $(a(2000), b(2000))$ in Figure 78. Notice that there are only **seven points**. It appears that $A(k)$ has converged to an attracting 7-cycle. If you pick any other (reasonably small) initial value, you will find that $A(k)$ again goes to the same 7-cycle.

If we had the time and inclination, we could compute $a(n+7)$ and

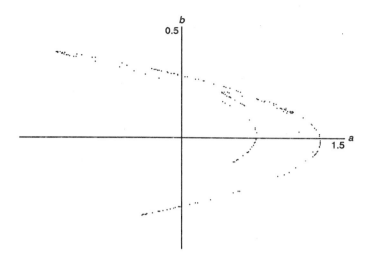

Fig. 77. Points $A(0)$ through $A(1000)$ when $x = 1.3$.

$b(n + 7)$ in terms of $a(n)$ and $b(n)$, that is, the dynamical system

$$\begin{aligned} a(n + 7) &= F(a(n), b(n)) \\ b(n + 7) &= G(a(n), b(n)) \end{aligned}$$

(where F and G represent seven compositions of f and g). We could then (try to) find the seven fixed points corresponding the the attracting 7-cycle of dynamical system (13) for $x = 1.3$. After linearization, we could show that each of these seven points was attracting. This would show, algebraically, that we have an attracting 7-cycle, or that we have an attractor consisting of seven points when $x = 1.3$.

Let's repeat this process for $x = 1.4$, that is, let's study the dynamical system

$$\begin{aligned} a(n + 1) &= 1 + b(n) - 1.4a^2(n) \\ b(n + 1) &= 0.3a(n). \end{aligned}$$

Again, we let $(a(0), b(0)) = (0.1, 0.1)$. In Figure 79, we plot $A(0)$ through $A(1000)$. As in the $x = 1.3$ case, the points take on a strange shape. Maybe they are slowly converging to a cycle. To see if this is true, we plot $A(1001)$ through $A(2000)$ in Figure 80. The points take on the same shape again. If we keep plotting the points $A(k)$ for large values of k,

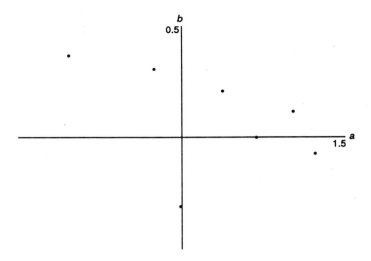

Fig. 78. Attracting 7-cycle when $x = 1.3$. This was found by plotting $A(1001)$ through $A(2000)$.

they will keep taking on this same shape, so they do not appear to form a cycle. If you plot points $A(k)$ for different (reasonably small) initial points, they will still form this strange shape.

The strange shape in Figures 79 and 80 is an **attractor**, much like the circle in Section 7.4. How do we describe this attractor, algebraically?

To answer this question, we consider the quadrilateral in Figure 81 with vertices

$$(-1.33, 0.42), \quad (-1.06, -0.5), \quad (1.245, -0.14), \quad (1.32, 0.133).$$

We will consider each point on this quadrilateral as an initial value $A(0)$ and use that value to compute $A(1)$. In Figure 82, we have plotted all these $A(1)$ points. Note that when $A(0) = A_0$ in Figure 81, then $A(1) = A_1$ in Figure 82. The same relationship holds between B_0 and B_1, C_0 and C_1, and so forth. If any point inside the quadrilateral of Figure 81 is used as an $A(0)$ value, then the $A(1)$ value will be inside the **horseshoe** of Figure 82.

Also, if Figure 82 were laid on top of Figure 81, then the horseshoe would fit entirely within the quadrilateral. Loosely speaking, our nonlinear dynamical system **stretches** the quadrilateral, then **folds** it over. This is sometimes called the **baker's map**, since it streches and folds the quadrilateral like a baker stretches and folds dough when making pastries.

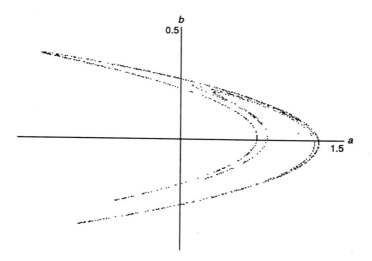

Fig. 79. Points $A(0)$ through $A(1000)$ when $x = 1.4$.

In Figure 83, we plot all the $A(2)$ points, where the $A(0)$ points are on the quadrilateral of Figure 81. Notice that this shape is somewhat like the shape formed by the points on the attractor of Figure 80. What happens is that, when we compute the $A(2)$ points, we stretch our horseshoe of Figure 82 and fold it, forming more branches. When we compute $A(3)$ points, we stretch the graph in Figure 83 and then fold it, forming even more branches.

Continuing, the points $A(k)$ will be inside a shape that is much like dough stretched and folded k times. It will have many thin branches, much like the thin layers of a croissant. This can be seen in Figure 84, which is a magnification of the rectangle drawn on the attractor in Figure 80. The coordinates of the corners of this rectangle are $(1, 0.08)$, $(1, 0.12)$, $(1.1, 0.08)$, and $(1.1, 0.12)$. We have computed the points $A(0)$ through $A(100\,000)$, and plotted those which lie in this rectangle. Notice that these points appear to lie on thin layers or lines.

In Figure 85 is a magnification of the rectangle in Figure 84. In Figure 85, the horizontal axis goes from $a = 1.072$ to $a = 1.082$, while the vertical axis goes from $b = 0.091$ to $b = 0.094$. Notice that what appeared to be one curve in Figure 84 can actually be seen as a collection of several thin curves in Figure 85. It seems that if we continue magnifying our figures, what appears to be one line under a certain magnification will actually be seen as a series of lines under higher magnification.

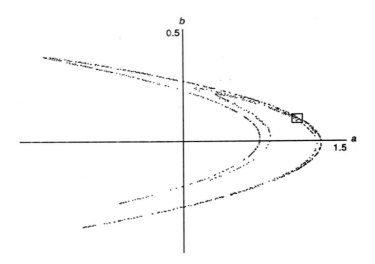

Fig. 80. Attractor when $x = 1.4$. This was found by plotting $A(1001)$ through $A(2000)$.

We have seen that the nonlinear dynamical system

$$
\begin{aligned}
a(n+1) &= 1 + b(n) - 1.4a^2(n) \\
b(n+1) &= 0.3a(n)
\end{aligned}
\tag{14}
$$

appears to satisfy three conditions.

Condition 1, sensitive dependence on the initial values: Recall that Definition 4.30 stated that we have sensitive dependence if there is some number c such that, no matter how near the initial point $A(0)$ is to the initial point $A'(0)$, eventually the solutions $A(k)$ and $A'(k)$ will be at least c units apart, that is,

$$
|A(k) - A'(k)| > c
$$

for some values of k.

Condition 2, existence of an attractor: Definition 4.24 states that we have an attractor S if there is a set of points S such that, for any initial value in a neighborhood of S, we have

$$
\lim_{k \to \infty} |A(k) - S| = 0.
$$

Condition 3, the attractor is transitive: From Definition 4.29, this means that for any initial value in our quadrilateral, the corresponding

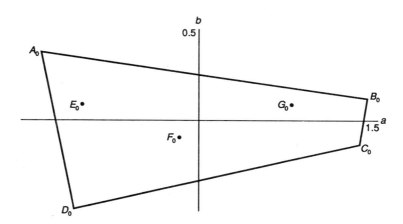

Fig. 81. Set of initial values $A(0)$ is the interior and boundary of this quadrilateral.

solution $A(k)$ gets close to every point in the attractor S, that is, for any point $P \in S$ and for any ϵ, there is some value of k such that

$$|A(k) - P| < \epsilon.$$

Condition 1 tells us the following. Suppose we estimate that the real world is starting at point $A(0)$, while in reality it is starting at point $A'(0)$. Then our predictions $A(k)$ of the real world will only be close to the actual behavior $A'(k)$ of the real world for a short time. Eventually our predictions will be off by at least c units. This statement will be true no matter how accurately we measure the world. Condition 2 tells us that although we don't know precisely where the real solution $A'(k)$ will be, we do know that it will be somewhere 'on' the set S. Condition 3 tells us that not only will the real solution $A'(k)$ be somewhere on S but every point of S will be part of the solution.

Definition 7.11

Suppose a dynamical system satisfies conditions 1, 2, and 3 above. Then the attractor S is called a **strange attractor***.*

Remark: It must be pointed out that the concept of strange attractors is not very well understood, and is therefore the object of a considerable amount of research, not only in mathematics, but in many other fields as

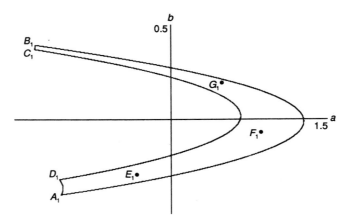

Fig. 82. Set of points $A(1)$ when $A(0)$ is the set of points given by the quadrilateral of the previous figure.

well. In fact, there is not even a unanimous agreement on the definition of a strange attractor. There are attractors that are strange attractors by one definition, but not by another. Thus, some people may have alternative definitions of strange attractor. Loosely, we might say that an attractor is 'strange' if it is not totally understood.

There is good news and bad news. The bad news is that sensitive dependence of the initial values means that we cannot accurately predict the future for such systems. The good news is that since there is an attractor we can predict the future, in that we know the solution $A(k)$ is close to this strange region and every point on that region will occur. Loosely speaking, solutions to such a dynamical system will move in a **chaotic but regular** fashion.

The first reference to strange attractors was by the meteorologist, Edward Lorenz, in 1963. Lorenz developed a system of differential equations to model weather patterns. The solutions to his system go to a strange attractor, called the **Lorenz attractor**. Strange attractors are therefore thought to explain why the weather is unpredictable (condition 1), and in some sense predictable (condition 2: it doesn't snow in Virginia in July). Condition 3 implies that every possible type of weather for a season will

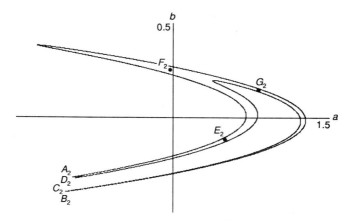

Fig. 83. Set of points $A(2)$ when $A(0)$ is given by the quadrilateral of Figure 81.

occur (if you don't like the weather, wait a few minutes).

Strange attractors are thought to explain similar chaotic or turbulent processes in a variety of fields, such as chemistry, economics (the stock market?), geophysics (the irregular changes in the earth's magnetic field?), ecology (irregular oscillations in the populations of several interacting species?), and so on.

How do our three conditions relate to dynamical system (14) considered earlier? Suppose we are given two initial points, $A(0)$ and $A'(0)$, which are close together. Because this map stretches the quadrilateral, eventually the points $A(k)$ and $A'(k)$ will be pulled apart so condition 1 is satisfied. The crescent-shaped region of Figure 80 is the attractor S so condition 2 is satisfied. Note that we can see a picture of S in that figure, but we are unable to define the points of S algebraically. Finally, if we take any $A(0)$ in the quadrilateral and plot the points $A(1001)$, $A(1002)$, ..., then these points will form a picture of the entire set S, so condition 3 is satisfied. This attractor S is called the **Hénon attractor**.

Some readers may question the rigor of the above argument that the Hénon attractor is a strange attractor. They would be correct. In fact it has not been shown rigorously that the Hénon attractor is a strange at-

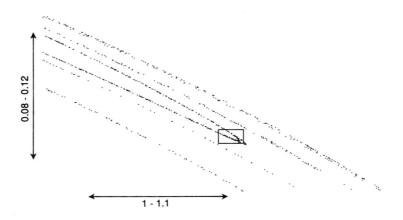

Fig. 84. Magnification of portion of the attractor that is inside the rectangle in Figure 80.

tractor. Maybe this attractor is just a large stable cycle. Since computers have round-off error, computation of solutions will not help decide which is true. Despite the fact that no proof has been given, many mathematicians feel that the Hénon attractor is a strange attractor. Their reasoning is that 'it looks like a strange attractor'.

So far, we have discussed the qualitative behavior of dynamical system (13) for different values of x. We have found that there is an attracting fixed point for x in the interval $(0, 0.3675)$, and that this fixed point bifurcates into an attracting 2-cycle at $x = 0.3675$. We also have indications that there are values of x for which the system has attracting 7-cycles, attractors that are curves, and strange attractors. We would like to have a complete bifurcation diagram for this system on the interval $0 < x < 2$, that is, we would like to know the behavior of this system for every x value.

We would also like to know x-intervals which are structurally stable, that is, for all x in that interval, the behavior remains the same. For example, does the system have an attracting 7-cycle for all x near 1.3? Does the system have a strange attractor for all x near 1.4?

Unfortunately, the complete bifurcation diagram for this nonlinear dynamical system is unknown, that is, the qualitative behavior of solutions to this system is unknown for some values of x between 1 and 2. This is expected since we are still not certain the system has a strange attractor for $x = 1.4$.

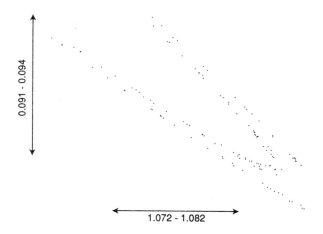

Fig. 85. Magnification of portion of the attractor that is inside the rectangle of Figure 84.

Let's consider another simple dynamical system

$$
\begin{aligned}
a(n+1) &= a^2(n) - b^2(n) + x \\
b(n+1) &= 2a(n)b(n) + y,
\end{aligned}
\tag{15}
$$

where x and y are two fixed numbers. For this system, we consider x and y as two parameters. We would like to know the behavior of this system for every value of x and y. As might be expected after studying the dynamical system, this problem is too difficult for us to solve. Let's try to answer a simpler question. For what values of x and y and for what initial values $A(0)$ do solutions to this system go to infinity, that is,

$$
\lim_{k \to \infty} |A(k)| = \infty?
$$

Also, for what values (x, y) does the solution remain bounded? We can construct a graph of the answer for a fixed $A(0)$ vector by plotting all points (x, y) in the xy plane for which the particular solution starting at this value of $A(0)$ remains bounded, that is, $A(k)$ goes to an attracting fixed point, an attracting cycle, a strange attractor, or some other type of attractor. We do not plot the point (x, y) if this solution goes to infinity.

Again we resort to mathematical experimentation. Pick a fixed $A(0)$. Fix values for x and y. Compute $A(1)$, $A(2)$, ..., $A(N)$. If $|A(N)| > C$, we will assume that $A(k)$ is going to infinity. If $|A(N)| < C$ we assume that solutions remain bounded and we plot that point (x, y) on the plane.

We divide a portion of the xy plane into a large number of points and repeat this procedure for each of these points, using $A(0) = (0, 0)$, $N = 20$, and $C = 2$. This gives us Figure 86. Our experiment implies that solutions $A(k)$ remain bounded for each point (x, y) in the shaded region and, consequently, solutions go to infinity for points outside that region. There is nothing sacred about our conditions. We could use a different point for $A(0)$. We could compute $A(1000)$ instead of $A(20)$. The only draw back would be the increased computer time required to draw our figure.

It happens that 2 is a good choice for c in that if $|A(k)| > 2$ for any value of k, then it can be shown (Devaney 1989) that

$$\lim_{k \to \infty} |A(k)| = \infty.$$

Note that since $a(0) = 0$ and $b(0) = 0$, it follows that $a(1) = x$ and $b(1) = y$. Thus the above result shows that if $\sqrt{a^2(1) + b^2(1)} = \sqrt{x^2 + y^2} > 2$, then $|A(k)|$ goes to infinity, that is, **no point (x, y) is plotted outside the circle of radius 2 centered at the origin**. This result depends on the particular dynamical system, that is, for another dynamical system we might need to pick $c = 50$ or some other 'large' number.

For dynamical system (15), the shaded region of Figure 86 is an approximation of the set of points S for which solutions starting at $(0, 0)$ remain bounded. The set S is called the **Mandelbrot set**, and it looks somewhat like Figure 86. It is a bifurcation diagram in the sense that if, in changing x and y, you cross the boundary of S, then you go from bounded to unbounded solutions (or vice versa). It tells nothing about the behavior of the bounded solutions.

To understand this bifurcation diagram better, we need a magnification of the boundary of this set. In Figure 87 is a magnification of the rectangle given in Figure 86, although we used $N = 200$ instead of $N = 20$ in the construction of Figure 87. Notice that when magnified, the boundary of this region resembles the boundary of the original region.

Remark: If any magnification of a part of a figure has the same shape (in some sense) as the shape of the original figure, then that figure is said to be **fractal**. The Mandelbrot set is fractal. An extreme example of the fractal nature of S is seen in Figure 88, which is a magnification of the rectangle in Figure 87. In Figure 88, we used $N = 300$ to get a better detail of the boundary of S. While this portion of S seems to be an island, it is actually connected to S.

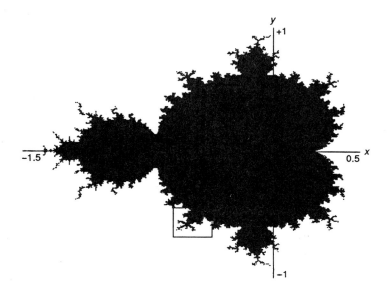

Fig. 86. The Mandelbrot set is the set of parameter values that lead to bounded solutions of dynamical system when $a(0) = b(0) = 0$.

You might ask why we are studying the strange dynamical system (15). Let $c(n) = a(n) + ib(n)$ and let $z = a + iy$. Then

$$c^2(n) = [a(n) + ib(n)]^2 = [a^2(n) - b^2(n)] + [2a(n)b(n)]i.$$

We now have

$$
\begin{aligned}
c(n+1) &= a(n+1) + b(n+1)i \\
&= [a^2(n) - b^2(n) + x] + [2a(n)b(n) + y]i \\
&= c^2(n) + x + yi \\
&= c^2(n) + z.
\end{aligned}
$$

Thus, when using complex numbers, dynamical system (15) is the same as the (complex) nonlinear dynamical system

$$c(n+1) = c^2(n) + z, \tag{16}$$

which is one of the simplest and most natural of all nonlinear dynamical systems.

From our discussion, it appears that even if we can develop complicated models that describe the world, it is likely that many of these models

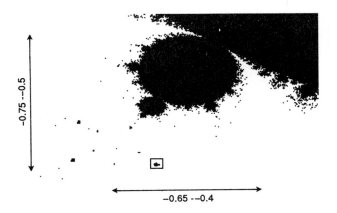

Fig. 87. Magnification of the portion of the Mandelbrot set inside the rectangle of the previous figure.

will not have stable equilibrium or stable cycles. Some will exhibit chaos while others will have a strange attractor.

As a further study of dynamical system (15) (or (16) if you prefer), we could fix the values of x and y and ask ourselves, for what initial values $(a(0), b(0))$ does the solution remain bounded? To 'answer' this question, we could first pick a point (x, y), say in the Mandelbrot set. Second, we could fix a grid in the ab plane, and pick any point on that grid as $a(0)$ and $b(0)$. We could then compute $A(1)$, ..., $A(N)$ for a large value of N, and if $|A(N)| < 2$, we plot the point (a, b). The points plotted would then represent bounded solutions for the particular dynamical system determined by the fixed values x and y. The set of plotted points is called the **Julia set** for that dynamical system. (Actually, the Julia set is the boundary of the set of plotted points.) Remember that the Julia set only gives initial values giving bounded solutions. It does not give the behavior of those solutions.

Note that, for each point (x, y), there is a different Julia set. It happens that Julia sets are also fractal, but the size and shape of Julia sets can vary considerably. In fact, the description of Julia sets is not known for all values of x and y for dynamical system (15). For a good introduction to Julia sets, as well as programs for generating Julia sets and the Mandelbrot set, see Devaney (1989).

While the subjects of chaos, Julia sets, the Mandelbrot set, and fractal sets are interesting results of dynamical systems, these topics require whole texts even to begin understanding them, and thus we will encourage

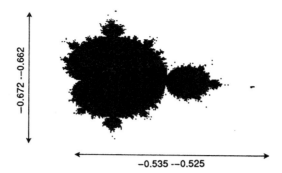

Fig. 88. Magnification of the portion of the Mandelbrot set inside the rectangle of the previous figure.

the reader to do further reading instead of lengthening this text. A good history of the development of this topic can be found in Gleick (1987). For a good introduction to the mathematics of chaos, see Devaney (1989) (and Devaney (1986) for a more advanced discussion). The book by Peitgen and Richter (1986) gives an advanced mathematical treatment, but has many beautiful color illustrations of the Mandelbrot set and Julia sets. For a good introduction to fractal geometry, see Barnsley (1988). The above listed books will give references for further study.

We are often asked what a mathematician does for a living. Isn't everything about mathematics already known? The answer is an emphatic **no!** We are at a stage in mathematical development where we can't completely analyze even simple nonlinear dynamical systems such as systems (13) and (15). For this reason, many mathematical models of the real world must be overly simplified before we can do any analysis. One of the goals of mathematicians is to be able to develop and analyze more realistic models of the world. You can see that our work has only just begun.

Bibliography

Barnsley, M. (1988). *Fractals Everywhere.* Academic Press, Boston.

Baumol, W. J. (1961). Pitfalls on contracyclical policies: some tools and results. *Review of Economics and Statistics* **43**, 21–6.

Cavalli-Sforza, L. L. and **Bodmer, W. F.** (1971). *The Genetics of Human Populations.* W. H. Freeman, San Francisco.

Devaney, R. L. (1986). *An Introduction to Chaotic Dynamical Systems.* Benjamin/Cummings, Menlo Park, California.

Devaney, R. L. (1989). *Chaos, Fractals, and Dynamics: Computer Experiments in Mathematics.* Addison-Wesley, Menlo Park.

Gleick, J. (1987). *Chaos: Making a New Science.* Viking, New York.

Hoppensteadt, F. C. (1982). *Mathematical Methods of Population Biology.* Cambridge University Press.

Malkevitch, J. and **Meyer, W.** (1974). *Graphs, Models, and Finite Mathematics.* Prentice Hall, Englewood Cliffs, New Jersey.

Peitgen, H.-O. and **Richter, P.** (1986). *The Beauty of Fractals.* Springer-Verlag, New York.

Richardson, L. F. (1960). *Arms and Insecurity: A Mathematical Study of the Causes and Origins of War.* Boxwood Press, Pittsburgh.

Samuelson, P. A. (1939). Interactions between the multiplier analysis and the principle of acceleration. *Review of Economics and Statistics* **21**, 75–8.

Smith, J. M. (1968). *Mathematical Ideas in Biology.* Cambridge University Press.

Answers

1.1 1) (a) $A(n+1) = 1.05A(n)$

(b) $A(1) = 210.00$, $A(2) = 220.50$, $A(3) = 231.52$, $A(4) = 243.10$

(c) $A(k) = 200(1.05)^k$

3) (a) $A(1) = 1040.00$, $A(2) = 1083.20$, $A(3) = 1129.86$, $A(4) = 1180.24$

(b) $A(n+1) = 1.08A(n) - 40$

5) (a) $A(n+1) = 1.02A(n)$

(b) $A(4) = 108.24$

(c) $100(1.02)^n$

(d) $100(1.02)^{4t}$

1.2 1) (a) is 4th order nonlinear,

(b) is 1st order affine,

(c) is not a dynamical system, nor is (d) or (h)

(e) is 2nd order nonlinear,

(f) is 5th order affine,

(g) is 4th order linear, and

(i) is 1st order nonhomogeneous.

3) (a) $A(n) = A(n-1) - 2A(n-2)$,   for $n = 3, 4, \ldots$

(b) $A(n) = A(n-1) + 2n + 6$,   for $n = 1, 2, \ldots$

(c) $A(n) = A(n-1)A(n-2)$,   for $n = 3, 4, \ldots$

1.3 1) $A(n+1) = A(n) + 0.20$ with $A(0) = 120$

3) $A(n+1) = A(n) - 0.05$ with $A(0) = 12$

5) $A(n+1) = 0.8A(n) + 200$ with $A(0) = 200$

1.4 1) (a) -6

(b) 1.4

(c) none

(d) 2 and -1

(e) 0, 0.5, and -0.5

3) (a) If $A(0) = 0.1$ then $A(3) = 0.67$, so not stable.

(b) If $A(0) = -0.1$ then $A(3) = -0.95$, so not stable.

1.5 1) $a = 2$ and $(2, 2)$ is point of intersection of $y = x$ and $y = -1.5x + 5$.

3) $A(0) = 2$

5) (a) 5 and -3

(b) and (c) 5 is stable and -3 is unstable.

7) $1 < A(0) < 7$

1.6 1) $f'(t) = 0.08 f(t) + 1000$

2.1 1) (a) $A(5) = -3.22$, $A(k) = 2(-1.1)^k$, solution oscillates to infinity.

(b) $A(5) = -1.61$, $A(k) = -(1.1)^k$, solution goes to negative infinity, exponentially.

(c) $A(5) = -0.32$, $A(k) = 1000(-0.2)^k$, solution oscillates to zero.

(d) $A(5) = -0.32$, $A(k) = -1000(0.2)^k$, solution increases exponentially to zero.

(e) $A(5) = -2.38$, $A(k) = 8(0.8)^k - 5$, solution decreases exponentially to -5.

(f) $A(5) = -2$, $A(k) = 3.5(-1)^k + 1.5$, solution forms the 2-cycle of -2 and 5.

(g) $A(5) = -5.59$, $A(k) = (-1.5)^k + 2$, solution oscillates to infinity.

3) (a) $A(k) = 4(3)^k$

(b) $A(k) = 4(-0.5)^k$

(c) $A(k) = 4(-1)^k$

(d) $A(k) = 4 + 3k$

(e) $A(k) = -6(1.5)^k + 10$

(f) $A(k) = 2(-0.9)^k + 2$

5) 8.5

7) 5

9) 0.5

11) $A(k) = c(\frac{2}{3})^k - 5$

2.2 1) (a) 1082.43

(b) 256.02

3) (a) $A(n+1) = 0.995A(n)$ $A(k) = (0.995)^k A(0)$

(b) $A(120) = 547.99$

5) 41 210.74

7) 2149.29

9) 273.02

11) (a) 21 914.91

(b) 2 130 530.72

(c) 181.09

13) 14.47 per cent

15) (a) 15 (or 14.21)

(b) 9 (or 8.04)

2.3 1) (a) $P(n+1) = -\frac{4}{3}P(n) + \frac{35}{3}$

(b) 5

(c) unstable

3) (a) $P(n+1) = -0.75P(n) + 35$, $P = 20$ is stable

(b) $S(n+1) = -0.75S(n) + 3.5$

(c) $D(n+1) = -0.75D(n) + 3.5$

5) (a) $S(n+1) = \frac{2}{3}P(n) + \frac{20}{3}$

(b) $D(n+1) = -P(n+1) + 14$

(c) $P(n+1) = -\frac{2}{3}P(n) + \frac{22}{3}$, $P = 4.4$ is stable

7) 200

9) $T(n+1) = 0.8T(n) + 20$, stable at 100 billion dollars.

11) (a) 1327

(b) 486

13) 34.31 or 35 years

15) 9901 years

17) 66 698 years

2.4 1) (a) $P(n+1) = \frac{7}{24}P(n) + \frac{3}{8}$

(b) $P(k) = c\left(\frac{7}{24}\right)^k + \frac{9}{17}$, $P(k) \to \frac{9}{17}$

(c) 0.533,

(d) $P(k) = \left(-\frac{1}{34}\right)\left(\frac{7}{24}\right)^k + \frac{9}{17}$, $P(4) = 0.529$

2.5 1) (a) 0.16, 0.48, and 0.36, respectively

(b) $q(n) = 0.4$, and 0.36 are dominant homozygotes

(c) 400, 3200, and 6400, respectively; 4000; $P(1) = 0.4$

3) (a) 50

(b) 83.3 or 84

(c) $\frac{50}{3}$ or 17

5) $a(n+1) = \left(\frac{1+\sqrt{\mu}}{1-\sqrt{\mu}}\right)a(n) + \frac{1}{1-\sqrt{\mu}}$; $a(k) = c\left(\frac{1+\sqrt{\mu}}{1-\sqrt{\mu}}\right)^k - \frac{1}{2\sqrt{\mu}} \to \infty$, so $q(k) \to \sqrt{\mu}$

7) $\frac{2}{7}$, $\frac{5}{7}$, and $\frac{4}{49}$, respectively

9) (a) $q(n+1) = 2q(n)(1 - q(n))/[2 - q^2(n)]$

(b) $q(n+1) = (1 - \mu)2q(n)(1 - q(n))/[2 - q^2(n)]$

2.6 1) (a) $A(k) = c\,2^k + 1 + k$

(c) $A(k) = c\,(-1)^k + 2k^2 - 2k - 1$

(e) $A(k) = c\,(-3)^k + 3\,(2)^k$

(g) $A(k) = c - 0.5(-1)^k$

(i) $A(k) = (c - 0.5k)\,2^k + 3^k$

(k) $A(k) = c\,3^k + 2\,(4)^k + 3$

2) (a) $c = 0$

(c) $c = 2$

(e) $c = -2$

(g) $c = 1.5$

(i) $c = 0$

(k) $c = -4$

3) $A(k) = c\,2^k + (k-3)\,3^k$

5) $A(k) = c\,r^k + \left(\frac{k}{s-r} - \frac{s}{(s-r)^2}\right) s^k$ if $r \neq s$; $A(k) = s^k \left(c + \frac{k(k-1)}{2s}\right)$ if $r = s$

7) (a) $A(n+1) = A(n) + 2\pi + 0.004n\pi$,

   (b) $A(k) = 1.998\pi k + 0.002\pi k^2$

   (c) 4709.25 inches

   (d) 1.15 inches

9) 141 277.50

11) (a) $A(n+1) = 1.1A(n) - (10.5)^{n+1}\, 40\,000$

   (b) $A(k) = c\,1.1^k + 840\,000\,(1.05)^k$

   (c) $c = A - 840\,000$

   (d) 508 707.53

13) (a) 3

   (b) $\frac{2}{3}$

   (c) $\frac{1}{48}$

   (d) $\frac{25}{21}$

3.1 1) (a) $a = 0$ is unstable, $a = 5$ is stable, and $(c, d) = (0, \frac{85}{7})$

   (c) $a = 0$ and $a = 1$ are unstable.

3) (a) $f'(-1) = 5$ so $a = -1$ is unstable

   (b) $f'(3) = -3$ so $a = 3$ is unstable.

5) (a) $f'(-1) = 5$ so $a = -1$ is unstable

   (b) $f'(1) = 1$ so no conclusion.

3.2 1) (a) $a = 2 \pm \sqrt{4-b}$ if $b < 4$, $a = 2$ if $b = 0$, and none if $b > 4$

   (b) $a = 2 - \sqrt{4-b}$ is unstable for $b < 4$, and $a = 2 + \sqrt{4-b}$ is stable for $0 < b < 4$ and unstable for $b < 0$

   (c) negative infinity

(d) semistable from above

3) (a) $a = 2 - 4b$ is stable for $-1.5 < b < 0.5$

(b) $H = 0.25$ when $b = 0.25$

3.3 1) $p(n+1) = 0.98p(n)[-0.4p(n)+2]/[1.4+1.2p(n)+3p^2(n)]$; $f'(0.33) = 0.38$ so $a = 0.33$ is stable, $f'(-5.637) = -0.02$ so $a = -5.637$ is stable, and $f'(0) = 1.4$ so $a = 0$ is unstable. Since $0 < p(0) < 1$ then $p(k) \to 0.33$.

3.4 1) $A(n+1) = \frac{m-1}{m} A(n) - \frac{a}{mA^{m-1}(n)}$

3) (a) -1.2207 and 0.7245

(b) 1.2419

5) (a) 12

(b) 4

7) 12.225

9) $g'(a) = \frac{2}{3}$

4.1 1) (a) $a = -2$

(b) semistable from below

3) (a) $a = 0$ and 1

(b) $a = 1$ is attracting and $a = 0$ is semistable from below.

5) $g'(a) = f'(a)f'(b)$

4.2 1) (b) $f'(a_1)f'(a_2) = 0.59$

3) (a) $a_1 = 0.4794$ and $a_2 = 0.8236$

(b) $f'(a_1)f'(a_2) = -0.29$

5) (a) $a_2 = 1.224\,996\,169$, $a_3 = 0.535\,947\,556\,2$, and $a_4 = 1.157\,716\,989$

(b) $f'(a_1)f'(a_2)f'(a_3)f'(a_4) = -0.03$

7) Let $F(x) = f(f(x))$. Then $-2F'''(a_1) - 3(F''(a_1))^2 = -3c^2[f'(a_1)^4 + f'(a_2)^2] < 0$, so it is attracting.

4.3 1) (a) $a = 2 \pm \sqrt{4-b}$ for $b \le 4$

(b) negative infinity

(c) $a = 2 - \sqrt{4-b}$ is repelling for $b < 4$. $a = 2 + \sqrt{4-b}$ is attracting for $3 \le b < 4$, repelling for $b < 3$, and semistable for $b = 4$.

3) (a) $a = 0$ is attracting for $0.5 < b \le 2.5$, repelling for $b > 2.5$ and $b < 0.5$, and semistable for $b = 0.5$. $a = 2 - 4b$ is attracting for $-1.5 \le b < 0.5$, repelling for $b < -2.5$ and $b > 0.5$, and semistable for $b = 0.5$.

5) (a) $a = 1$ is stable for $1 < b < \sqrt{3}$ and $-\sqrt{3} \le b < -1$, is repelling for $b < -\sqrt{3}$, $-1 < b < 1$, and $b > \sqrt{3}$, and is semistable for $b = \pm 1$. $a = b^2$ is attracting for $-1 < b < 1$, is repelling for $b < -1$ and $b > 1$, and is semistable for $b = \pm 1$.

5.1 1) (a) $x^2 = x + 2$, $x = 2$ and -1, $A(k) = c_1 2^k + c_2 (-1)^k$, $c_1 = 2$, $c_2 = 1$

(c) $x^2 = -2x + 15$, $x = 3$ and -5, $A(k) = c_1 3^k + c_2 (-5)^k$, $c_1 = 2$, $c_2 = -1$

(e) $x^2 = 4x - 5$, $x = 2 \pm i$, $A(k) = c_1 (2+i)^k + c_2 (2-i)^k$, $c_1 = c_2 = 1$

3) (a) $c_1 = [A(1)s - A(2)]/[r(s - r)]$, $c_2 = [A(1)r - A(2)]/[s(r - s)]$

(b) $c_1 = [A(0)s^N - A(N)]/[s^N - r^N]$, and $c_2 = [A(0)r^N - A(N)]/[r^N - s^N]$

5.2 1) (a) $A(k) = 5 - k$

(c) $A(k) = (-1+i)^k (0.5 - 0.5i) + (-1-i)^k (0.5 + 0.5i)$

5.3 1) (a) 0.88

(b) 0.60

(c) 0.55

(d) 0.52

(e) 0.51

3) (a) $P(0) = 1$, $P(1) = \frac{30}{41}$, $P(2) = \frac{18}{41}$, $P(3) = P(4) = 0$

(b) $P(n+1) = 0.1P(n+3) + 0.3P(n+2) + 0.6P(n)$ or $P(n+3) = -3P(n+2) + 10P(n+1) - 6P(n)$, $P(0) = 1$, $P(N) = 0$, and $P(N+1) = 0$

5.4 1) 9 per cent of women and 30 per cent of men; 42 per cent

3) (a) 0.85

(b) $P(k) = \frac{13}{15} + \frac{1}{30}(-0.5)^k$

(c) $\frac{13}{15}$

5) $P(n+2) = 0.5(1-\mu)P(n+1) + 0.5(1-\mu)^2 P(n)$, $P(k) = c_1(1-\mu)^k + c_2(0.5\mu - 0.5)^k$

5.5 1) (a) $A(k) = c_1 3^k + c_2(-2)^k$

(b) [part (a)] -5^k

(c) [part (a)] $+2k - 1$

(d) [part(a)] $- 2^k$

(e) [part(a)] $-2(3)^k$

3) (a) $A(k) = c_1 + c_2(-2)^k$

(b) [part(a)] $- 2^k$

(c) [part(a)] $+k(-2)^k$

(d) [part(a)] $+3k$

(e) [part(a)] $-2k^2$

5) (a) $c_1 = 3.2$, $c_2 = -0.2$

(c) $c_1 = -4$, $c_2 = 5$

7) (a) $A(k) = c_1 + (c_2 + c_3 k)2^k + 0.5(3)^k$

(c) $A(k) = c_1 + (c_2 + c_3 k - k^2)2^k$

5.6 1) 1904.1

3) (a) $P(1) = 0.25$

(b) $P(2) = \frac{3}{8}$

(c) $P(k) = c_1(0.809)^k + c_2(-0.309)^k + 1$ where $c_1 = -0.5 - 0.2\sqrt{5}$ and $c_2 = -0.5 + 0.2\sqrt{5}$

5) $P(0) = 0$, $P(1) = 0.5$, $c_1 = -0.5 - 0.1\sqrt{5}$, and $c_2 = -0.5 + 0.1\sqrt{5}$

5.7 1) (a) $20 + 17i$

(b) $-17 + 11i$

(c) $-45 - 24i$

(d) $\sqrt{53}$

(e) $\sqrt{5}$

3) (a) $A(k) = c_1 (-0.5 + 0.5i)^k + c_2 (-0.5 - 0.5i)^k$

(b) $A(k) = 0.5^{0.5k} (c_3 \cos \frac{3k\pi}{4} + c_4 \sin \frac{3k\pi}{4})$

(c) attracting

(d) $c_1 = i$ and $c_2 = -i$

(e) $c_3 = 0$ and $c_4 = -2$

5) (a) $A(k) = c_1 (-0.5 + 0.5i)^k + c_2 (-0.5 - 0.5i)^k - 2$

(b) $a = -2$ is attracting

5.8 1) $\frac{2}{1-a}$

3) $T(n+2) = 1.35T(n+1) - 0.45T(n) + (1.05)^{n+2}$, $T(k) = c_1 (0.75)^k + c_2 (0.6)^k + \frac{49}{6} (1.05)^k$

5) (a) $\frac{3}{1+a-ab}$

(b) $0.5(ab \pm \sqrt{a^2 b^2 - 4a})$

(c) $a = 4b^{-2}$

(d) $a < 1$

5.9 1) $A(n+2) = 2A(n+1) + 3A(n)$, $(A : B) = (15 : 4)$

3) $B(n+2) = 2.6B(n+1) + 0.56B(n)$, $(A : B) = (4 : 1)$

5) $(A : B : C) = (1.84 : 1 : 4.84)$

6.1 1) $P(n+1) = R P(n)$ where $P(n) = \begin{pmatrix} p(n) \\ a(n) \end{pmatrix}$ and $R = \begin{pmatrix} 0.5 & 0.5 \\ 1 & 0 \end{pmatrix}$

6.2 1) (a) $r = -3$ and 1

(b) $A = \begin{pmatrix} -3 \\ 1 \end{pmatrix}$ and $B = \begin{pmatrix} 1 \\ 1 \end{pmatrix}$ (or any multiple), respectively

(c) $2A + 4B$

(d) $2(-3)^3 A + 4B = \begin{pmatrix} 166 \\ -50 \end{pmatrix}$

3) (a) $r = 1, -1,$ and 2

(b) $A = \begin{pmatrix} 2 \\ 3 \\ -4 \end{pmatrix}$, $B = \begin{pmatrix} 1 \\ 0 \\ -3 \end{pmatrix}$, and $C = \begin{pmatrix} 1 \\ 1 \\ -2 \end{pmatrix}$, respectively

(c) $A - 3B - 2C$

$$\text{(d)} \quad A + 3B - 2^6C = \begin{pmatrix} -59 \\ -61 \\ 115 \end{pmatrix}$$

6.3 1) (a) $A(k) = a(-4)^k \begin{pmatrix} 1 \\ -1 \end{pmatrix} + b\,3^k \begin{pmatrix} 2 \\ 5 \end{pmatrix}$

(c) $A(k) = a\,i^k \begin{pmatrix} 5 \\ 2 - i \end{pmatrix} + b(-i)^k \begin{pmatrix} 5 \\ 2 + i \end{pmatrix}$

2) (a) $a = -\frac{29}{7}$ and $b = \frac{4}{7}$

(c) (i) $a = 0.4 + 0.2i$ and $b = 0.4 - 0.2i$

3) $A(k) = \begin{pmatrix} a(k) \\ b(k) \end{pmatrix} = 2(0.5)^k \begin{pmatrix} 1 \\ 2 \end{pmatrix} + 2(-0.25)^k \begin{pmatrix} 2 \\ 1 \end{pmatrix}$

6.4 1) (a) 4

(c) 1

3) 4-cycle

6.5 1) (a) No, total is not one.

(b) yes

2) (a) No, total of first column is not one.

(b) No, there is a negative entry.

(c) yes

3) (a) $\begin{pmatrix} 3/7 \\ 4/7 \end{pmatrix}$

(c) $\begin{pmatrix} 6/11 \\ 9/22 \\ 1/22 \end{pmatrix}$

5) 60 per cent

6.6 1) $P(\text{red}) = 0.6$ and $P(\text{blue}) = 0.4$

3) (a) $P(\text{red}) = \frac{5}{9}$ and $P(\text{blue}) = \frac{4}{9}$

(b) $P(\text{red}) = \frac{121}{225}$ and $P(\text{blue}) = \frac{104}{225}$

5) $P = \begin{pmatrix} 5/57 \\ 20/57 \\ 32/57 \end{pmatrix}$

6.7   1) $P(A) = 0.208$, $P(B) = 0.217$, $P(C) = 0.469$, and $P(\text{none}) = 0.106$

3) 123 148 for Marketing and 186 851 for Manufactoring

5) (b) $P(E_1) = P(E_2) = 0.5$

   (c) $P(E_1) = 0.75$ and $P(E_2) = 0.25$

6.8   1) 1.64

3) (a) $r_1 = 2$, $r_2 = -0.5$, $a = 1$, and $b = 2$

   (b) 2.000 61

   (c) $a' = 0.798$ and $b' = 1.597$

   (d) $\frac{b}{a} = 2$ and $\frac{b'}{a'} = 1.9997$

5) (b) 1.0994

   (c) 1.1048

   (d) $(1.832 : 1 : 4.865)$

6.9   1) (b) $a_1 = 4$, $a_2 = 8$, $a_3 = 12$, and $a_4 = 16$

   (c) $a_1(4) = 7.875$, $a_2(4) = 13.125$, $a_3(4) = 15.375$, and $a_4(4) = 16$

   (d) 0.9

3) (a) $a_2(n+1) = p\,a_1(n) + (1 - 4p)a_2(n) + p\,a_3(n) + 40p$, $a_3(n+1) = p\,a_2(n) + (1 - 4p)a_3(n)$

   (d) $a_1 = \frac{265}{14}$, $a_2 = \frac{110}{7}$, and $a_3 = \frac{55}{14}$

   (e) $\|R\| = 0.3535$

6.10 1) (a) $A(k) = c_1 \begin{pmatrix} 2 \\ 3 \end{pmatrix} + c_2 \left[\begin{pmatrix} 2 \\ 4 \end{pmatrix} + k \begin{pmatrix} 2 \\ 3 \end{pmatrix} \right]$

   (b) $A(k) = \begin{pmatrix} 1 + 2k \\ 3 + 3k \end{pmatrix}$

3) (a) $A(k) = c_1 \begin{pmatrix} 1 \\ -1 \end{pmatrix} + c_2 \left[\begin{pmatrix} 0 \\ 3 \end{pmatrix} + k \begin{pmatrix} 1 \\ -1 \end{pmatrix} \right]$

   (b) $A(k) = \begin{pmatrix} 3 + k \\ -k \end{pmatrix}$

5) (a) $\begin{pmatrix} 2 \\ -1 \end{pmatrix}$

(b) $A(k) = c_1(-2)^k \begin{pmatrix} 5 \\ -3 \end{pmatrix} +$

$$c_2 \left[(-2)^k \begin{pmatrix} -3 \\ 2 \end{pmatrix} + k(-2)^{k-1} \begin{pmatrix} 5 \\ -3 \end{pmatrix} \right] + \begin{pmatrix} 2 \\ -1 \end{pmatrix}$$

(c) $A(k) = (-2)^{k-1} \begin{pmatrix} 6 + 5k \\ -4 - 3k \end{pmatrix} + \begin{pmatrix} 2 \\ -1 \end{pmatrix}$

7) (a) $\begin{pmatrix} 2 \\ 1 \\ -1 \end{pmatrix}$

(b) $A(k) = c_1 2^k \begin{pmatrix} 1 \\ 0 \\ 1 \end{pmatrix} + c_2(-2)^k \begin{pmatrix} 1 \\ 0 \\ -1 \end{pmatrix}$

$$+ c_3 \left[2^k \begin{pmatrix} 0 \\ 1 \\ 0 \end{pmatrix} + k\,2^{k-1} \begin{pmatrix} 1 \\ 0 \\ 1 \end{pmatrix} \right] + \begin{pmatrix} 2 \\ 1 \\ -1 \end{pmatrix}$$

(c) $A(k) = 2^{k-1} \begin{pmatrix} 2 + k \\ 2 \\ 2 + k \end{pmatrix} + (-2)^k \begin{pmatrix} 1 \\ 0 \\ -1 \end{pmatrix} + \begin{pmatrix} 2 \\ 1 \\ -1 \end{pmatrix}$

7.1 1) (a) For $\begin{pmatrix} 0 \\ 0 \end{pmatrix}$, $\|R\| = 1.8$ so it is unstable; for $\begin{pmatrix} 1 \\ 0 \end{pmatrix}$ and $\begin{pmatrix} 0 \\ 1 \end{pmatrix}$, $\|R\| = 1.6$, so they are unstable; and for $\begin{pmatrix} 0.8 \\ 0.8 \end{pmatrix}$, $\|R\| = 0.52$ so it is stable.

7.2 1) $r < 1 + \frac{1}{c-1}$

7.3 1) (a) $A(k) = c_1(1.15)^k \begin{pmatrix} -3 \\ 1 \end{pmatrix} + c_2(0.7)^k \begin{pmatrix} 0 \\ 1 \end{pmatrix}$, so the solution moves toward A_3 along the b axis and away from A_3 along the line $a = -3b$.

3) Points below $a + 3b = 1$ move to the right and points above that line move to the left. Points below $b + 3a = 1$ move up and points above that line move down. Therefore, solutions move toward the equilibrium points $(a, b) = (0, 1)$ and $(a, b) = (1, 0)$. The particular point depends on the initial values.

5) Solutions cycle counterclockwise about the point $(a, b) = (4, 1)$.

7.4 1)   (a) $c(n+1) = [1.6 - 0.15c^2(n)]c(n)$

      (b) Since $f(c) = (1.6 - 0.15c^2)c$, then $f'(0) = 1.6 > 1$.

      (c) $f'(2) = -0.2$ so $c = 2$ is stable.

      (d) 4-cycle

      (e) Goes to 4-cycle.

  3)   (a) $c(n+1) = [1 + x - c^2(n)]c(n)$

      (b) Since $f(c) = (1 + x - c^2)c$, then $f'(0) = 1 + x$ so $c = 0$ is stable if $-2 < x < 0$. When $x = 0$, $f'(0) = 1$, $f''(0) = 0$, and $f'''(0) < 0$ so $c = 0$ is stable for $-2 < x \leq 0$.

      (c) $f'(\sqrt{x}) = 1 - 2x$ so $c = \sqrt{x}$ is stable if $0 < x < 1$.

Index